# ESSAYS IN
# GEOMORPHOLOGY

*Books by G. H. Dury*

# ESSAYS IN GEOMORPHOLOGY

*Edited by*

## G. H. DURY

M A, PH D, F G S

*McCaughey Professor of Geography*
*University of Sydney, Australia*

**HEINEMANN**

LONDON

Heinemann Educational Books Ltd

LONDON   MELBOURNE   TORONTO

SINGAPORE   CAPE TOWN

HONG KONG   NAIROBI

AUCKLAND   IBADAN


© Heinemann Educational Books Ltd 1966

First published 1966
Reprinted 1967


Published by
Heinemann Educational Books Ltd
48 Charles Street, London W.1
Printed in Great Britain by
Butler and Tanner Ltd, Frome and London

# Contents

# List of Plates

*(between pages 212 and 213)*

# Editor's Preface

During the past few years, geographers in general and geomorphologists in particular have increasingly been appearing in print at essay length. The ostensible purpose of certain collections of essays has been to celebrate the fame, retirement, or memory of some notable scholar, or to mark an anniversary in the progress of the discipline. But the willingness of authors to contribute combines with developments elsewhere in publishing practice, to demonstrate that our purposes cannot be fully served by comprehensive texts on the one hand and by single papers on the other. The technical essay, like the long short story, discharges a unique function: distinct from the review article, it gives room for the development at some length of the author's work, and in addition permits this work to be set in a wide perspective.

The present collection results from the demonstrable fact that geomorphology is producing swift and copious results. Whether this science constitutes a branch of geography or geology, or whether it should be regarded as an independent discipline, need not be argued here. Indeed, the current trend of amalgamation of disciplines promises to make argument of this kind purposeless. The fact remains, however, that workers in geomorphology are currently so productive that their rightful demands on available space for publication meet a wholly comprehensible resistance from some geographers and some geologists who are not engaged in the study of landform. At the same time, years of labour on the part of single individuals are producing results which, to be treated adequately, need space—specifically, the space afforded by an essay.

As the editor of, and a contributor to, this collection, I count myself highly fortunate in my fellow-writers. My one regret is that additional prospective contributors were, in various ways, prevented from joining the rest of us between these covers. All of those whose essays are included have prepared and supplied their material in the face of manifest difficulties—mainly the difficulties of time which press hard upon every practising geomorphologist. Most of my fellow-authors have patiently dealt with manuscripts, and with queries relating to them, in the course of working journeys about the world, and all have borne with the delays and disruptions occasioned by my own movements. Those who sent in material early have been tolerant of the subsequent delay, as late-comers have tolerantly borne pressure from myself to complete. Because we are so scattered and so mobile, I have had to ask my fellow-writers to accept certain short-cuts of editorship: this they have freely done.

The unifying theme of this collection is a systematic approach to morphological problems. The first six essays relate to specified areas, but state and examine principles of general significance, while the last three essays are wholly thematic.

N. Stephens and F. M. Synge adduce and review a mass of evidence relating to Pleistocene shorelines, which they discuss with principal reference to northwest Europe; in addition to clarifying the problems and reservations which apply to the interpretation of the shorelines discussed, these two writers give useful fixes of time and of form, which promise to be of the greatest help in future work. R. Common treats slope failure mainly with reference to Alberta, Macedonia, and northwest Europe, although drawing examples also from many other environments: he emphasizes the illuminating principle that the proximate cause of failure may be one of a whole range of possible factors, and commends an inter-disciplinary or inter-professional approach to the matters he discusses. J. A. Mabbutt, selecting for investigation a part of central Australia, deals with questions of inheritance and periodicity in an arid environment, describing a complex of morphogenetic events which, at least in large part, must be ascribed to climatic fluctuations. J. C. Pugh and W. W. Bishop, basing their observations chiefly upon African landscapes, considerably advance the prolonged debate of slope-retreat, pedimentation, and the correlation of great erosional platforms. M. M. Sweeting specifies the nature and origin of the weathering-forms of limestones, principally with reference to the limestone outcrops of northern England, giving quantitative data on rates of weathering. My own contribution is a review of the concept of grade, which suggests that a substantial part of foregoing discussions of this matter has been inconclusive on account of linguistic difficulties. J. I. Clarke reveals far more problems in the morphometric analysis of contour maps than are normally realized, while so clarifying the effects of the various available techniques as greatly to simplify choice among them. R. J. Chorley supplies an account of the application of statistical methods to geomorphology—an account which is most timely, at a juncture where statistical analysis, quantification, and data-processing are doing much to revolutionize geography and all cognate disciplines.

Sequential studies, critical appraisal and re-appraisal of earlier work, and the use of numerical data in a whole range of ways, bulk large in the collection as a whole. The groups of themes—strandline movements, slope retreat and the forms of slope associations, weathering-processes, and quantification—well exemplify the direction in which geomorphology is moving, under the guidance of some of its most active practitioners. The wealth of material already on record is well shown by the reference-lists which are here included. Without exception, however, these essays are forward-looking. Author after author, recording what has already been accomplished, signalizes questions which are urgently outstanding, and suggests means of further advance. We hope that the works here included will assist in making that advance possible.

It would be ungenerous to conclude this introduction without acknowledging the kindness of our publishers, who have calmly suffered the repeated redistribution of the authors throughout the world, and who have maintained effective contact with myself across two hemispheres: or without thanking our draughtsman, Mr A. Bartlett of the Department of Geography, University of Sydney, who drew the diagrams. In addition, I may suitably take this occasion to make a block statement of gratitude, on behalf of all authors, to the numerous friends and colleagues who have, at various stages, read parts or all of our manuscripts, and have supplied comments, criticisms, and suggestions.

G. H. DURY

The University of Sydney
1965

# Pleistocene Shorelines

## N. STEPHENS and F. M. SYNGE

The study of the changing sea-levels of the Pleistocene period has been the subject of much local research. Charlesworth (1957) and Fairbridge (1961) make notable attempts at world-wide synthesis and correlation. Valentin (1952, 1953) and McGill (1958) direct themselves to analysis of the world's coastlines with the aid of world maps; C. A. Cotton and A. Guilcher give descriptions of coastal evolution. Writers on coastal geomorphology are too numerous to list; but even the six already named exemplify many conflicting arguments of principle and conflicting interpretations of field data, especially in the context of Pleistocene evolution.

Recent studies of Pleistocene stratigraphy by Zeuner (1959), Mitchell (1960) and West (1963) for parts of northwest Europe, and by Fairbridge (1961) in his world survey of eustatic sea-levels, not only provide much information, but also emphasize some of the difficulties of correlating remnants of beaches, or drift deposits of various kinds on which some of the beaches rest, over considerable linear distances and time ranges. Nevertheless, it is proposed here to examine some of the principles and proble ms inherent in the study of the Pleistocene shorelines, making use of examples drawn from the coasts of northwest Europe.

Shorelines vary greatly in type and distribution, depending on their situation on the open coast, in sheltered bays, or around lakes. Those developed under conditions of severe wave action naturally differ from those in sheltered situations, and those subject to the impact of winter pack-ice have their own special character. Material forming the shoreline can vary from exposed shores, in bedrock so resistant that scarcely any notch is formed, to neighbouring stretches in boulder clay or soft sandstone which develop pronounced cliffs. Really hard rocks with massive structure can be very resistant indeed, requiring a considerable time for cliffing of any magnitude (Cotton 1955).

Shorelines differ in distribution according to whether they occur on stable or on unstable parts of the earth's crust: that is, parts affected either by tectonic movements or by isostatic displacement

1

because of glaciation. In tectonic areas the shorelines are deformed or tilted by local crustal movements, which can sometimes be detected by eye. The true tilt associated with isostatic movements can only be detected from measurements, never by eye.

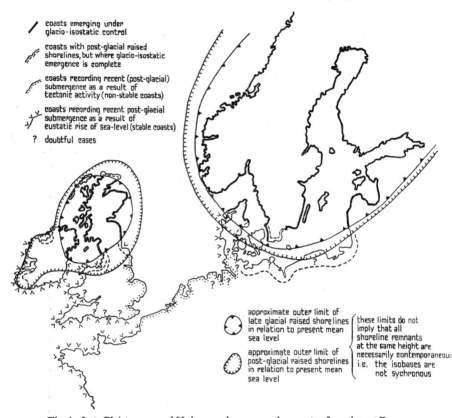

coasts emerging under
glacio-isostatic control

coasts with post-glacial raised
shorelines, but where glacio-isostatic
emergence is complete

coasts recording recent (post-glacial)
submergence as a result of
tectonic activity (non-stable coasts)

coasts recording recent post-glacial
submergence as a result of
eustatic rise of sea-level (stable coasts)

?  doubtful cases

approximate outer limit of
late glacial raised shorelines
in relation to present mean
sea level

approximate outer limit of
post-glacial raised shorelines
in relation to present mean
sea level

these limits do not
imply that all
shoreline remnants
at the same height are
necessarily contemporaneous
i.e. the isobases are
not sychronous

Fig. 1. Late Pleistocene and Holocene changes on the coasts of northwest Europe.

In northwest Europe (Fig. 1) Pleistocene shorelines have been studied in four different kinds of environmental condition:

Stable Coasts, where for the greater part or even the whole of the Pleistocene Period neither tectonic nor isostatic activity has occurred. Old shorelines should be horizontal, both above and below the present shoreline. They can be recognized as eustatic shorelines formed during periods of higher or lower sea-level. These were periods when sea-level was raised or lowered by a variety of means, which have been ably summarized by Fairbridge (1961, p. 193), under four main headings. Tectono-eustasy is envisaged as directly affecting the volume capacity of ocean basins by deforming their floors or margins in some way; sedimento-

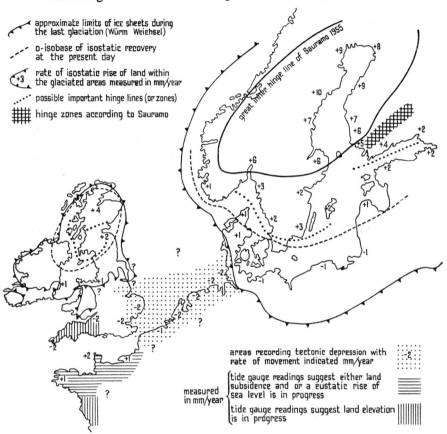

approximate limits of ice sheets during the last glaciation (Würm Weichsel)

o-isobase of isostatic recovery at the present day

+3 rate of isostatic rise of land within the glaciated areas measured in mm/year

possible important hinge lines (or zones)

hinge zones according to Sauramo

areas recording tectonic depression with rate of movement indicated mm/year

tide gauge readings suggest either land subsidence and or a eustatic rise of sea level is in progress

tide gauge readings suggest land elevation is in progress

measured in mm/year

Fig. 2. Isostatic and Eustatic movements on the coasts of northwest Europe.

eustasy involves the addition of sediments to oceans and seas, raising their surface level; glacio-eustasy involves the removal and return of water to the oceans during alternate glaciation and deglaciation; and the fourth category constitutes the addition of juvenile water from volcanoes, or the change in the total volume of oceans as a result of expansion or contraction of the water bodies through temperature-change.

**4**      ESSAYS IN GEOMORPHOLOGY

Perhaps the only strictly stable coasts of the British Isles lie along the south coast of England (Godwin 1960), outside the extreme limit of the Quaternary ice-sheets, the present range of activity of the North Sea geosyncline, and any late movement along Tertiary fold axes or faults near the English Channel coast (cf. Wooldridge and Linton 1955). Part of the south coast of Ireland and segments of the coast of northwest France can probably be regarded as stable, recording only marine submergence since the end of the last glaciation; all their series of fragments of raised shorelines appear, so far as is yet known, to be unwarped. This is the very area where Zeuner (1960 etc.) has attempted to carry to Britain the raised shoreline chronology of the Mediterranean and the Atlantic coasts of Portugal, Spain and France. But, as will appear later, other interpretations of the shoreline sequence in southern Britain are possible, differing markedly from Zeuner's strictly altimetric system. It is possible therefore that the word *stable* should probably not be applied indiscriminately to both sides of the English Channel, especially as the tide-gauge records on the French and English coasts do not accord in sign (Fig. 2). The French tide-gauges record a positive movement, and suggest that land elevation is taking place or that sea-level is falling; the English tide-gauges record a negative movement —a subsidence of the land, or eustatic rise of sea-level. If the English Channel should occupy a tectonically controlled depression, movement along which has perhaps controlled to some extent the development of some drainage systems (Everard 1953), then stability in the strict sense is unlikely (cf. King 1954; see also Bourcart 1939, 1950, Cotton 1955). The appearance in Fig. 1 of the symbol for coastal stability and marine submergence, on west Denmark and on the southern Baltic Sea coasts, indicates merely one factor in the modification of the coastline in an area where tectonic and glacio-isostatic movements are also most certainly involved. Wherever mixtures of symbols occur on any coastal segment in Fig. 1, stability of the landmass cannot be accepted for much of the late-Pleistocene, even though submergence (depending in part upon the present world-wide rise in sea-level) may be the dominant process operating.

*Unstable Coasts.* Instability can be caused in three main ways; the coasts of northwest Europe exemplify each type:

1. In the coastal areas buried—probably more than once—by thick ice-masses during the Pleistocene period, the essentially emergent features of raised shorelines occur. These permit measurement of that isostatic upheaval (recovery) of the land *above present*

*sea-level only* which has taken place since the phase of maximum glaciation, but do not tell us the *total amount* (Figs. 1 and 2). Calculations for the coasts of the northern part of the Baltic Sea indicate that the coast has still some 200 metres of recovery to complete (Gutenberg 1941). Isostatic depression and recovery rarely affects large areas in exactly the same way throughout, for example on account of unequal weight of ice or variation in solid geology; isostatic shorelines are therefore generally tilted, or deformed in some other manner. Degree and direction of tilt can be detected only by very careful survey. Coasts of this description belong to mobile coasts of isostatic type, as distinct from those affected by epeirogenic movements or by volcanic activity.

2. Immediately outside the area still dominated by isostatic control [uplift] there is a zone, at present impossible to define with any accuracy, where isostatic upheaval has ceased, but where raised shorelines are recorded. Eustatic effects are now predominant, with features of submergence recorded. Consideration of Figs. 1 and 2 shows that these coastal segments may lie only within the areas of post-glacial raised beaches, but where late-glacial shorelines are absent; all such segments lie outside the zero isobase of isostatic recovery at the present day.

3. In some areas, former shorelines have been tilted or deformed by local crustal movements which can sometimes be detected by eye, and are not due to glacio-isostatic control. The lands around the southern part of the North Sea have been down-warped towards the North Sea depression; their coasts are noteworthy for evidence of submergence, rising tide-gauge measurements at the present day, and serious problems of erosion, protection and reclamation (Schou 1949, 1960, Godwin 1960; Steers 1953, 1959). On these local crustal movements are superimposed the effects of Pleistocene events, for the crustal activity is known to date from the Tertiary. Investigations of shorelines, ancient and modern, within this area have been numerous and detailed, but it seems important to stress the difficulties and dangers of attempting to correlate remnants of fossil beaches, and above all river terraces (which have sometimes been used to aid determination of past sea-levels), between this tectonically active zone and other and dissimilar coasts.

Considerable problems must be solved in this particular environment before the different interpretations of coastal phenomena and Pleistocene stratigraphy on different sides of the North Sea can be appreciated. They apply not merely to a tectonically active area, but also to one invaded by considerable ice-sheets of British and Continental origin during various glacial advances. As far south as the latitude of London and the mouth of the Rhine, isostatic adjustments may well have been superimposed on the slower movements due to tectonic forces. If combined movement occurred more than once during the early Pleistocene, the precise age of any marine deposit or shoreline must be known before it can be correlated on a purely altimetric basis with beaches outside the affected area. For example, it is necessary to know to what part of an interglacial period a particular beach may be dated, and in the case of some of the older beaches, this need of precision may account for certain difficulties of altitudinal correlation outlined by Mitchell (1960) between East Anglia (March gravels, Nar Valley deposits), the south coast of England (Selsey raised beach), and southwest England and Ireland (pre-Saale or pre-Eastern General beaches).

Concerning these four different environments, knowledge is still very far from complete—even as to the precise geographical limits, and ages, of many of the fossil shorelines which post-date the last glaciation of northwest Europe. It is important to recognize that *outside* the isostatically and tectonically affected areas, world sea-level cannot but have been fractionally altered by the formation and decay of the northwest European ice-sheets. There is much evidence against strict contemporaneity between events in northwest Europe and those in the other large continental areas which were covered by huge ice-sheets (Charlesworth 1957, Flint 1961). Local isostatic and tectonic movements may have further emphasized the discordance of phase, making it all the more difficult to achieve accurate correlations of past sea-levels. It should never be *assumed* that because ice-advances were being recorded in the British Isles and Scandinavia, the ocean level outside the area immediately affected by the ice-sheets was necessarily being lowered rapidly and catastrophically. Conversely, the rate of post-glacial rise of sea-level (Godwin, Suggate and Willis 1958; Fairbridge 1961) was also largely controlled by the rate and manner of melting of the great extra-European continental ice-sheets. This circumstance may be of supreme relevance to the fossil shorelines of a small island group such as the British Isles, where the ice-sheets probably had a climatic history not precisely identical with that of the large continents.

We must now examine critically with the aid of specific examples some of the methods which have been used to investigate the Pleistocene sea-levels, recalling the risks in correlation outlined, e.g.

by Charlesworth (1957), Farrington (1945), Sparks (1960) and Zeuner (1952, 1959).

A shoreline must be accurately described, with cliff, wave-cut platform, and beach material distinguished from each other. On coasts of low relief the shoreline may be represented by beach ridges of sand or shingle, variation in the heights of ridges sometimes contributing to our knowledge of land- and sea-level changes during their formation (Lewis and Balchin 1940), but much care is needed in their interpretation (Jonsson 1957). On some very flat coasts the shore deposits may form a zone without any marked surface relief, obscuring the position of the high water mark (marine limit). Wave erosion produces a very distinctive landscape where transgression has taken place across hilly country. Notches, caves, shoreline terraces, and washed areas may be mapped where the hills are of solid rock, and where, for example, a drumlin belt has been invaded, good cliffs may be cut, and the hills of boulder clay may be completely truncated, as for example in Strangford Lough (Plate 1).

Sometimes the only evidence of a former transgression is given by terrestrial deposits—peat, fossil soil, or freshwater mud, beneath marine silt or below present high water mark (e.g. Godwin 1945, 1960); some deposits have been dated by Carbon-14 and their stratigraphy proven by excavation. But some coastal peats can have achieved their present position below high water mark—outcropping on the modern foreshore—without any change of relative level between land and sea. Marine invasion of lagoon flats by the sea (e.g. when a shingle beach system moves inland) or the invasion of an area of hummocky drift (e.g. a drumlin belt or moraine system with deep kettle holes) can both result in marine sedimentation over peat. In the absence of independent stratigraphical evidence or obvious height-differences it is unwise to assign inter-tidal outcrops of peat to a lower sea-level than the present.

The same argument can be applied where freshwater marls and marine silts interdigitate, or where blanket peat bog descends into the sea to below high water mark, as in West Mayo (near Belmullet) and West Donegal (Rosbeg). The permanent breaching of a drift barrier, or the occasional overwhelming of a strong shingle-sand dune complex, may account for at least some of these phenomena, without the need to invoke changes of level.

In tectonically stable areas and outside the range of glacio-isostatic movements the mapping and surveying of fossil-raised shorelines is a relatively simple matter, but it is not always possible to determine the upper marine limit for a particular beach over long distances. Once the height range of a given rock platform or beach has been accurately determined in a number of places, and the shoreline proved to be horizontal and unwarped, it can then be recognized elsewhere at this same level—the *reference level*. The sequence of fossil strandlines can be determined by positions relative to the reference level. As will be shown, the use of reference levels is also of particular importance in areas where glacio-isostatic movements have occurred (Fig. 9).

Very serious difficulties are often encountered in the study of wave-cut rock platforms, on which beach deposits are sometimes found. Just as a beach has a height range, so too does the wave-cut platform; and the limiting notch at the base of the fossil cliff is often difficult to locate. Variation of tidal ranges, length of fetch, exposure of particular segments of coastline to gale force winds and hence to great storm waves, geological controls imposed by soft or hard rocks, especially where these permit selective etching—all these can markedly affect the height range of platforms and beaches (Plate 3).

Wave-cut platforms are rarely flat; it is not always possible to ascertain their upper and lower limits, and usually even less possible to indicate the depth of water under which they formed. They usually slope most steeply near the cliff, ending in a notch (Fig. 3A). In Palaeozoic grits or slates a bold notch is likely to be preserved, and more than one for each particular level of the sea is unlikely. Such a notch can usually be attributed to wave attack at the high water level of ordinary tides. But in less resistant rocks, not only can the height of the platforms be controlled by lithological differences, but there may be more than one notch, and the question immediately arises of which should be used (Fig. 3B). In some extreme cases on exposed coasts (e.g. Chalk and basalt cliffs of northeast Ireland) occasional exceptional high storm waves and wind-driven spray have been observed to reach notches well above normal wave action. Where these high notches occur in weak rocks they must obviously be regarded as inconclusive evidence for the existence of former high sea-level stages, unless supported by the presence of beach material, marine clays and high-level notches at the same height in less exposed places (Plate 3).

At Porthleven in west Cornwall, re-excavation of fossil notches in quite resistant rock is taking place (Fig. 3C). Beach deposits are firmly cemented to the sides and back of the old notches, in front of which a well-developed wave-cut rock platform extends seawards (Plate 2). Thick head-deposits blanket the coastal slope and must at one time have extended seawards across the fossil cliff and the rock platform. Most of this material has now been cleared away by wave action,

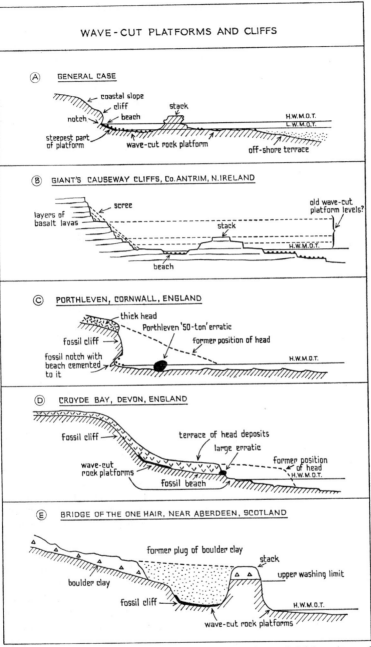

# WAVE-CUT PLATFORMS AND CLIFFS

(A) GENERAL CASE

coastal slope
cliff
notch
beach
stack
H.W.M.O.T.
L.W.M.O.T.
steepest part of platform
wave-cut rock platform
off-shore terrace

(B) GIANT'S CAUSEWAY CLIFFS, Co. ANTRIM, N. IRELAND

scree
layers of basalt lavas
old wave-cut platform levels?
stack
H.W.M.O.T.
beach

(C) PORTHLEVEN, CORNWALL, ENGLAND

thick head
Porthleven '50-ton' erratic
fossil cliff
former position of head
fossil notch with beach cemented to it
H.W.M.O.T.

(D) CROYDE BAY, DEVON, ENGLAND

fossil cliff
terrace of head deposits
large erratic
wave-cut rock platforms
former position of head
H.W.M.O.T.
fossil beach

(E) BRIDGE OF THE ONE HAIR, NEAR ABERDEEN, SCOTLAND

former plug of boulder clay
stack
upper washing limit
boulder clay
fossil cliff
H.W.M.O.T.
wave-cut rock platforms

Fig. 3. Some examples of wave-cut platforms, cliffs and superficial deposits, and their interpretation, in the British Isles.

and the modern cliff now coincides with the fossil cliff in places. A comparable sequence (Fig. 3D) occurs at many places in southwest England (Orme 1960). Similarly, boulder clay plugging gaps between former stacks and the mainland cliffs on the Kincardineshire coast has been only partially eroded by wave action since the last glaciation, so that the fossil cliffline is not re-exposed completely (Fig. 3E). In both cases it is quite clear that the very marked wave-cut notch, and much of the rock platform are fossil, and that the present beach deposits lie uncomformably on the platform. This problem can be a serious one: many post-glacial shingle beaches rest upon wave-cut platforms developed across hard, resistant strata in eastern Ireland and southwest Scotland. In a number of cases it has been shown that whereas the fossil raised beach is strictly post-glacial, the rock platform on which it rests, and the rock cliff at the rear of the platform, must be attributed to wave action which pre-dates at least one, if not two glacial phases (Stephens 1957, Stephens and Synge 1958).

It is sometimes necessary to consider the case of a beach deposit whose upper and lower limits are unknown, and where no abrasion-platform or cliff can be attributed directly to the period of beach formation. The Burtle Beds of Somerset (Bulleid and Jackson 1937) are fossiliferous sands and fine gravels, where the faunal content suggests a last interglacial age for the deposit. But there seems to be no way of measuring the former upper limit of the deposit, and hence the sea-level during the period of accumulation cannot be determined with any accuracy.

Fossil faunas of molluscs, ostracods, and foraminifera contained in beach and off-shore deposits have been used in a variety of ways in the study of Pleistocene sea-levels—to distinguish between beaches attributed to different interglacial phases of high sea-level, to ascertain water depths, and to permit calculations of the temperature of the sea at the time of the formation of a particular beach, (Baden-Powell 1927, 1934, Movius 1942, Charlesworth 1957). But there is need for great caution here: as Praeger (1896) shows, there was no clear-cut division between northern and southern molluscan species inhabiting the sea during the post-glacial transgression, nor is there at the present time such a division off the coasts of northeast Ireland. Praeger does not argue for *major* changes in the physical character of the sea water; he emphasizes that the extinction of some southern species after the Climatic Optimum was not followed by an immigration of more northern types. Research by Williams (1954) and others has shown a surprising mixture of cold-water (northern types) and southern types of molluscs today off the Co. Down coasts, these having presumably invaded the area by the North Channel and St George's Channel respectively. Thus a mixture of 'northern' and 'southern' mollusca might also be expected in the post-glacial raised beach and estuarine deposits in eastern Ireland, possibly confusing the issue of the Climatic Optimum. Southward and Crisp (1954) discuss the relationship between the distribution of certain molluscs and various environmental factors off the Irish coasts. Their study further emphasizes the need for caution, and the problem remains of whether or not assemblages (often small) of molluscs from fossil beaches can be used to indicate warmer or cooler conditions during deposition, and to what extent they can be used for long-distance correlation of fossil raised beaches, (Baden-Powell 1955, Richards 1960, 1962). Important environmental changes occur during rises and oscillations of sea-level, which not only alter the shape of the coastline, but bring sea water into contact with (geologically) different kinds of bottom ground. Moreover, a marine transgression to even the 50 ft contour would produce large areas of comparatively shallow water among the drumlins of Co. Down, but hardly any change along the steeply cliffed, rock coast of Co. Antrim. Speeds of current, wave activity, temperature and salinity variations might all be affected, and could influence markedly the local distribution of certain molluscan fauna. The wide geographical range of some molluscs (e.g. *Cyprina islandica*, from Greenland to the Bay of Naples) must also contribute to the problem of defining sea water temperatures, and of using them as aids to correlation of fossil beaches over long distances. In general, there seems to be a need to study large populations of molluscs, and where possible to examine off-shore deposits (clays, muds etc.) where there may also be pollen-bearing horizons, rather than beaches (Wooldridge 1960).

The excavation of raised beaches (and of river terraces) frequently brings to light archaeological material which can be used in dating; the Carbon-14 technique supplies absolute dates; and other means of achieving dates are also possible (Fairbridge 1961). However, it is often very difficult to be quite sure of the time-relationships between artifacts on the one hand and beach or terrace gravels on the other (*Pleistocene Dating and Man*, 1960).

Rock platforms and cliff-foot notches are more rarely seen and measured than the literature might suggest. Their study connects with that of two other classes of feature—caves, and surfaces of washed-rock from which glacial drifts have been cleaned by wave action. Caves and cave-deposits figure prominently in discussions of Pleistocene shorelines, but it does not seem to be always appreciated that cave roofs can be excavated by storm waves in bedrock at heights well above the extreme limit of high spring tides, especially in well-jointed rock. If the cave mouth is widened and the cave cuts deeply into the cliff, a very great range of height may be suggested for a particular shoreline—and indeed, indicated by beach accumulation inside the cave. But even where terrestial deposits, containing datable archaeological material, form part of the stratigraphy in the cave, it may still be extremely difficult to work out an accurate chronology for the cutting of the cave and the accumulation of the marine and terrestial deposits inside it. Furthermore, a large cave can result from more than one period of marine abrasion at a particular height (e.g. Gower Caves of south Wales: George 1932).

In areas bearing any distinct beach deposits (southwest Finland Archipelago and the drumlin belt of east County Down, Northern Ireland), the level of the washed rock indicates only the minimum level of a transgression. Additional evidence is needed to determine the maximum height of the former shoreline; the actual notch is often cut entirely in drift 5–10 ft above the platform and the feather-edge of the boulder clay.

If wave-cut notches and platforms in rock be accepted to represent some phase of still-stand of the sea, or perhaps progressive transgression, because these are the optimum conditions for the development of such erosional features, then it is necessary to consider the attendant beach deposits most carefully. Do they represent the *transgressive phase* of submergence, or do they in part form the beaches deposited during subsequent (relative) emergence of the platform or regression of the sea, assuming that platform and beach are approximately contemporaneous? Beach deposits constructed during the regression of the sea from its original high level, for whatever reason, may now appear firmly cemented to the rock platform at variable distances and altitudes from the fossil cliff notch, and cannot be used indiscriminately as indicators of the levels (usually the maximum levels) attained by a particular raised beach at a particular place. The multiplicity of beaches recorded by George (1932) at Heatherslade Bay in the Gower Peninsula of south Wales can probably be explained as parts of a single beach. Progressive transgression may be indicated by the overlap of the deposits resting upon the rock platform—see for example, Wooldridge and Linton (1955) on the Pliocene beach of southeast England. Rock platforms may also show several different levels by inter-cliffing; in the absence of transgressive beach deposits across a series of such levels (Barnstaple Bay sequence in north Devon) it is difficult to decide upon the relative age and importance of the several notches and benches (cf. Nonn 1960).

Buried channels in rock and in glacial drifts are known from many dock sections and estuaries of our coastlines, and extravagant claims have sometimes been made for the accuracy of the sea-levels that can be determined from them. Comparatively little is known of the conditions under which they were cut, although it is usually assumed that the deep rock-girt channels were formed in some glacial phase of low sea-level, when rivers were cutting down (McFarlane 1955). It is only in a few places that the fills of such channels, and hence the post-channel history of the area, are known accurately (cf. Zeuner 1960, on the River Thames). One particularly puzzling feature is the presence of deep rock-girt channels both within and outside the glaciated areas of the British Isles—they are known from Glasgow, Belfast, Liverpool, south Wales, Barnstaple Bay, London and Plymouth. It seems most unlikely that all of them can be assigned to the *same* phase of low sea-level, even when the *investigated* parts of such channels reach to approximately the same depth. In the northern parts of the British Isles the relevant areas presumably lay below the ice, and were depressed isostatically, while channels in southern England were being cut. But it might be argued that sea-level was controlled by the growth of ice-sheets of continental size, and that before glaciation of the British Isles had taken place, sea-level might have been lowered sufficiently to promote incision of streams. Some of the channels may represent the over-deepening of pre-existing valleys by sub-glacial streams, and others may be pre-glacial. There will also be difficulties in making use of such buried channels when they occur in tectonically active areas—witness the cases of the River Thames and River Rhine.

The use of river terraces to provide the heights of former sea-levels has been grossly misapplied, especially in the extra-glacial areas, because in many cases assumptions have been made about the type of terrace—whether it is (a) tectonically and isostatically controlled; or (b) thalassostatic, resulting from eustatic movements of sea-level; or (c) climatic, an outwash terrace from a moraine, or an aggradation terrace developed under periglacial conditions—and also about the former regime of the river, which may be unverifiable (Dury 1958). Cotton (1958), Zeuner (1959), Tricart (1952, 1953, 1960), and Troll (1954) discuss certain problems of the use of river terraces, while Wills (1938) shows, for example, that the glacial succession used for the West Midlands of England is based upon an interpretation of the complex of terraces in the Severn and Avon valleys. The interpretation is most difficult where, as at Kidderminster, a *single terrace surface* represents *three* different sets of conditions—periglacial with frost heaving, followed by wind erosion, followed by a thin spread

# RIVER TERRACES AND EUSTATIC MOVEMENTS OF SEA-LEVEL

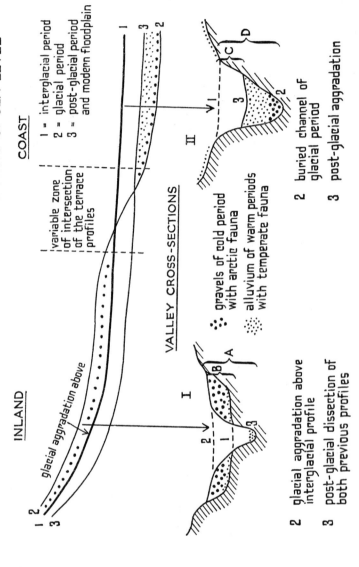

### INLAND

glacial aggradation above

### COAST

1 = interglacial period
2 = glacial period
3 = post-glacial period and modern floodplain

variable zone of intersection of the terrace profiles

### VALLEY CROSS-SECTIONS

:·:· gravels of cold period with arctic fauna

⁖ alluvium of warm periods with temperate fauna

I

II

2 glacial aggradation above interglacial profile

3 post-glacial dissection of both previous profiles

2 buried channel of glacial period

3 post-glacial aggradation

of alluvial sand, involving the investigator in an analysis both of terrace height and of drift chronology (Fig. 4).

Many wide-ranging correlations have been made between terrace fragments and sea-levels, even where the terraces cannot be traced into a raised beach or submerged terrace, and where too the relationship of the terrace to the position of the former coast-line (L.W.M.S.T.) is very imperfectly known. Mathematical formulae have been applied to existing long profiles and terrace profiles of rivers in order to project forward in linear distance, and backwards in time, in an effort to achieve a *precise* sea-level for a particular river or terrace segment. It has been shown by Miller (1939) that the mathematical method is at best very approximate, and may be down-right misleading, while correlation by eye is open to many obvious criticisms. Cotton (1958) has considered the case when eustatic (thalassostatic) river terraces are complicated by seaward or land-ward flexuring. Flexuring may affect thalassostatic or climatic terraces indifferently, further emphasizing the need for extreme caution in using this type of evidence.

Submerged shorelines present special problems, and are perhaps more numerous than one suspects (Fairbridge 1960). Little can be said of these shorelines (perhaps dating from the glacial maximum lowering of sea-level or from stages during the post-glacial eustatic rise of sea-level), except that possible lines of submarine cliffs have

---

Fig. 4. River Terraces and eustatic movements of sea-level.

IA.  Post-glacial valley incision has dissected the glacial and interglacial deposits laid down formerly in the wider pre-glacial valley.

IB.  The gravels of the cold period rest upon the alluvium of the previous warm period, the section indicating two different periods of contrasting aggrada-tion. The glacial terrace (profile 2) is the dominant morphological feature and the interglacial alluvium may not be readily seen. Where both glacial and interglacial deposits are composed of gravels there may be extreme difficulty of interpretation.

IIC. Post-glacial incision has been sufficient to lower the present profile *below* the interglacial profile, but post-glacial aggradation has been considerable, and the lower part of the valley may be drowned.

IID. During glacial times with a lower sea-level there was sufficient time for the river to erode a deeply incised valley in rock, in the base of which glacial gravels are found. Post-glacial alluvium may cover these glacial gravels to a considerable depth. In contrast to IA, the depth of the valley in rock, IID, does not represent the total amount of post-glacial incision.

Considerable difficulties of interpretation occur where some of the deposits may be missing or concealed, or where in the variable zone of intersection of terrace profiles the three different stages of valley develop-ment are compressed into a small height range. Tectonic movements or coastal flexuring may be additional factors which have to be considered when interpretation is made.

been recorded in a few places; and in tectonically active areas such as the Netherlands, littoral deposits of the Eem (Last Interglacial) Sea lie *below* present sea-level. Similarly, on the Polish Baltic coast, portions of the Littorina shoreline are now hidden below the sediments of the Vistula delta, while elsewhere a raised, fossil cliff has been mapped. Differential tectonic movements, probably of post-humous type, have been suggested (Galon 1960), but the fact remains that here is an example of the displacement of a shoreline trending generally east–west. Too often, perhaps, attention inside glaciated Europe is concentrated upon displacements and tilting of shorelines along north–south axes because of the position of ice-centres and the direction of ice movement during the glacial phases of the Pleistocene, to the neglect of differential changes of level in other directions as a result of tectonic or glacio-isostatic forces.

### Pleistocene shorelines in unglaciated areas of the British Isles: Devon and Cornwall

The approximate limits of the ice-sheets during some of the glacial phases of the Pleistocene are indicated in Fig. 5. This map and the correlation table (Table I) permit comparisons of the Pleistocene stratigraphy of the coastlands of the southwest peninsula, south Wales, and southern Ireland. The limits of the ice-sheets of early Pleistocene age (Mitchell 1960) constitute but one problem. The map area displays many similarities in the coastal sections of drifts, raised beaches and exposures of wave-cut rock platforms (below 60 ft O.D.), if head (frost-rubble) or solifluction deposits and other evidence of cryoturbation in Devon and Cornwall be equated with some of the boulder clays of the glaciated areas. It is with the interpretation of fossil raised beaches, head deposits, certain large (50-ton) erratics, the Fremington boulder clay (Maw 1864) and the rock platforms on which these superficial deposits rest, that this discussion is mainly concerned. The origin and age of the so-called hogs-backed cliffs (Arber 1911) and of certain 'hanging' coastal valleys is also intimately bound up with the Pleistocene history of north Devon.

In Barnstaple Bay, near Croyde, a series of rock platforms can be seen at different heights above low-water mark, for example, at Pencil Rock (45 and 25 ft) and Freshwater Gut (40 and 30 ft). Near Middleborough the 40–50 ft and the present tidal platforms are the most striking, but can be seen in places to grade into one another, or to inter-cliff each other. It is thus by no means certain that three *distinct* platforms are present, within the height range 0–50 ft O.D. (Fig. 6).

The transgression of these rock platforms by a suite of periglacial and raised beach deposits, in the same stratigraphical sequence

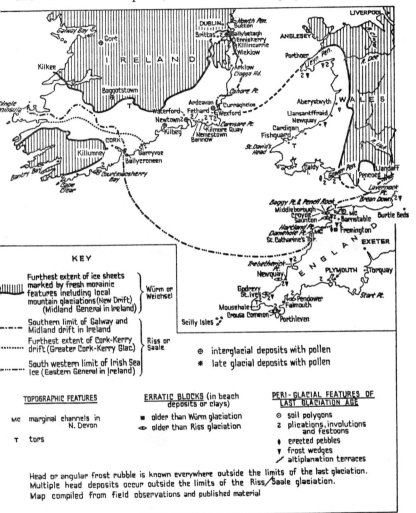

Fig. 5. Ice limits, glacial and peri-glacial deposits, and important Pleistocene sites in southern Ireland, Wales and southwest England.

everywhere between Baggy Point and Saunton, indicates that the platforms pre-date the superficial deposits, and that even the lowest, which is awash at high water, cannot be regarded as post-glacial, whether modern or Flandrian. Admittedly there has been some post-glacial modification of the lowest platform, but at many places (in Barnstaple Bay, Godrevy, Porthleven, and at sites in south Wales and

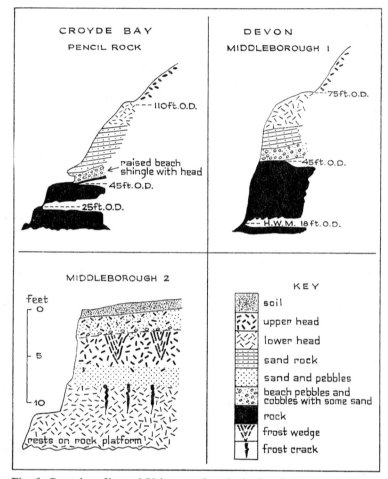

Fig. 6. Coastal profiles and Pleistocene deposits in Croyde Bay, north Devon. The frost cracks actually begin in the Upper Head alongside the frost wedges.

southern Ireland) this amounts merely to stripping of the superficial deposits with re-exposure of a much older abrasion-platform.

Great care is necessary in correlating isolated exposures of raised beach shingle lying upon rock shelves—the criterion of height is not alone sufficient. There is one, and only one, raised beach to be seen around Barnstaple Bay; it has a height range of 45 ft from below present HWM to about 60 ft O.D., and transgresses the series of rock platforms described above.

Even though the age of the wave-cut platforms is unknown, the distribution of platforms within the same height range is known throughout the southwest peninsula, in south and west Wales, and in Ireland along the south and east coasts (Wright and Muff 1904, Stephens, 1957) as far north as Belfast Lough. Similar platform remnants are known in northwest France, the Channel Islands, and possibly on some parts of the coast of western Ireland and west Scotland, while Mitchell (1960) identifies the Sewerby and Brighton platforms as part of the same sequence. If allowance is made for the three different levels at which the platforms have been recorded, and if 60 ft O.D. is the extreme height of these features, then it seems very probably that the three levels, often grading into or cliffing one another, must date from the same general period of wave planation. The fossil cliffs of the three benches are not always seen, but there seems to be no clear evidence of warping of this shoreline. If this is so, then on the coasts where glacial deposits bury the rock platforms, isostatic recovery has presumably returned the depressed landsurface to its original position.

In Barnstaple Bay at Freshwater Gut, as at Saunton, large erratics (Dewey 1913, Taylor 1956) rest upon one or other of the wave-cut platforms; the erratics are sealed below either the main head (frost rubble), or else by sandrock which is part of the raised beach sequence and which is in turn sealed below the main head. These erratics compare in size with the Porthleven erratic of some fifty tons weight (Flett 1912). Beyond all doubt, they were delivered on to a pre-existing rock platform and later sealed by a variety of Pleistocene deposits. But the problems of whether these large erratics were moved into position by a regional ice-sheet (Mitchell's Mindel/Elster or Lowestoft stage; Mitchell 1960) or by floating icebergs has not been resolved. The very large erratics in Devon and Cornwall are few in number and appear to be confined to a narrow zone along the coast, below 35–40 ft O.D. No boulder clay has been found which on the coasts could be associated with giant erratics. Erratics have not been recorded from inland localities except at Fremington, where, however, the boulder clay also recorded is thought to be a much younger deposit, stratigraphically separated from the large coastal erratics by the raised beach (Maw 1864); around Barnstaple Bay and on the north Devon coastal slope the main head contains only a small number of pebble-sized erratics. Many greenstone boulders recorded in the literature are not true erratics. Flint 'erratics' have wide horizontal and vertical distributions in a variety of deposits, and must be placed in a different category from either the giant erratics (Rogers and Simpson 1937) or the many smaller erratic pebbles. If an ice-sheet extended as far as Porthleven, as Mitchell requires, then difficulties arise from erratics weighing up to half a ton on the Cornish coasts east of the Lizard, in the same kind of position on the rock platforms and in the same raised beach; the St Erth deposits, which in Mitchell's view occur in terrain traversed by ice, have been interpreted as glacial or pre-glacial in origin.

Mitchell (1960) emphasizes that it is unlikely that the large erratics were delivered by floating icebergs during an interglacial phase of high sea-level, and dismisses ice-rafting during glacial phases on the grounds that the sea-level would then have been far too low (cf. Arkell 1943). However, it is not proven that Early Pleistocene sea-levels during glacial phases were depressed below present-day sea-levels. Late Tertiary to Early Pleistocene sea-levels were probably high, accounting for the coastal marine erosion surfaces at 650 ft and below, and the Crousa Common and other high-level shingle deposits in Cornwall; the St Erth clays, if they are marine in origin, suggest a 200 ft sea-level (Mitchell 1960, Zeuner 1959). Glacial eustatic lowering of sea-level during the Early Pleistocene, super-imposed upon tectonic eustatic lowering of world sea-levels, may have succeeded in lowering sea-level only to about the present mark. Icebergs might thus have been able to carry the erratics into position (see also Fig. 7, and Fairbridge 1961, who argues for high Early Pleistocene sea-levels during certain of the glacial phases). The weak-ness of this argument is the problem of determining the age and origin of the rock platforms if these were submerged below tens of feet of sea during the early interglacials, or were awash during the glacial phases—at present there seems to be no clear proof of either hypothesis. Again, the rock platforms may not always represent wave planation during interglacial phases; they may perhaps be analogous to the Norwegian strandflat, where wave planation is considered to have been materially assisted by glaciers and frost action (Wright 1937, Charlesworth 1957). There are many such rock platforms below 100 ft O.D., in various parts of the British Isles, where age and origin is obscure—for example, there is as yet no adequate explana-tion of the anomalous platforms found on some of the Western Isles of Scotland (e.g. Colonsay, Oronsay) and described by Wright (1937).

The delivery of the large erratics (Fig. 5) is complementary to the evidence of an early full glacial period, (probably the Lowestoft-

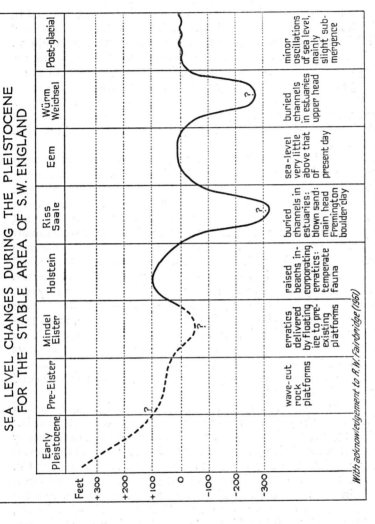

Fig. 7. Sea level changes during the Pleistocene in southwest England: a tentative summary of the available evidence.

Elster–Mindel of Mitchell) in East Anglia and in Ireland, which on the basis of known glacial stratigraphy must place the raised beach and main head in later, younger, phases of the Pleistocene. For the present it is perhaps best to refer the rock platforms below 100 ft, the St Erth deposits, and the large erratics, to the 'Early Pleistocene' of Britain, without attempting specific correlation with the continent. The raised beach which rests upon the rock platforms and the large erratics, and which itself contains erratics, consists of beach shingle and of cemented shelly sands with a temperate fauna, capped in places by a system of fossil sand dunes (sandrock) (Fig. 6, Plate X). But contained in the shingle and sand are many sharply angular blocks of all sizes, which can only be described as derived head (Plate 5).

The considerable bulk of angular material in these beaches seems unlikely to be due wholly to occasional cliff-falls. There has clearly been insufficient time for this material to be rounded into a typical beach shingle comparable to the rest of the raised beach. It seems possible that in many places the exposures of raised beach do not represent a lengthy period of formation, and that they were rapidly sealed-off by the overlying head when sea-level was lowered during an ensuing glacial period. On this view, these parts of the fossil raised beaches were deposited during the relative *regression* of the sea, independently of the *cutting* of the rock platforms on which they rest. Alternatively, raised beaches containing angular material in their lowermost layers, with many feet of shelly beach above, imply progressive *transgression*. But whichever explanation be adopted, the existence of abundant head in the lowermost beach gravels implies that head had already formed, or was forming contemporaneously with the beach on *pre-existing* rock platforms, in southwest England and southern Ireland.

The raised beach shingle reaches a maximum height of about 50 ft O.D. near Croyde (the shelly sand extending to 60–70 ft O.D.; Plate 5), but the best exposed sections of the beach are frequently lower, the base being just within reach of storm waves at the present day. Considerable height ranges are recorded, for instance, in Co. Cork. Thus the correlation of beaches between Ireland and Great Britain upon the basis of altitude alone is indefensible, and the continued use of such terms as, the '100 ft beach', '45 ft beach', '25 ft beach', '10 ft beach', and 'Patella beach', to denote beaches belonging to different interglacial periods cannot be admitted without other supporting evidence. The complete stratigraphy of each section must be judged upon its own merits (Arkell 1943, Green 1943).

A correlation of Pleistocene stratigraphy between Ireland and

Great Britain has been previously attempted by Mitchell (1960), and the following interpretation (Table I) is very similar to his, but for a much more limited area. The chief arguments in favour of the present interpretation may be summarized as follows:

(i) Within the range 0 to 50 ft O.D. there exists at least one wave-cut rock platform, on which rest glacial erratics (without boulder clay); a raised beach, sometimes containing a shelly temperate fauna, and sometimes including angular blocks (old head?); and occasional fossil sand dunes. The erratics resting upon the rock platforms and those contained in the raised beach suggest that the beach is not wholly contemporaneous with the cutting of the platforms. The inclusion of some head in the beach gravels, even where a temperate fauna is also present, suggests the inclusion of an old head deposit, perhaps equivalent in age to the cold period when the erratics were delivered to these coasts, probably by floating ice, for no boulder clay has yet been found on the south coast of Ireland, in south Wales, nor in the Southwest Peninsula *below* the raised beach and associated with the erratics.

(ii) The fabric analysis of the Fremington boulder clay shows it to be closely similar in most respects to the Eastern General till, which also suggests a correlation with the 'Older Drift' of south Wales. Mitchell (1960, 1962) and Watts (1959) have shown the Eastern General till to be almost certainly of Saale age.

(iii) Analysis of the series of head deposits and cryoturbation phases (cp. Dylik 1960), and the equating of the most massive head with the 'Older Drifts' (Eastern General and Fremington tills) allows a reasonable correlation to be made. Nowhere in Ireland or Wales is it possible to trace the really massive head deposits (or deeply cryoturbated boulder clay) right up to the end moraines of the Weichsel advance. In each of these areas, as in southwest England, there is a distinct 'upper head' which can be followed northwards, increasing slightly in thickness (or severity of cryoturbation) towards the southern limit of the ice-sheets of the last glaciation. The solifluction deposits in the coastal sections of west Wales, where their maximum thickness is 5–6 ft, correspond closely with the Irish evidence (Mitchell 1951, Synge 1962). There is nothing to compare with the huge thicknesses of the main head in Devon and Cornwall or the intense frost-churning in the older main head recorded at Godrevy (Fig. 8 and Plate 6) and at certain of the sites in Co. Cork. Instead, there is a thin fresh upper head, such as that recorded at Middleborough (Fig. 6), Trebetherick (Arkell 1943,

Stephens 1961), Godrevy, and at many other sites, which is often distinctly separated from the lower, main, head, and is much the less weathered. Furthermore, as shown in Fig. 5, the Fremington boulder clay and the Eastern General till of south Wexford and southeast Cork cannot be younger than the Saale glacial phase, because the southern limit of the Weichsel advance leaves these areas everywhere outside its maximum southerly extension. The approximate southern limit in Ireland of the Irish Sea ice responsible for the Eastern General and Fremington tills is near Cork Harbour. In the southwest peninsula the ice-front is judged to have pressed against the high cliffs near Clovelly, to have pivoted about Hartland Point, and to have extended southwards sufficiently far enough to allow certain marginal drainage channels (Damehole Point; St Catherine's Tor; Fig. 5) to form between

GODREVY - CORNWALL

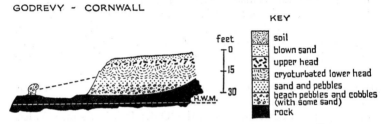

KEY

feet
0
15
30

H.W.M.

soil
blown sand
upper head
cryoturbated lower head
sand and pebbles
beach pebbles and cobbles
(with some sand)
rock

Fig. 8. Some Pleistocene deposits at Godrevy, Cornwall.

the ice and the coastal slope. Indeed, it may be argued that the Valley of the Rocks and similar features on the north Devon coast may owe part of their form to ice-marginal streams (see Arber 1911, and Scott-Simpson 1956, for alternative views). The fact remains that Carboniferous Limestone erratics (of south Wales origin?) have been recovered from the head on the coastal slope of the hogs-backed cliffs at places between Saunton and Lynmouth; and a series of channels (some dry) more or less parallel to the coast and declining in height towards the southwest are known between Lynmouth and Hartland Quay.

(iv) There is no known evidence for a raised beach of Saale–Weichsel interglacial (Last Interglacial or Eem) age in southern Ireland, south Wales or southwest England. No detected beach cuts into or rests upon the Eastern General and local Saale-age tills of southern Ireland, nor upon the Fremington boulder clay or the main head (Arber 1960, Stephens 1961). The main and upper heads have sludged downhill, spreading out as a great apron or solifluction-terrace at the foot of the coastal slope. The surface of this terrace slopes at low angles—less than three degrees—and smooth convex-concave profiles result (Saunton Down). It must not be confused with raised-beach platforms; there is no evidence that the terrace-like surfaces of the solifluction deposits owe their form to wave action, for no marine deposits have been found to cap the main or upper head. Alternative explanations are possible for the Trebetherick Point sections described by Arkell (1943); a tentative reassessment is here made in the correlation table. Neither the field evidence nor the literature gives conclusive evidence of a raised beach of Last Interglacial age in the Gower Peninsula. Where raised beaches are known to lie below the main head, or an equivalent deposit, they are placed in the Great Interglacial (Elster/Saale) (Stephens 1961).

(v) Where the raised beaches of the southwest peninsula are not covered by massive main head deposits, then their age must be regarded as problematical, regardless of height-relationship to present sea-level. Neither height nor contained fauna justify the placing of the beach in a specific panel of the correlation table. The great storm ridge of Chesil Beach (crest at 52 ft O.D.) could be considered to be of 'Great Interglacial' age on the basis of height alone; and Baden-Powell has dealt with some of the problems of the contained faunas of beaches in several publications. In general, great thicknesses of boulder clay and of solifluction and other deposits in coastal sections suggests that waves have not been able to reach these deposits at levels above the present limits. Survival of these on western coasts exposed to Atlantic storms suggests that a moderate transgression of, say, 30 ft seems unlikely since deposition. On this view, at no time since the Great Interglacial has the sea achieved such a height. The well-known hogs-backed cliffs in north Devon also indicate both the great importance of periglacial processes, and the lack of marine transgressions high enough to clear much of the head from the coastal valleys and coastal slopes and to change the coastal profile during the last interglacial. Mitchell (1960) summarizes some of the evidence for the relatively low level of the last interglacial sea in northwest Europe and the British Isles. Although it is perhaps unwise to attempt exact height-correlations for the Eem marine deposits between the unstable (tectonic) areas of Holland and north Germany and southeast England, and the supposedly more stable area of southwest England, Mitchell's evidence is nevertheless convincing in itself and in accord with that of the present writers. Thus the strictly altimetric systems of Green (1943) and Zeuner (1959) may be incorrect, demonstrating once more some of the problems of long-range correlation. There has been further discussion of some of the related problems of Pleistocene sea-levels and stratigraphy by Apsimon, Donovan and Taylor (1961), where the Brean Down section has been analysed in detail. Further investigation may be necessary to ascertain the age of the period of greatest periglacial activity (at Brean, deposit 13), for this deposit may be considerably older than the last glaciation. It may be of Saale (Riss) age, when it is believed that all the really great thicknesses of head accumulated. Büdel (1960) discusses many of these problems in relation to European stratigraphy and sea-levels, and Shotton (1962) presents certain alternative viewpoints.

### Isostatic Shorelines

Shorelines of the isostatic class abound in all areas formerly covered by the great continental ice-sheets. They were formed during deglaciation in areas where thick ice once depressed the crust, and where the sea or proglacial lakes formed shorelines at successively lower levels on a rising land area. The rate of uplift would seem proportional to the former thickness of ice, the crust rising like a cork both during and after the melting of the ice. Where the bedrock is uniform in hardness—as in the great shield areas of Canada and Scandinavia—the amount of uplift appears to be uniform over large areas. There seems no convincing evidence of recent differential movements along faults, although such movements have been claimed. But where a major geological contact occurs between large masses of rock of very different hardness, a line or zone of sudden change in the rate of rise may occur, e.g. between the shield rocks of southern Sweden and the softer rocks of Skäne, or between the rocks of the Grampians and the Carboniferous formations of the Midland Valley of Scotland (Fig. 2).

Although isostatic shorelines are very numerous in Scandinavia, they usually cannot be traced laterally to any great distance (Hyyppä 1936, Granö 1958, Okko 1957, Donner 1952). Lower shorelines frequently cut out higher ones, while ground of high enough relief to preserve a whole sequence is limited in extent. The greatest care is necessary in selecting sites for measurement, because beaches and shorelines can be simulated by outwash terraces, kame terraces and solifluction terraces; the problem of distinguishing between lake and marine shorelines arises throughout.

One of the clearest types of shoreline, or *reference level* as it may be termed, is constituted by the upper marine limit in a particular area (A in Fig. 9). Usually in one place or another such a limit can be easily determined. For localities below this limit, the tilt may be difficult to determine. Sometimes closely spaced measurements can reveal a particular clearly marked beach sequence (B in Fig. 9). It may be possible to identify and survey a particular type of beach that cannot be confused with those above and below it—for example, a cliff with a series of shingle bars in front of it, in an area where similar assemblages are lacking at other levels (C in Fig. 9). If all such reference levels of different type give consistent results, then it is safe to assume that the tilt has been correctly determined.

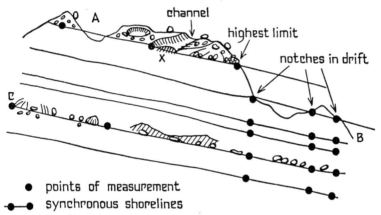

Fig. 9. Types of shoreline in drift that can be used as reference levels:
A. The highest washing limit in supra-aquatic drift; × marks the position of a shingle bar at the lowest limit of an ice-marginal channel.
B. A repeated shoreline pattern.
C. A single shoreline of distinct type that can be consistently followed.
    All these must be followed over short distances only.

Shorelines of isostatic type are different from other shorelines because of their very temporary character. In Scandinavia they generally do not notch bedrock, on account of rapid crustal uplift, and are recognizable only as washing zones, as lines of ice-thrust boulders, or as shingle bars. Only in exposed situations was the till cover removed to produce a zone of washed bedrock. A special feature of many of the shorelines is the concentration of boulders pressed against these old coastlines by sea-ice in winter. They are readily recognized as blocks pushed in line, and arranged with their long axis parallel to the ice-pressure, that is, parallel to the shore. The blocks are usually derived from a very blocky till and in strongly glaciated areas of bare rock, the highest shoreline is easily recognized as the lower limit of perched blocks (Fig. 10A and Plate 7).

Some isolated hills with till-covered tops remaining above the marine limit are surrounded by very pronounced rings of washed rock. These, termed *kalotteberg* or 'ring hills' in Lapland, exemplify a marine limit (Fig. 10B).

In areas strewn with subglacial channels cut in till or gravel, the marine limit can also be clearly determined; for a very clear lower

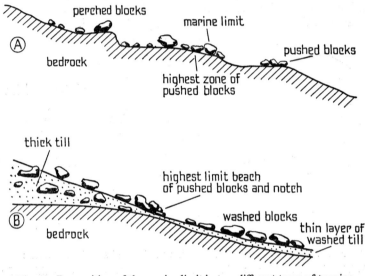

Fig. 10. Recognition of the marine limit in two different types of terrain:
A. In drift-free terrain the scattered erratic pebbles and blocks have been removed and concentrated at particular levels at and below the marine limit.
B. In drift-covered terrain the drift surface has been washed clear of the finer particles below the marine limit. At the latter limit, boulders washed out of the drift have been concentrated and aligned by the thrusting action of winter ice forming on the surface of the sea.

limit of such channels marks the highest water level, with the channels generally terminating in a shingle or sand bar. The presence of deep, fresh kettle holes in glacial gravels is no proof that sea-level was always at lower levels. Fluvioglacial material containing large blocks of ice can have survived temporary submergence by the sea, with blocks of ice not melting until uplift, raising the land above the sea, later allowed a series of beaches to form (I, II, III in Fig. 11) which overlap the height of the kettle hole.

Various fluvioglacial formations are often little affected by wave action, probably because each strandline endured but briefly. Eskers,

especially, are deformed in a particular way (Fig. 12). The usual
undulating crest of an esker tends to be levelled off and strewn with

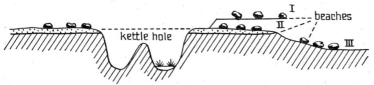

Isostatic Shorelines - an example of a series of beaches which predate
the final melting out of the ice blocks which
formerly occupied the kettle hole

Fig. 11. Shorelines I and II pre-date the melting of ice in the kettle hole. The
absence of kettles below Shoreline III show that it post-dates the melting of the
ice-blocks.

boulders below the marine limit, which is defined by a notch and the
upper limit of ice-pushed blocks. The steep sides of the esker tend to
survive intact.

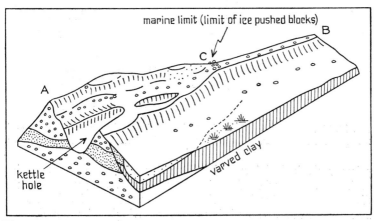

Fig. 12. Deformation of eskers by wave action. The usual undulating crest of an
esker tends to be levelled off and strewn with boulders below the marine limit (C),
which is defined by a notch and the upper limit of ice-pushed blocks. The steep
sides of the esker tend to survive intact, but kettle holes may be partially filled
with materials if they were free of ice at the time. The lower limit of kettle holes
will sometimes indicate a particular marine limit.

Regressive shorelines, formed by erosion during crustal uplift,
possess hardly any beach deposit. On level drift surfaces such shorelines may consist of just a foot or two of beach gravel. Only with a

still-stand of sea-level or with an actual transgression do the deposits thicken.

Transgressions can produce an additional type of shoreline, as along the big Finnish eskers. The first main transgression during the post-glacial period occurred here when much ice still remained buried. Erosion by the sea tended to expose and disperse the masses of ice, planing off the eskers but failing to produce a well-defined shoreline because melting ice-blocks still persisted. The next transgression is much more clearly marked, for it affected kettle holes, most of which were ice-free, so that it could completely fill depressions with sea-water. The shoreline of this phase consequently marks the lower limit of kettle holes (Fig. 13). It is not always easy to distinguish

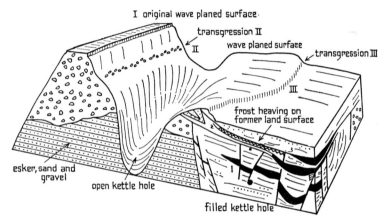

Fig. 13. Transgressive shorelines in fluvioglacial deposits. In the diagram each transgressive beach (2 and 3), and the associated marine silts (2 and 3) are shown.

primary fluvioglacial material from littoral and offshore marine sediments. Only when deep-water marine silts are present can the distinction be made with absolute certainty, the deposits above being marine and those below being primary fluvioglacial material.

Because of the great difficulties in determining the tilt of the shorelines in the field, appeal is made to various mathematical systems. The degree of tilt and the extent of the earlier shorelines are still disputed. Only the later shorelines—from the Littorina to the present —are fixed in time and extent with certainty by means of archaeology, pollen analysis, C–14 dating and studies of diatoms, ostracods, foraminifera, and mollusca.

Methods of determining the supposed tilt or levels of the late glacial shorelines have changed since the time of the earliest investigations, which relied in part on determination of the highest marine limit. But although this limit is synchronous in some areas, in others it is not: some tilted synchronous shorelines can be traced up to an upper marine limit, which may be either horizontal or slightly tilted. In such a case the upper limit of each shoreline marks the position of the retreating ice border—a horizontal limit (by no means rare) resulting from the interaction between uniform uplift and a regular recession of the ice margin (Sauramo 1958). The upper marine limit often varies considerably from place to place. Its irregular pattern is difficult to fit into the usual scheme of tilted shorelines. Hence the postulate that all shorelines above an undoubted tilted series of shorelines are not marine, but were formed in ice-dammed lakes or

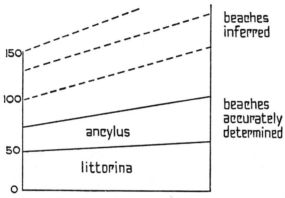

Fig. 14. Traditional shoreline diagram. The tilt of the Littorina and Ancylus shorelines is determined accurately by pollen, diatom, archaeological and geomorphological evidence. The position of older and higher shorelines is inferred by carrying this system upwards gradually increasing the tilt. The actual shorelines are positioned so as to pass through the greatest concentrations of plotted points.

in pro-glacial lakes around nunataks. There are difficulties in such a concept, as positive evidence of both lakes and nunataks is usually lacking (cp. Sissons 1958, 1961).

The extent, altitude, and age of certain post-glacial raised beaches (Littorina and Ancylus beaches) has been accurately determined. By plotting the heights of the beaches against distance, along lines drawn at right angles to the isobases (lines joining beaches of equal height), the lower beaches can be projected upwards to the older beaches. The procedure assumes that the land surface rises at a rate inverse to the distance from the area of greatest ice-thickness, and that the rate of uplift is diminishing at a constant rate. It also assumes that

32     ESSAYS IN GEOMORPHOLOGY

the rate of uplift always outstripped the eustatic rise of sea-level. Thus the older beaches are the highest ones, and are tilted at greater angles than the younger beaches (Fig. 14). Over short distances the beaches appear as straight lines, but if they are traced laterally for tens of kilometres a curved line becomes apparent. This is well seen in the measurements of the Littorina beach (Sauramo 1955a). Although this system seems to work in a great many instances there is a growing body of evidence suggesting other factors than those

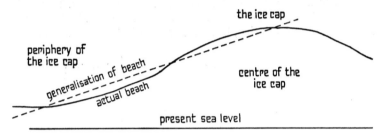

Fig. 15. Relationship between hypothetical and actual tilted shorelines. The 'straight-line' representation cuts the line of the actual beach at three points; it can be used as a rough approximation.

envisaged. A logical corollary of the curved line of gradient of a beach would be a similar flattening of the curve towards the area of greatest uplift, with the straight line beach profile being really the generalization of a sigmoidal curve (Fig. 15).

Detailed investigations show that certain beaches appear to possess a tilt greater than that generally accepted; pollen investigations show that beaches at different levels on the diagram appear to be similar in age. In order to eliminate these anomalies Sauramo (1955a, 1958) formulated his ingenious hinge line hypothesis with sharp changes of gradient in the tilt of particular beaches (Fig. 16). But this idea may be too extreme, because little evidence of zones of geological weakness can be found along the postulated hinge lines by geophysical means, while some beaches can be traced laterally across a major hinge line without showing any signs of deformation (Virkkala 1948, 1953).

By work on the micro-fauna and flora of late- and post-glacial deposits, Florin (1948) finds evidence for one or more major transgressions of the sea during the pre-Boreal period in Sweden. Silts with marine diatoms overlie terrestrial peats containing pollen from this period. Tynni (1960, 1961) obtains identical results in South

Finland, where the shorelines at levels above his highest transgressive beach have a very high tilt (e.g. 1·5 m per km). This evidence shows

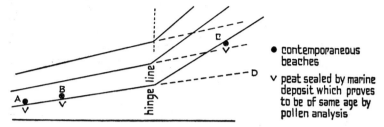

Fig. 16. Principle of hinge lines. In the diagram sites A, B, and C are dated the same age by pollen analysis. Therefore the older representation of the shoreline (A–D) may be incorrect so that it is necessary to introduce a bend or hinge line. The tilt of the more steeply inclined shorelines is based on field-evidence.

that isostatic uplift was extremely rapid at the end of the younger Dryas period (Zone III), and must have produced large areas of dry land. During the pre-Boreal period a sudden eustatic rise of the ocean

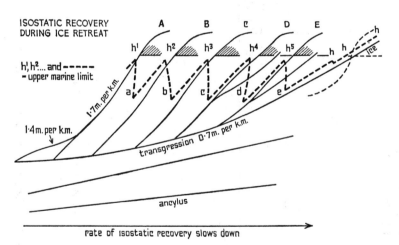

Fig. 17. Diagram illustrating the shoreline pattern in south Finland. This conception does not use hinge lines. Highly tilted shorelines are related to a series of recessional moraines; thus the upper marine limit fluctuates—the 'lows' represent a stationary ice-front during continued uplift—the 'highs' can be inferred from particular shorelines: it ranges from 1·7 m per km near the ice margin to 1·4 m per km in more peripheral areas. The lower series of shorelines were initiated by a major transgression (eustatic) that occurred when crustal uplift had slowed down.

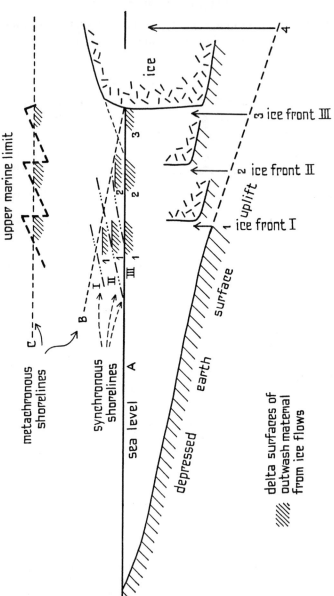

ISOSTATIC RECOVERY
DURING ICE RETREAT

Fig. 18. The principles of isostatic uplift, assuming a constant rate of uplift, and an ice margin retreating and halting at regular intervals.

inundated the Baltic area at a time when isostatic uplift had considerably slowed down.

Beaches levelled by Synge at localities along the same isobase as that of Tynni's localities gave a tilt of 1·4 m per km, and could be extended north some 50 km to beaches with a tilt of 1·7 per km which were formed close to the receding ice margin. These ideas are expressed diagrammatically in Fig. 17.

The principles of isostatic recovery can be best expressed in Fig. 18, where for the sake of argument a constant sea-level is assumed. The ice margin is receding by stages in a uniform manner, 1, 2, 3 . . . At any given stage of the ice retreat, say stage 3, the successive ice marginal features form a metachronic beach B tilting towards the centre of glaciation; such beaches are recorded from Central Finland (Sauramo 1958). By the time recovery is complete (Stage 4), the marginal features have assumed horizontality. Thus, although the metachronous features may form the most prominent shorelines, they cannot be linked together in a synchronous sequence. If the ice retreat slows down, then the delta surfaces will rise above the horizontal; but if ice retreat speeds up they will pitch below this line. Because the land masses near the centres of glaciated areas were depressed isostatically—by hundreds of metres in Scandinavia—the first shorelines on the rising land mass during ice retreat and in the beginning of the eustatic rise of sea-level were cut well *below* present sea-level. The height of these shorelines above present sea-level allows a direct measurement to be made of *only* the amount of isostatic recovery above this datum since deglaciation began (cp. Daly 1934).

If a eustatic rise of the sea-level occurs at the same time, the results are more complicated (Fig. 19). But it can be shown that if the rate of the eustatic rise of sea-level equals the isostatic rise of the land surface a synchronous shoreline coincides with the metachronous delta levels. In this case the upper marine limit is horizontal.

Thus the presence of horizontal beach levels in an isostatically affected area does not necessarily imply separate block movements of the sections of the earth's crust, but is a natural result of the relationship between rate of land uplift and rise of sea-level.

### Pleistocene shorelines in the glaciated area of the British Isles: Southwest Scotland and the North of Ireland

Very little detailed work on the late-glacial shorelines has been carried out in the British Isles (Anderson 1939, Farrington 1945, Mitchell 1963, Sissons 1962). Beaches of this age are confined to the northern parts of these islands, in those areas that lay beneath the greatest ice-load during the Last Glaciation (Figs. 1, 2). The highest beaches recorded occur in Scotland near Oban at about 130 ft O.D. Along much of the coast of Scotland, two beach levels, at 100 ft and 50 ft, are found in many places. They occur between Dunbar and Brora on the east coast, and between Stranraer and Loch Eriboll on the west coast. In the past these have been regarded as two distinct synchronous levels throughout their length and the various sites have

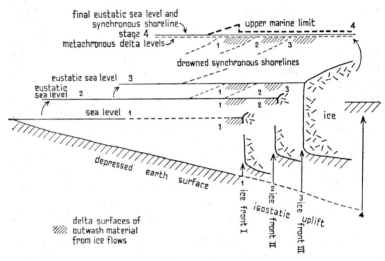

ISOSTATIC RECOVERY DURING ICE RETREAT
AND EUSTATIC RISE OF SEA LEVEL

Fig. 19. The principles of isostatic uplift accompanied by a rising eustatic sea-level. In this example both the rate of uplift of the land and that of sea-level are taken as equal.

been linked with isobases drawn concentric to the area in the western Highlands which is believed to have carried the greatest weight of ice. But as we have seen from the considerable work carried out in Scandinavia, mere horizontality of beaches cannot be accepted as proof of contemporaneity. Synchronous levels are explicable either by a eustatic fall of sea-level by 50 and 100 ft, or by unwarped crustal uplift of the same amount, but there is little evidence to support either view. Furthermore, as has been stressed in many of the Geological Memoirs, these 'beaches' have much more the character of glacial outwash gravels than of true beaches, and the gravels are always unfossiliferous. If they did in fact originate as outwash, they cannot possibly be synchronous. It has already been shown (Figs. 18, 19) that a regular rate of ice recession and a regular rate of uplift account adequately for the general accordance of level of these features, assuming that isostatic recovery is now complete.

If the 100 ft beach is to be regarded as largely an ice-marginal feature, then one must visualize a stage during the late-glacial period at which the sea rose eustatically to a particular level, while Scotland was still isostatically depressed. Then followed a regular recession of the ice-front up the various western lochs, outwash being deposited at the ice-front in the sea all the time. The extreme limits of the 100 ft beach, at Dunbar and Brora, mark the points at which the ice margin stood at the culmination of the late-glacial eustatic rise of sea-level. At these places the synchronous shorelines should extend outwards as tilted strandlines into the less deeply depressed areas. One would expect very small features, probably just a weak washing limit, to indicate the position of a particular temporary strandline.

The Kintyre peninsula (Fig. 20) is most suitable for the study of the problem of the late-glacial 100 ft beach (Donner 1959, 1963). Notches at this level are found along the coast at many places, especially in the west, the highest recorded lying at 130 ft O.D. near Oban, where it is associated with a terminal moraine. At Ford a large terminal moraine is associated with an alluvial outwash terrace that merges into a delta with a level surface of 133 ft O.D. just south of Kilmartin. Farther south, the highest beach was clearly defined at Cretshengan at 110 ft O.D. and again at Stewartfield at 98 ft O.D. These three localities are situated on the same line (Fig. 20). If they are synchronous they indicate a tilt of 1·3 ft per mile (approximately 0·3 m per km) or about ⅕ the amount of tilt of beaches of similar age in Finland. A comparison of size between the Scottish and the Scandinavian ice-caps suggests that the stated tilt is of about the correct order, allowing for the fact that the datum line in Scotland may not be at right angles to the isobases.

The higher marine limit at Rosehill (106 ft O.D.) may mean that, during the period of the retreat of the ice-front from Rosehill to Stewartfield, the almost continuous isostatic land recovery produced an overall *lowering* of the upper marine limit. But it is possible that the marine limits at Rosehill, Stewartfield and Cretshengan lie on the same tilted shoreline, which would indicate a synchronous shoreline. This example demonstrates one of the difficulties of interpreting raised shorelines, where the slight variation in height range (98–110 ft O.D.) might be explained as a function of coastal configuration affecting exposure to wave action at the different sites, of variation in fetch, and even of the accuracy of the surveying technique used in the fieldwork. The highest beach at Rosehill is a shingle bar, resting on boulder clay which overlies bedrock; striae in the bedrock show that the last ice flowed southwestwards.

The Mull of Kintyre itself possesses a landscape highly contrasted

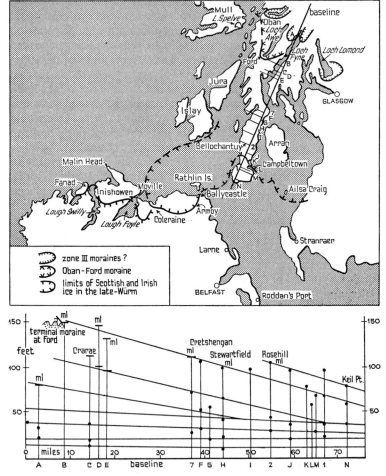

Fig. 20. A shoreline diagram and late-Pleistocene ice limits in the north of Ireland and southwest Scotland. The letters A, B, C . . . refer to sites surveyed by the authors, and the numbers to sites surveyed by J. J. Donner. All sites have been projected to the common baseline and the shoreline diagram constructed. The *dots* represent wave-cut notches in drift, the thick *horizontal bars* are strong terrace levels, and *ml* signifies the *marine limit*.

with that north of Campbeltown; the difference is due to thick solifluction deposits and massive landslides associated with the very definite till-moraine extending from Campbeltown to Bellochantuy. The extensive solifluction deposits have a lower limit at 220 ft on the south coast of the Mull, perhaps corresponding to an earlier washing or ice limit. As the marginal drainage channels cut in fresh drift at Bellochantuy descend well below this level, such a high limit in the Mull must have pre-dated the deglaciation of this part of the coast.

Solifluction in the Mull of Kintyre is so marked that it can only be compared to that immediately outside the limits of the Last Glaciation in Ireland and England. Therefore, it seems likely that when the ice in southwest Scotland reached its maximum extent, which it did later here than elsewhere in the British Isles, it covered most of Kintyre but not the Mull. It is even possible that before the Scottish ice had reached its maximum extent in Kintyre and extended to Ulster, the sea-level had already risen considerably and occupied areas which were subsequently invaded by this ice. The western continuation of the Campbeltown moraine in the north of Ireland (Dwerryhouse 1923) is associated with a till that overlies a contorted silt of possible marine origin at Portballintrae (Stephens 1963).

Both the North Channel and Firth of Clyde must have been heavily weighed down by ice during the maximum of the Last (Würm = Weichsel) Glaciation, as they were the main discharge route of the Scottish ice. But on the other hand, the lack of sharpness of the 220 ft 'washing' limit in the Mull might mean that it is much older at least in part, and possibly of late Riss = Saale age; that is, it might be associated with the deglaciation of the older ice-sheet. Much further work is necessary to elucidate this problem.

Late-glacial marine deposits occur along the north and east coasts of Ireland between Fanad Head and Skerries (Fig. 21). Within the limits of the Last Glaciation, marine waters failed to extend above 50–60 ft O.D. But just outside these ice limits, evidence of wave-action extends as high as 74 ft O.D. on the northwest coast. Thus it appears that in the northwest, isostatic recovery was already taking place *before* the ice started to decay. Respecting ice limits in the northwest, it is suggested that the thick accumulations of morainic drift at Buncrana and Moville mark the Last Glaciation limit in Inishowen. North of this limit the drumlins are absent, no fresh drift forms occur, and widespread solifluction is apparent. The Irish ice extended across the present coastline to the east of Coleraine at the drumlins stage, but the drumlins have been destroyed by the later readvance of the Scottish ice.

On Malin Head the marine limit stands at 68–74 ft O.D. but

declines westward. In Lough Swilly the high strandline is absent. At Greencastle, overlooking the entrance to Lough Foyle, the marine limit stands at 72 ft O.D. Farther south, inside the limits of the Irish Ice Cap the highest beach, 40–50 ft O.D. at Moville, and 48 ft at Ture

Fig. 21. Late-Pleistocene shorelines, marine deposits, terraces, and some ice limits in the north and northeast of Ireland. Diagram heights refer to Irish Datum: heights in the text refer to British Datum:—note a difference of about 8 feet.

rises along the shores of Lough Foyle to Derry where it merges with terraces of glacial outwash that slope northwards. Similar heights (42–67 ft between Coleraine and Fair Head) are recorded along the coast farther east, in terrain that was covered by Scottish ice readvancing from the northeast (in the so-called Scottish Re-advance of Dwerryhouse 1923; Charlesworth 1939). There is no doubt that these beaches represent a transgression that followed the withdrawal of the Scottish ice from the Ballycastle–Coleraine moraine, but the presence of a possible marine clay between the tills of the Irish and Scottish ice at Portballintrae could mean an earlier incursion of marine waters before the re-advance of Scottish ice. Farther south, in Co. Down, a late-glacial shoreline notches the coastal drumlins at levels between 50 and 60 ft O.D. Below this notch occur extensive spreads of red brick clay containing shells of *Yoldiella lenticula*, marine foraminifera and marine ostracods (*Cypridea puntillata*) (Stephens 1963). The actual shoreline is seldom sharp, as it is often buried by solifluction deposits. There is no evidence of any shoreline above this level.

In Dundalk Bay and near Drogheda there is some evidence of late-glacial beaches at a low level. The most southerly so far recorded reaches some 37 ft O.D. The general absence of late-glacial beaches on this low coastline is not surprising, as it is largely drift-covered and subject to considerable coastal erosion. Thick deposits of silt and clay in Dublin Bay may be marine, but no corresponding shoreline has been noted above present sea-level.

Such is the distribution and upper limit of the late-glacial beaches in the north of Ireland. But in character the beaches vary, and can be subdivided on a regional basis. Most of the beaches lying outside the extreme limit of glaciation (that is, Northern Inishowen) differ markedly from those elsewhere, and especially from those in Kintyre. Typically these consist of massive storm-shingle beaches or ridges of rounded boulders at the marine limit (Stephens and Synge 'In Press'). They are not related to glacial outwash, but must represent a synchronous level of considerable duration, as indicated by the well-rounded nature of the deposits. The contrast between the roundness of the beach shingle and angularity of the thick head deposits that clothe the slopes above the limit of wave action is striking. Below the level of the shingle beach bars a wave-cut rock platform extends, sloping outwards from a fossil cliff; the maximum width of this feature is about 300 ft. Examination of this platform and the rock cliff reveals several interesting facts:

1. The platform has a very low gradient (Fig. 22).
2. The platform seldom joins the old rock cliff in a sharp angle—the angle or notch is usually completely hidden by heavy block scree, and angular blocks litter the surface of the platform except in the vicinity of the shingle deposits. There is no boulder clay on it.

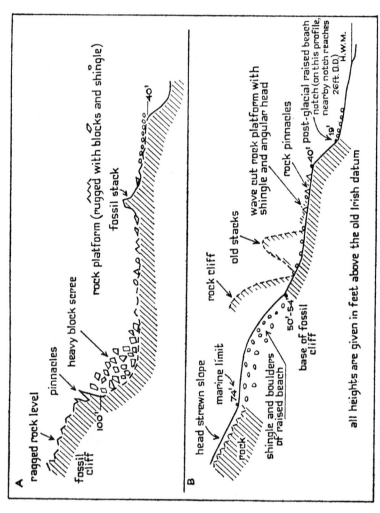

**A**

ragged rock level

pinnacles

heavy block scree

rock platform (rugged with blocks and shingle)

fossil cliff

fossil stack

100'

40'

**B**

head strewn slope

marine limit

rock cliff

old stacks

wave cut rock platform with shingle and angular head

rock pinnacles

74'

shingle and boulders of raised beach

50'-54'

base of fossil cliff

40' post-glacial raised beach notch (on this profile, nearby notch reaches 26ft. O.D.)

19'

H.W.M.

all heights are given in feet above the old Irish datum

Fig. 22. Late-Pleistocene beachs and platforms near Malin Head, north Donegal, Ireland.

3. The fossil cliff, whose base is hidden by angular block scree, may have an irregular profile, that is seldom vertical but is studded with rock buttresses and pinnacles that break the line of the free cliff face and scree slope. These suggest cliff retreat under periglacial conditions, as the sea no longer washed the platform and the notch at the foot of the cliff. The block scree mantling the cliff extends *below* the marine limit.

4. The uppermost 5–6 ft of the shingle that composes these deposits has been churned by frost action, showing that severe periglacial conditions persisted after isostatic recovery had begun, these conditions also being responsible for producing the mantle of debris clothing the cliffs and for etching the rocky crags into pinnacles. The rock platform results from a combination of marine planation, and frost action which occurred between tides and shattered the rock surface. The rock debris was swept away into deeper water, pounded to shingle and rounded on the platform, or flung above normal storm-wave limits in severe gales. Such processes account for a platform as smooth in profile as any described from non-glaciated coastlines. There is therefore every reason to regard the late-glacial beach deposits as resting on their own platform, above which rise some residual stacks.

As yet, the precise chronological relationship has still to be worked out for the 60–70 ft late-glacial beaches of Northern Inishowen, those of Rathlin Island (68 ft), those of Co. Down (50–60 ft) which are associated with the red brick clays, and those of Kintyre. At Killough, Co. Down, there is some evidence of an oscillation of the ice-front into the 'Red Clay Sea' which may correspond to accumulations of outwash at Kilrea, and along the Faughan in Co. Derry. Thus an oscillation of the Irish ice mass, in sympathy with the advance of Scottish ice to the northeast coast, could have occurred after a marine transgression. The moraine of the Scottish Re-advance from Coleraine to Ballycastle might be correlated with a stage of the Irish Ice Cap running through the Faughan (South of Derry), to Kilrea, Dunmurry (esker and kame deposits), and to the west of Dundalk. The transgression associated with this stage of glaciation post-dates the higher beaches of Inishowen.

The presence of possible marine clay deposits below the till of the Scottish Re-advance at Portballintrae has already been mentioned. A similar succession is recorded from Rosehill in Kintyre. As both sites are at low altitudes (less than 100 ft), it is not possible to correlate these clays with the very high 220 ft 'washing' limit in the Mull of Kintyre. Indeed, even if we accept the evidence of a sea-level higher than that of the present, before the re-advance, we have no evidence to show that it was higher in all areas than that which followed the decay of this ice (Fig. 20). Nevertheless, it is possible to say that the first recorded eustatic rise of sea-level occurred some time after the maximum of the Last Glaciation, flooding the more deeply depressed areas that were free of ice, such as Inishowen, when Kintyre was still protected by an ice-barrier. At that time the sea-level was not high enough to transgress the present coastline in the less isostatically depressed areas.

It is quite clear, however, that *all* the late-glacial shorelines of southwest Scotland and northeast Ireland cannot be synchronous. The Irish and Scottish ice-centres acted more or less independently, and there is no reason to regard ice-dissolution as precisely in phase in the two areas. Indeed Donner (1959) suggested that certain important ice re-advances in Zone III in Scotland can be linked with certain phases of the high Late-Glacial sea-levels, whereas in Co. Down the Zone III deposits at Roddans Port show no trace of marine influence, even though today they are awash at high tides. The complexity is probably explained by the different rates of isostatic recovery of the Scottish and Irish landmasses, and perhaps too by the presence of an important tectonic break (Cook and Murphy 1952) between Scotland and Ireland, which may have acted as a hinge zone.

The non-synchronous nature of the late-glacial shorelines in Scotland and Ireland seems to be repeated when the post-glacial raised beaches are studied. The outer limit of the post-glacial shorelines is shown in Fig. 1, the limiting line lying for the most part of its length inside the limit reached by the ice-sheets during the Last Glaciation, as in Scandinavia (Fig. 2). In Ireland the post-glacial shoreline is recorded at 22–24 ft I.O.D. [Irish Datum, which is some 7–8 ft lower than the datum for Great Britain; thus this height range becomes 14–16 ft O.D. for Great Britain] on the south side of Sligo Bay. This shoreline may be present in a few isolated localities in Mayo, and is seen again at a low level in Connemara, in the Shannon estuary and in Bantry Bay. It is high on the north and east coasts of Ireland as far south as Carlingford Lough, ranging from 25–33 ft I.O.D. (Stephens 1957), declines to about 20 ft I.O.D. just south of Dublin Bay, and then disappears. The archaeological, pollen-analytical, and C–14 evidence summarized by Movius (1942), Mitchell (1956), Charlesworth (1957), Watts (1960), Stephens and Collins (1961), Morrison and Stephens (1960, and 'In Press'), Wright (1937) and Godwin (1960) demonstrates conclusively that this shoreline cannot be regarded as synchronous throughout its length. The beach *contains* Mesolithic material in northeast Ireland, but Mesolithic and Neolithic artifacts in Dublin Bay. The degree to which this shoreline is now elevated above present sea-level probably reflects not only the weight of ice passing across a particular segment of coastline, but also the nearness of the coast to one of the major ice-centres (Synge and Stephens 1960). In Scotland the shorelines rise to greater heights than those recorded in Ireland (Wright 1937), a circumstance explained by marine invasion of the more deeply depressed Scottish landmass, although in Scotland, as in Ireland, the post-glacial transgression seems to be a dramatic event brought about by a renewed surge of eustatic rise, temporarily exceeding the rate of isostatic recovery (Jardine 1964).

## Conclusion

The study of Pleistocene shorelines is clearly difficult, especially in heavily glaciated areas where marine transgressions have taken place, but it can nevertheless provide the geomorphologist with a great deal of valuable information. Problems of isostasy and eustasy can be investigated, and river terrace sequences may be elucidated. Full explanatory descriptions of the morphology of existing coastlines, especially in high latitudes, will be incomplete and even inaccurate unless some of the principles here outlined are understood. In addition, the morphogenic approach to the study of world shorelines (Davies 1964) is of considerable value to the research worker concerned with Pleistocene shorelines, and should make for fresh appraisal of attempts at world-wide correlations.

The few actual examples described in some detail are meant to illustrate the complexity of sea-level changes during the Pleistocene, in unglaciated as in glaciated areas. Attention has been confined to certain types of fossil shorelines which can be observed above present mean sea-level, but research is necessary also on fossil marshes and tidal flats, and on shorelines which now are either hidden below many feet of more recent sediments, or are submerged below present sea-level. Perhaps geomorphologists may be induced to examine afresh the whole concept of cyclic or non-cyclic evolution of coasts (Cotton 1958, Valentin 1952), and to examine as closely as possible drift and detrital deposits, both in the field and in the laboratory. A strong case can be made for geomorphologists working on problems of the Pleistocene to adopt some of the rigorous scientific methods, and equipment, used in pedological studies. Shoreline studies may also lead botanists and zoologists to investigate the migration of plants and animals during and after the glacial periods.

## References

Anderson, F. W., 1939. 'Possible late-glacial sea-levels at 190 and 140 ft. O.D. in the British Isles.' *Geol. Mag.*, 76, 317–21.

Apsimon, A. A., Donovan, D. J., and Taylor, H., 1961. 'The stratigraphy and archaeology of the late-glacial and post-glacial deposits at Brean Down, Somerset.' *Proc. Univ. Bristol Spelaeol. Soc.*, 9, 67–136.

Arber, E. A. N., 1911. *The Coast Scenery of North Devon.*

Arber, M. A., 1960. 'Pleistocene sea-levels in North Devon.' *Proc. Geol. Assoc.*, 71, 169–76.

Baden-Powell, D. F. W., 1927. 'On the present climatic equivalence of British raised beach mollusca.' *Geol. Mag.*, 64, 433–8.

Baden-Powell, D. F. W., 1934. 'On the marine gravels at March, Cambridgeshire.' *Geol. Mag.*, 71, 193–219.

Baden-Powell, D. F. W., 1955. 'The correlation of Pliocene and Pleistocene marine beds of Britain and the Mediterranean.' *Proc. Geol. Soc. Lond.*, 66, 271–92.

Baulig, H., 1935. 'The changing sea level.' *Inst. Brit. Geographers, Publn. no. 3*, 1–46.

Blake, W., 1961. 'Radiocarbon dating of raised beaches in Nordaustlandet, Spitsbergen.' *Geology of the Arctic*, pp. 133–45.

Bourcart, J., 1939. 'La marge continentale; essai sur les régressions et transgressions marines.' *Soc. Géol. France Bull.*, 8, 393–474.

Bourcart, J., 1950. 'La théorie de la flescure continentale.' *Congr. Géog. Internat.*, C–R. Lisbon, 2, 167–90.

Büdel, J., 1960. 'Die gliederung der Würmkaltzeit.' *Würzb. Geog. Arbeit.*, 8, 1–45.

Bulleid, A., and Jackson, J. W., 1937. 'The Burtle Sand Beds of Somerset.' *Proc. Somersets. Arch. Nat. Hist. Soc.*, 83, 171–95.

Cailleux, A., and Taylor, G., 1954. *Cryopédologie: étude des sols gelés.* Paris.

Charlesworth, J. K., 1957. *The Quaternary Era* (2 vols.). Arnold, Edinburgh.

Cook, A. H., and Murphy, J., 1952. 'Measurements of gravity in Ireland; gravity survey of Ireland north of a line Sligo–Dundalk.' *Dublin Inst. Adv. Studies, Geophys. Mem.*, 2, 1–36.

Cotton, C. A., 1958. 'Eustatic river terracing complicated by seaward downflexure.' *Trans. Edinburgh Geol. Soc.*, 17, 165–78.

Daly, R. A., 1934. *The Changing World of the Ice Age.* Yale Univ. Press, New Haven.

Davies, J. L., 1964. 'A morphogenic approach to world shorelines.' Zeitschrift für Geomorphologie, 8, 127–42.

Dewey, H., 1913. 'The raised beach of North Devon: its relation to others and to Palaeolithic Man.' *Geol. Mag.*, 10, 154–63.

Dinham, C. H., 1927. 'The geology of the Stirling District.' *Proc. Geol. Assoc.*, 38, 470–94.

Donner, J. J., 1952. 'On the early post-glacial shoreline displacement in southeast Finland.' *Ann. Acad. Sci. Fenn.* A. III, 29, 1–22.

PLEISTOCENE SHORELINES       47

Donner, J. J., 1959. 'The late- and post-glacial raised beaches in Scotland.' *Ann. Acad. Sci. Fenn.*, 53, 1–25.

Donner, J. J., 1963. 'The late- and post-glacial raised beaches in Scotland II.' *Ann. Acad. Sci. Fenn.*, 68, 1–13.

Dury, G. H., 1954. 'Contribution to the general theory of meandering valleys.' *Amer. Journ. Sci.*, 252, 193–224.

Dury, G. H., 1958. 'Tests of a general theory of misfit streams.' *Trans. Inst. Brit. Geographers, Publn. no. 25*, 105–18.

Dylik, J., 1960. 'Sur le système triparti de la stratigraphie du Pléistocène dans les pays d'accumulation glaciaire.' *Biuletyn Peryglacjalny*, 9, 25–39.

Espenshade, E. B. (chairman), 1961. *Coastal Geography*. Nat. Acad. Sci., Nat. Res. Council. Washington D.C.

Everard, C. E., 1954. 'The Solent River—a geomorphological study.' *Trans. and Papers, Inst. Brit. Geog., Pubn. no. 20*, 41–58.

Fairbridge, R. W., and Stewart, H. B., 1960. 'Alesca Bank, a drowned atoll on the Melanesian Border Plateau.' *Research*, 7, 100–16.

Fairbridge, R. W., 1961. 'Eustatic changes in sea level.' *Physics and Chemistry of the Earth*, 4, 99–185.

Farrington, A., 1945. 'The level of the ocean in glacial and late-glacial times.' *Proc. Roy. Irish Acad.*, 50B, 237–43.

Farrington, A., 1959. 'The Lee valley: part one, glaciation.' *Proc. Roy. Irish Acad.*, 60B, 135–66.

Flett, J. S., and Hill, J. B., 1912. 'Geology of Lizard and Meneage.' *Mem. Geol. Soc.*

Flint, R. F., 1961. *Glacial and Pleistocene Geology*. Wiley, New York.

Florin, S., 1948. 'Kustförskjutningen och Bebyggelseutvecklingen i östra Mellan sverige under senkvartär Tid.' *Geol. Fören.*, 70, 17–196.

Galon, R., 1960. 'Problem of geomorphological classification of the Polish coast.' *Przeglad Geograficzny*, 32 Supp., 67–77.

George, T. N., 1932. 'The Quaternary beaches of Gower.' *Proc. Geol. Assoc.*, 43, 291–324.

Godwin, H., 1945. 'Coastal peat-beds of the North Sea region as indices of land- and sea-level changes.' *New Phytologist*, 44, 29–69.

Godwin, H., 1960. 'Radiocarbon dating and Quaternary history in Britain.' *Proc. Roy. Soc.*, B, 153, 287–320.

Godwin, H., Suggate, R. P., and Willis, E. H., 1958. 'Radiocarbon dating of the eustatic rise in ocean-level.' *Nature*, 181, 1518–19.

Granö, O., 1958. 'The Vessö esker in southern Finland and its economic importance.' *Fennia*, 82, 1–33.

Green, J. F. N., 1943. 'The age of the raised beaches of southern Britain.' *Proc. Geol. Assoc.*, 54, 129–40.

Guilcher, A., 1958. *Coastal and Submarine Morphology*. Methuen, London.

Gutenberg, B., 1941. 'Changes in sea-level, post-glacial uplift, and mobility of the earth's interior.' *Bull. Geol. Soc. Amer.*, 52, 721–2.

Hyyppä, E., 1936. 'Über die spätquartäre Entwicklung Nordfinnlands mit Ergänzungen zur Kenntnis des spätglazialen Klimas. Vorläufige Mitteilung.' *Bull. de la Comm. Géol. Finlande*, 115, 401–46.

48     ESSAYS IN GEOMORPHOLOGY

Jardine, W. G., 1964. Post-glacial sea-levels in South-west Scotland. *Scot. Geog. Mag.*, 80, 5–11.

Johnson, D., 1933. 'The correlation of ancient marine levels.' *Internat. Geog. Congr.*, Paris 1931, 2, 42–54.

Jonsson, J., 1957. 'Notes on changes of sea-level in Iceland.' *Geografiska Annaler*, 37, 143–212.

King, W. B. R., 1954. 'The geological history of the English Channel.' *Quart. Journ. Geol. Soc.*, 110, 77–101.

Kuenen, H., 1955. 'Sea-level and crustal warping.' *Crust of the Earth (A Symposium), Geol. Soc. Amer., Spec. Paper 62.*

Lewis, W. V., and Balchin, W. G. V., 1940. 'Past sea levels at Dungeness.' *Geog. Journ.*, 96, 258–85.

McFarlane, P. B., 1955. 'Survey of two drowned river valleys in Devon.' *Geol. Mag.*, 92, 419–29.

McGill, J. T., 1958. 'Map of coastal landforms of the world.' *Geog. Review.*, 48, 402–5.

Maw, G., 1864. 'On a supposed deposit of boulder clay in North Devon.' *Quart. Journ. Geol. Soc.*, 20, 445–51.

Miller, A. A., 1939. 'Attainable standards of accuracy in the determination of preglacial sea levels by physiographic methods.' *Journ. Geomorph.*, 2, 95–115.

Mitchell, G. F., 1951a. 'Studies in Irish Quaternary deposits, No. 7.' *Proc. Roy. Irish. Acad.*, 53B, 111–206.

Mitchell, 1951b. 'The Pleistocene period in Ireland.' *Meddelelser fra Densk Geol. Foren., Bd.* 12, 111–14.

Mitchell, G. F., 1956. 'An early kitchen-midden at Sutton, Co. Dublin.' *Journ. Roy. Soc. Antiq. Ireland*, 86, 1–26.

Mitchell, G. F., 1960. 'The Pleistocene history of the Irish Sea.' *Adv. Sci.*, 68, 313–25.

Mitchell, G. F., 1962. 'Summer field meeting in Wales and Ireland.' *Proc. Geol. Assoc.*, 73, 197–213.

Mitchell, G. F., 1963. 'Morainic ridges on the floor of the Irish Sea.' *Irish Geog.*, 4, 335–44.

Morrison, M. E. S., and Stephens, N., 1960. 'Stratigraphy and pollen analysis of the raised beach deposits at Ballyhalbert, Co. Down, Northern Ireland.' *New Phytologist*, 59, 153–62.

Morrison, M. E. S., and Stephens, N., 1965. 'A submerged late-Quaternary deposit at Roddans Port on the north-east coast of Ireland.' *Phil. Trans. Roy. Soc. Lond. B. In Press.*

Movius, H. L., 1942. *The Irish Stone Age.* C.U.P., Cambridge.

Movius, H. L., 1953. 'Graphic representation of post-glacial changes of level in Northeast Ireland.' *Amer. Journ. Sci.*, 251, 697–740.

Nansen, F., 1928. 'The earth's crust, its surface forms, and isostatic adjustment.' *Arhandl. det norske Videnskabs.-Akad.* Oslo, 1.

Nonn, H., 1960. 'The deposits of the western part of the Cantabrian "Rasa".' *Révue de Géomorph. Dynamique*, 11, 97–105.

Okko, V., 1957. 'The second Salpausselkä at Jylisjärvi, east of Hämeen-linna.' *Fennia*, 81, 1–46.

Olsson, I., and Blake, W., 1961. 'Problems of radiocarbon dating of raised beaches, based upon experience in Spitsbergen.' *Norsk Geog. Tidskr.*, 1–2, 1–18.

Orme, A. R., 1960. 'The raised beaches and strandlines of South Devon.' *Field Studies*, 1, 1–22.

'Pleistocene dating and Man: abstracts of a symposium.' 1962. *Adv. Sci.*, 18, 485–98.

Praeger, R. L., 1896. 'Report on the raised beaches of the northeast of Ireland, with special reference to their fauna.' *Proc. Roy. Irish Acad.*, 20, 30–54.

Ramsay, W., 1924. 'On relations between crustal movements and varia-tions of sea-level during the late Quaternary time, especially in Fenno-scandia.' *Bull. Comm. Géol. Finlande*, 66, *Fennia* 44, No. 5, 1–39.

Rice, R. J., 1961. 'The glacial deposits at St Fort in northeastern Fife: a re-examination.' *Trans. Edinburgh Geol. Soc.*, 18, 113–23.

Richards, H. G., 1960. 'Correlation of Pleistocene shorelines of North America with those of Europe.' *Rept. Internat. Geol. Congr. 21, Part 4, Chronology and Climatology of the Quaternary*, 58–61.

Richards, H. G., 1962. 'Studies on the marine Pleistocene.' *Trans. Amer. Phil. Soc.*, 52, 1–141.

Rogers, I., and Simpson, B., 1937. 'The flint gravel deposit of Orleigh Court, Buckland Brewer, North Devon.' *Geol. Mag.*, 74, 309–16.

Sauramo, M., 1955a. 'Land uplift with hinge-lines in Fennoscandia.' *Ann. Acad. Sci. Fenn.*, A44, 1–25.

Sauramo, M., 1955b. 'On the nature of Quaternary crustal upwarping in Fennoscandia.' *Acta Geog.*, 14, 334–48.

Sauramo, M., 1958. 'Die Geschichte de Ostsee.' *Ann. Acad. Sci. Fenn.*, A., *Geol-Geog.*, 51, 1–522.

Schou, A., 1949. *Atlas of Denmark: I, The Landscape.* H. Hagerup, København.

Schou, A., 1960. 'The coastline of Djursland: a study in east Danish shore-line development.' *Internat. Geog. Union, Guidebook Denmark*, 11–28.

Shotton, F. W., 1962. 'The physical background of Britain in the Pleisto-cene.' *Adv. Sci.*, 19, 1–14.

Simpson, S., 1953. 'The development of the Lyn drainage system and its relation to the origin of the coast between Coombe Martin and Porlock.' *Proc. Geol. Assoc.*, 64, 14–23.

Sissons, J. B., 1958. 'Supposed ice-dammed lakes in Britain with particular reference to the Eddlestone Valley, southern Scotland.' *Geog. Ann. Stock.*, 40, 159–87.

Sissons, J. B., 1961. 'Some aspects of glacial drainage channels in Britain, part II.' *Scot. Geog. Mag.*, 77, 15–36.

Sissons, J. B., 1962. 'A re-interpretation of the literature on late-glacial shorelines in Scotland, with particular reference to the Forth area.' *Trans. Edinburgh Geol. Soc.*, 19, 83–99.

Southward, A. J., and Crisp., D. J., 1954. 'The distribution of certain intertidal animals around the Irish coast.' *Proc. Roy. Irish Acad.*, 57B, 1-29.

Sparks, B. W., 1960. *Geomorphology.* Longmans, London.

Steers, J. A., 1953. 'The East Coast Floods, January 31-February 1, 1953.' *Geog. Journ.*, 119, 280-98.

Steers, J. A., 1959. 'Archaeology and physiography in coastal studies.' *Second Coastal Geog. Conference, Coastal Studies Inst. Louisiana.* Washington (pp. 317-40).

Stephens, N., 1957. 'Some observations on the "interglacial" platform and the early post-glacial raised beach on the east coast of Ireland.' *Proc. Roy. Irish Acad.*, 58B, 129-49.

Stephens, N., 1958. 'The evolution of the coastline of northeast Ireland.' *Adv. Sci.*, 56, 389-91.

Stephens, N., 1961. 'Re-examination of some Pleistocene sections in Cornwall and Devon (abstract).' *Roy. Geol. Soc. Cornwall, Camborne Conference*, 21-3.

Stephens, N., 1963. 'Late-glacial sea-levels in northeast Ireland.' *Irish Geog.*, 4, 345-59.

Stephens, N., and Collins, A. E. P., 1961. 'The Quaternary deposits at Ringneill Quay and Ardmillan, Co. Down.' *Proc. Roy. Irish Acad.*, 61C, 41-77.

Stephens, N., and Synge, F. M., 1958. 'The Quaternary deposits at Sutton, Co. Dublin.' *Proc. Roy. Irish Acad.*, 59B, 19-27.

Stephens, N., and Synge, F. M., 1965. 'Late-Pleistocene Shorelines and drift limits in North Donegal.' *Proc. Roy. Irish. Acad. In Press.*

Synge, F. M., 1963. 'A correlation between the drifts of SE Ireland and those of W. Wales.' *Irish Geog.*, 4, 360-6.

Synge, F. M., and Stephens, N., 1960. 'The Quaternary period in Ireland —an assessment.' *Irish Geog.*, 4, 121-30.

Tanner, V., 1931. 'L'étude des terrasses littorales en Fenno-Scandie et l'homotaxie intercontinentale.' *Union Geog. Int. III. Rapport de la Comm. pour l'Etude des Terr. Plioc. et Pleistoc. Paris*, 2, 61-76.

Taylor, C. W., 1956. 'Erratics of the Saunton and Fremington areas.' *Rept. Devon Assoc. Adv. Sci.*, 88, 52-64.

Tricart, J., 1952. 'Paléoclimats quaternaires et morphologie climatique dans le Midi méditerranéen.' *Eisz. und Geg.*, 2, 172-88.

Tricart, J., 1953. 'Résultats préliminaires d'expériences sur la désagrégation de roches sédimentaires par le gel,' *C-R Acad. Sci.*, 236, 1296-1298.

Tricart, J., 1960. 'Manifestation periglaciares du Quaternaire ancien en France.' *Biuletyn Peryglacjalny*, 9, 143-57.

Tricart, J., Michel, P., and Vogt, J., 1957. 'Oscillations climatiques quaternaires en Afrique Occidentale.' *Résumés V Congr. Internat. INQUA, Madrid-Barcelona*, 187-8.

Troll, C., 1954. 'Über Alter und Bilding von Talmaändern.' *Erdkunde*, 8, 286-302.

Tynni, R., 1960. 'Ostseestadium während der Allerødzeit in Askola, Ost-Uusimaa (Südfinland).' *C-R Soc. Geol. Finlande*, No. 32.

Tynni, R., 1961. 'Late- and post-glacial history of the Askola district near Helsinki.' Unpublished thesis, Geol. Surv. Finland.

Valentin, H., 1952. 'Die Küsten der Erde.' *Petermanns Geogr. Mitt.*, 264.

Valentin, H., 1953. 'Present vertical movements of the British Isles.' *Geog. Journ.*, 119, 299–305.

Virkkala, E., 1948. 'Late-glacial development of shorelines in southern Kainur and northern Karelia.' *Bull. Comm. Géol. Finlande*, 142.

Virkkala, E., 1953. 'Altitude of the Littorina limit in Askola, South Finland.' *C-R Soc. Géol. Finlande*, 26, 59–72.

Von Post, L., 1952. 'New aspects of the late-Quaternary displacements of Swedish sea shore.' *Medd. fr. Stockh. Högskol. Geol. Inst.*, No. 99.

Waters, R. S., 1960. 'Pre-Würm periglacial phenomena in Britain.' *Biuletyn Peryglacjalny*, 9, 163–76.

Watts, W. A., 1959. 'Interglacial deposits at Kilbeg and Newtown, Co. Waterford.' *Proc. Roy. Irish Acad.*, 60B, 79–134.

Watts, W. A., 1960. 'C-14 dating and the Neolithic in Ireland.' *Antiquity*, 34, 111–16.

West, R. G., 1963. Problems of the British Quaternary. *Proc. Geol. Assoc.*, 74, 147–86.

Williams, G., 1954. 'Fauna of Strangford Lough and neighbouring coasts.' *Proc. Roy. Irish Acad.*, 56B, 29–133.

Wills, L. J., 1938. 'The Pleistocene development of the Severn from Bridgnorth to the sea.' *Quart. Journ. Geol. Soc.*, 94, 161–242.

Wooldridge, S. W., 1960. 'The Pleistocene succession in the London Basin.' *Proc. Geol. Assoc.*, 71, 113–29.

Wooldridge, S. W., and Linton, D. L., 1955. *Structure, Surface, and Drainage in Southeast England* (2nd edn.). George Phillips, London.

Wright, W. B., 1925. 'Three short papers on isostasy.' *Geol. Mag.*, 62, 227–34.

Wright, W. B., 1928. 'The raised beaches of the British Isles.' *Internat. Geog. Union, Rept. Comm. Pliocene and Pleistocene Terraces*, 99–106.

Wright, W. B., 1937. *The Quaternary Ice Age* (2nd edn.). Macmillan, London.

Wright, W. B., and Muff, H. B., 1904. 'The pre-glacial raised beach of the south coast of Ireland.' *Proc. Roy. Dublin Soc.*, New Ser., 10, 250–324.

Zeuner, F. E., 1952. 'Pleistocene shorelines.' *Geol. Rundschau*, 40, 39–50.

Zeuner, F. E., 1959. *The Pleistocene Period* (2nd. edn.). London.

# Slope Failure
# and Morphogenetic Regions

## R. COMMON

Slope failure has been described as that part of the process of denudation in which the solid materials predominate (Ward 1945), but the expression is also employed to identify a distinctive physiographic form. Both aspects of the topic are surprisingly fruitful ones for the geographer with a scientific turn of mind, for they have the added attraction of being concerned with real problems and theoretical explanations.

Since the publication of Sharpe's pioneer study (1938), *Landslides and Related Phenomena*, the interest of several professions and the needs of certain sections of society have produced a considerable volume of fresh information upon both aspects of this subject. Much current literature (Baver 1956; Bull 1950; Cumberland 1947; Hills 1943; Krynine and Judd 1957; Taylor 1948; Terzaghi 1958) reaffirms that the failure process is normally the combined effect of several factors, acting at different rates for varying periods of time, which are responsible for the entrance of slopes upon a critical condition. Then the waxing and waning of a single force, the introduction or absence of only one additional factor seems enough to start or stop the deformation of a slope. Shearing stresses in the material of a slope cause creep when they exceed the 'fundamental' shearing resistance, but cause landslides when they are strong enough to produce shear failures (Terzaghi, *op. cit.* 1958, p. 85). The major factor in rapid flowages, however, is decreased internal friction in the material involved. Despite the generalizations which are possible about the processes involved in, and the geomorphological results of, slope failure there are no simple rule of thumb criteria for the safety of particular slopes in a given environment, without field observations. Nevertheless it is now possible to reduce the risk of unintentionally encouraging its occurrence and to take correct preventative action when certain of its undesirable manifestations appear.

Sharpe's original classification of slope failure processes and forms, although generally sound and acceptable, now requires some revision

c                                    53

and qualification: a number of quibbles appear in recent American literature (see e.g. Parizek and Woodruff 1957). Slope deformation in organic deposits deserve to be included and treated separately, since peat flows or slides can be regionally important and peat deposits are often very extensive,[1] e.g. their combined area in U.S.S.R., Canada, Sweden and Finland alone surpasses 150,000 square miles (for the U.K., see Bower 1960a, 1960b, Bowes 1960, Praeger 1950; cf. also Sjors 1961, for a map of northern peatlands). Sufficient data have now accumulated for the classification to recognize those composite forms in which slip and flow processes alike have taken place, with or without modification from other agents of denudation. Cumberland's earlier observations on this point (op. cit. 1947, p. 38), based upon New Zealand experience, have been adequately supported in later writings from other parts of the world (see for instance Common 1953, Horton 1945, Thomas 1959). Glacially-induced deformations and subsequent failures on glacially disturbed or weakened slopes, similar to those referred to elsewhere in this text, might eventually deserve a place in the classification. There is also a need for a subdivision to cater for anthropogenic forms, i.e. those due primarily to human disturbance of slope-equilibrium.

The number of variables involved, however, show that precise classification of deformation patterns or exact quantitative analysis of their processes are unobtainable ideals. Engineers and geologists alike admit that it can be very difficult to determine the various factors in slope stability at all accurately (Fig. 1). 'No physical property of cohesive soil is more complex than the shearing strength' (Taylor, op. cit. 1948, p. 362), and significant variations in this resistance to deformation among widespread, mixed deposits only increase the difficulty of measurement. Experience has also shown that the term water lubrication fails to give an adequate explanation of the mechanics in certain types of slope failure. Changes in cohesion (Dettmann 1958), pore water pressure, frictional resistance and the total weight of an earth mass are each distinguished instead and are recognized to upset slope equilibrium in many instances. Understandably, therefore, the rapid removal of excessive amounts of water in slide-prone areas, either by pumping from wells or by bleeding through galleries, has come to be an effective inhibiting technique in use by the engineers.

Recent work stresses the importance of events preceding sudden and occasionally catastrophic slope failures. Unexpected collapse of a

---

[1] The subject of bogflows in Ireland will be briefly reviewed in a forthcoming article on 'Recent mass movements in northeast Ireland' by Colhoun, E. A., Common, R., and Cruickshank, M.

SOME SELECTED PROPERTIES OF MIXED DEPOSITS

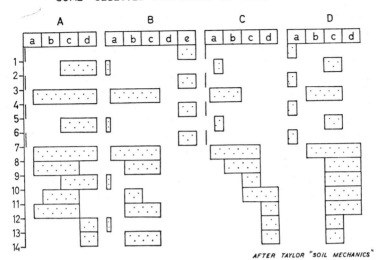

Fig. 1. Selected physical properties of certain mixed deposits.

A. DRY STRENGTH: (a) None to very slight, (b) Slight, (c) Medium, (d) High.
B. DRAINAGE CHARACTERISTICS: (a) Practically impervious to very poor, (b) Poor, (c) Fair, (d) Good, (e) Excellent.
C. SHRINKAGE, EXPANSION, ELASTICITY: (a) None to very slight, (b) Slight, (c) Medium, (d) High.
D. POTENTIAL FROST ACTION: (a) None to very slight, (b) Slight, (c) Medium, (d) High.

Materials involved.
1. Well graded gravel and gravel/sand mixtures. Little to no fines.
2. Well graded gravel/sand/clay mixtures.
3. Poorly graded gravel and gravel/sand mixtures. Little to no fines.
4. Gravel with fines; silty gravel; clayey gravel.
5. Well graded sands and gravelly sands. Little to no fines.
6. Well graded sand/clay mixtures.
7. Poorly graded sands. Little or no fines.
8. Sands with fines, very silty sands, clayey sands, poorly graded sand/clay mixtures.
9. Silts and very fine sands. Rock flour. Silty or clayey fine sands with slight plasticity.
10. (Inorganic) clays of low to medium plasticity, sandy clays, silty clays, lean clays.
11. Organic silt and organic silt clay of low plasticity.
12. Micaceous or diatomaceous fine sandy and silty soil.
13. (Inorganic) clay of high plasticity. Fat clays.
14. (Organic) clay of medium to high plasticity.

The importance of fine texture upon the physical properties is apparent and in particular the influence of silt and clay. In respect of column D, measurements show that frost heaving is not simply the result of freezing and thawing of pore moisture. Different materials have differing capacities to draw additional water from depth to take part in the freezing process and this suction is encouraged by a slow rate of freezing, but inhibited if the freezing is rapid.

slope that has withstood prevailing natural conditions without much apparent change was, in the past, all too easily attributed to an abnormal occurrence. Except with earthquakes, volcanic or other earth tremors and spontaneous liquefaction, any abnormality is merely an additional contributory factor to such events. Since documentation of slides, slumps, and flows associated with earthquakes is already adequate, the information will not be repeated here. Two comments are alone necessary: first, that flows due to seismic activity can be extremely large and rapid, e.g. the mudflow at Mt Olivet Cemetery in San Francisco involved 90,000 cu. yd of material, which moved almost 1000 yd in 3 minutes; second, that slope failures in the Chilean earthquakes of 1960 have now been described by Weischet (1960, p. 282). The material involved normally offers a declining resistance to deformation, and failure may be accelerated by the application of additional forces on a particular occasion. Norwegian investigations into slides in late-glacial clays near Trondheim, Oslo and Ullensaker, for example, prove that it is the simple process of leaching out of contained salt, by groundwater, which rapidly reduces the shearing strength of the deposits (Bjerrum 1955, Bjerrum and Eide 1955). Lessons painfully learnt in the Göta Valley of Sweden (Jarnerfors 1958, Odenstad 1957; Sandegren 1960) also demonstrate the same point, and illustrate how human ingenuity can devise effective warning systems for railways in slide-prone areas. The simplest form of warning system operates when movement of an earth mass is sufficient to close an electric circuit. Hollow metal tubes containing metal rods and connected to a power supply are driven vertically into the slide-prone ground. Electric power to operate the warning system is not available until earth pressures on the outer metal tube cause it to bend and touch the inner, vertical rod.

Other observations show that it is unwise to attach too much importance to the angle of surface slope, without considering the other safety factors of the material involved. Reviewing the distribution of Exmoor slides, Gifford (1953) noted that 'It was with vegetation cover, which is itself an indicator of groundwater conditions, rather than angle of slope, that the distribution of landslides can be most closely related. Most of the landslide scars lie within patches of "wet" vegetation on slopes varying in steepness from 30° or more to as little as 8°.' In contrast, the rapid collapse of original internal structures during spontaneous liquefaction chiefly accounts for the sand slope failures on gradients of only 1 in 4 in coastal Zeeland. Spontaneous liquefaction can result from a rapid rise in the water table or from sudden shocks causing an internal rearrangement of particles within certain deposits. During this process of reorientation the porosity also rapidly decreases and thus the equilibrium of the slope material is disturbed. Loss of cohesion on the other hand, due to swelling and shrinkage, is largely responsible for the fact that stable, naturally-cut slopes in London Clay seldom exceed gradients

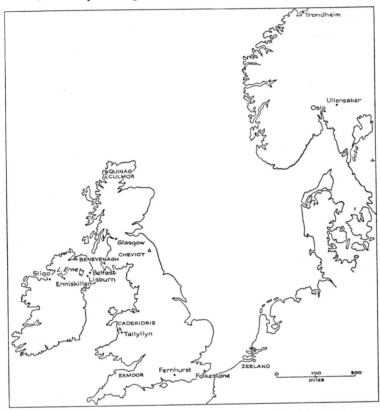

Fig. 2. Location of places in northwest Europe mentioned in the text.

of 1 in 6. Although relaxation of stress in homogeneous material forming the sides of natural or artificial cuttings can often be readily recognized as the prime factor producing slope instability, the role of the same factor in a succession of competent and incompetent deposits is apt to be overlooked. The collapse in recent years of the Peace River bridge in north Alberta, resulted from stress relaxation in incompetent deposits near the river which, undergoing creep, disturbed the equilibrium of overlying competent material (cf. Christiansen 1959).

Paradoxically, suitable conditions do permit steep, man-made slopes to be cut in materials which can be otherwise extremely unreliable. Hard shales can be graded safely at $\frac{1}{2}$ : 1 when the collective assessment of dip and joint systems, climatic regime, soil processes and vegetation cover, potential loading and susceptibility to change is favourable.

In spite of the wealth of new information upon the phenomena of slope failure, some aspects of the topic remain neglected. It is known for instance that there is a periodicity of 19–20 years in the Folkestone Warren slides and that many Norwegian slides (Rapp 1960) tend to coincide with spring thaws and autumn rains, but data generally on the matter of periodicity in slope failures is still slight. Similarly, the results of recent research by Rudberg (1958) in Sweden and Williams (1957) in Norway promise that the systematic and long-term collection of basic data upon earthflow rates will be profitable, and therefore worthy of attention in the future. Another neglected aspect concerns slope failure in landscape development, even though a number of field workers have hinted that it is likely to be a significant one (e.g. Hays 1942). While recognizing that the work of Davis and Penck was of the greatest value to the whole subject of geomorphology, few would deny that there was a considerable period of time in which their ideas on landscape development were accepted as moulds rather than as models. In more recent years, however, new models for landform evolution have been proposed by Peltier (1950), King (1951), and Cotton (1961). This work, allied with a succession of French studies (e.g. Cholley 1957), underlining the relative importance of climate in geomorphology, has made for fresh thinking on processes of subaerial denudation. The author's observations on the Mediterranean area, the Prairie Provinces, and northwest Europe suggest that the relative importance of slope failure still tends to be underestimated or ignored in these areas.

Fieldwork in central Macedonia (Fig. 3) located slope failures in third-order relief features which demanded more than passing attention. Valleys tributary to the Tripotamos, for example, often display lower slopes which are either cleanly scoured or debris-cluttered. The bare, scoured valley sides are clearly the products of sheet erosion, a process encouraged both by biotic and by climatic factors. Cluttered sections usually are composed of coarse heterogeneous deposits, distributed first on one bank and then on the other. This material is associated with slides, flows and catsteps which often involve faces 60–100 ft in height, as well as with depositional cones lying at the foot of valley-side gullies. The features are responsible for small and temporary derangements of drainage, but steady rain in the cool season or heavy convectional showers in summer seem likely to flush and grade the debris within comparatively short periods of time. Also common is slope failure on the flanks of minor spurs, producing low cliffs and recesses. An extreme sample of the variations produced by this type of erosion is a small corrie-like recess, floored with colluvium instead of till. It is therefore suggested that minor spurs can be segmented by slope failure which plays either a dominant role in the enlargement of recesses lying on opposite sides of the spur,

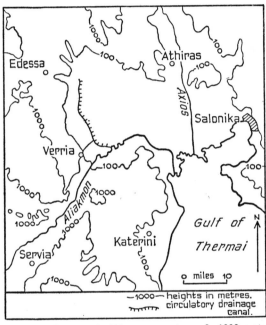

Fig. 3(a). Location diagram. 1. 100 metre contour, 2. 1000 metre contour, 3. Circulation (drainage) canal, 4. Salonika.

or a minor (but important) role in accelerating the headward extension of small opposed streams. Segmentation of spurs in these fashions may also represent the penultimate stage of butte development (Fig. 4).

Away from the higher ground of crystalline rocks and older sediments, but above 50 metres, the impress of slope failure appears on the youthfully dissected terrain of softer, mixed Tertiary deposits. Ephemeral perched water tables frequently appear to overload the sides of many seasonal gullies, whilst rapid drawdown is probably

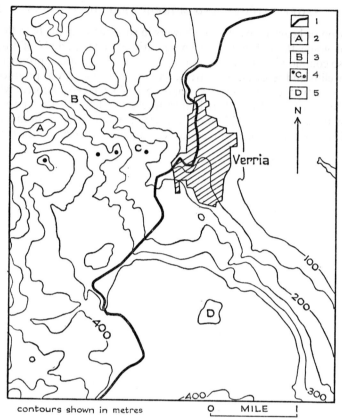

Fig. 3(b). Buttes and slope failures near Verria. 1. Tripotamos. 2. Minor spur being segmented by slope failures and gullying. 3. Locality where slides and slumps pronounced. 4. Example of a series of minor buttes which are probably derived from denudation of a former flight of terraces and benches. 5. Large butte on travertine deposits. (Contours drawn at 50 metre interval.)

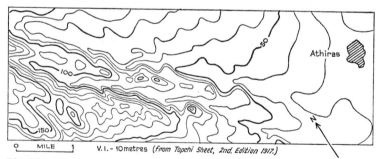

Fig. 3(c). Contour pattern northwest of Athiras, showing large and small butte features along minor watersheds.

responsible for some of the bank caving. The fine chain of residual buttes upon the minor watershed west of Athiras could possibly represent a larger scale version of the segmented spurs and minor buttes examined to the west.

The effectiveness of subaerial agents and their mode of combination differ from those of northwest Europe. Tentatively, therefore, the distinctive regional environment is taken to produce a hybrid

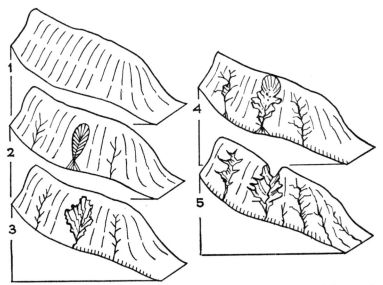

Fig. 4. Suggested sequence of changes often produced by slope failure and gullying to dissect spurs in Central Macedonia.
1. Spur segment from watershed to talweg in initial stages.
2. Recess developed because of slides and slumps.
3. Recess growth aided by other subaerial processes.
4. Recess head enlarged by fresh slides.
5. Watershed breached by coalescing of recesses working inwards from both flanks of the spur.

set of landforms, due partially to present fluctuating African and European climatic influences and partially to the local human geography and palaeogeography. The Prairie Provinces of Canada, however, reveal an even greater increase in the relative importance of slope failures during the evolution of regional landforms.

Genetically different types of slope occurring together alongside several of the larger streams, overburden with a quasi-morainic appearance, and the prevalence of buttes along with fresh landslide or slump scars, indicate that slope failures in Alberta and Saskatchewan have been quite common since deglaciation (Fraser and others 1935, Russell and others 1940, Williams and others 1930). The glacial deposits themselves also contain evidence of similar processes (Bayrock 1958, Gravenor and others 1960, Mollard 1960, Research

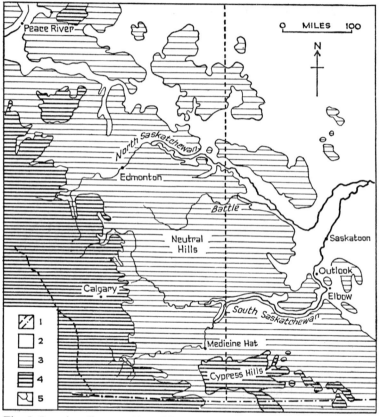

Fig. 5. Location diagram. (1) Political boundaries, (2) less 2000′, (3) 2–3000′, (4) over 3000′, (5) Rivers.

Council of Alberta 1958). Onset and release of considerable ice pressures are invoked to help explain the slumping of the Mud Buttes in Alberta. N. Stephens (University of Belfast: private communication) considers that ice pressure-fluctuations could have occurred on the eastern margin of the Antrim lavas, with comparable results. A similarly-located slide near Lennoxtown, Scotland, is worth investigating in this context. A décollement below the sole of a glacier is inferred to explain the unusual, bedrock slope failure which produced a set of small-scale fold and fault patterns in the Neutral Hills, Alberta. These ideas are by no means unreasonable either, for

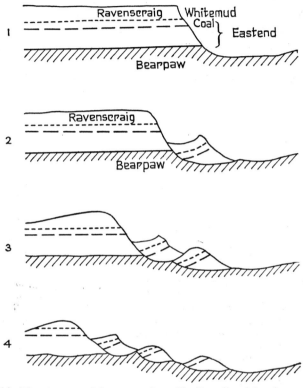

Fig. 6(*a*). The sequence of changes envisaged by Russell and Landes to produce buttes, hiatus in the stratigraphy and the undulating ground about the northwestern margin of the Cypress Hills. The Tertiary Ravenscraig beds lie unconformably upon Cretaceous measures—the uppermost of which is the Whitemud formation.

Mackay (1959, 1960) reports ablation-slide moraines from the Northwest Territories and glacier ice-thrust features in deposits of the Yukon.

Russell ascribes a primary role to mass movement in explaining some of the impressive, peripheral buttes of the Cypress Hills. Eagle Butte, for example, he considers a remnant of a Tertiary escarpment, the retreat of which was largely due to the repetition of a simple erosional sequence. Large blocks slumped on the scarp face; once detached, their material was the more effectively attacked by the agents of denudation. Meantime the safety factor declined on the free face of the remaining scarp, until conditions were ripe again for the next large block to be detached. Repetition of this sequence not only produced the distinctive terrain of a considerable area but also

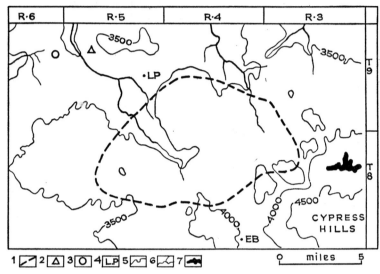

Fig. 6(*b*). SLOPE FAILURES NORTHWEST OF THE CYPRESS HILLS,
(1) Main slumped area recognized by Russell and Landes.
(2) Quasi-morainic slumped area.
(3) Spur subject to contemporaneous slumping and sliding.
(4) Settlements. L.P. Little Plume; E.B. Eagle Butte.
(5) Contours.
(6) Creeks.
(7) Elkwater Lake.
(Township and Range references provided on diagram margins.)

the hiatus in its stratigraphy (Fig. 6). This process still seems to affect certain localities today, but when the retreat of the scarp becomes uneven and produces small re-entrants then significant gully development appears to be associated with the free face in the re-entry. (It is not certain which comes first—the gully or the re-entry.) Again, when the detached blocks from the free face are only of moderate proportions then butte development seems to be discouraged, especially if the material is soft, although residual pinnacles can be produced. Speed and amount of retreat by the free face

are apparently governed both by local baselevel of fluvial erosion
and/or by the capability of denudational agents to reduce, remove
and grade the debris accumulating in front of it. Thus when the
retreat is slow, or ceases altogether, the free face tends to become
serrated by minor slips and gullies. Subsequent slope development
then seems to depend upon the difference in denudation rates below
the free face, at the free face and upon the crest surface above the
free face. When erosion is most rapid below the free face, consequent
slope failure will tend to preserve the original form of the free face.
Should the free face itself possess the greatest rates of erosion, then
debris will gradually accumulate in front of it. Being thus masked,
the surface available for further slope failure will diminish until the
free face has finally disappeared. If erosion is most active upon the
crest surface above the free face, however, and fluvial processes are
important, then gullies (associated with minor slides for a period)
will eventually change the nature of the crest surface, free face and
lower slope. Combinations of these three different possibilities would
explain the mixed slopes which can develop side by side, as about
Medicine Hat.[1]

Where the scarp retreat has been rapid, however, some of the local
creeks often appear to have had insufficient time to readjust themselves to the changing conditions and consequently look anomalous
in transverse and longitudinal profile. They frequently appear to be
graded to the exposed base of the free face and display markedly
different cross-sections above and below the same reference point.

Minor buttes again appear upon spurs and, while they apparently
develop in a similar fashion to those observed in Macedonia, climatic
conditions here vary sufficiently for them to be distributed both in
subhumid gully lands and in semi-arid badlands. Once again, therefore, a distinctive environment seems to be responsible for geomorphological features similar to those observed in Macedonia. Evidence
for rates of fluvial erosion in different environments and that of the
world climatic maps both suggest a different blending of the sub-
aerial processes in these two areas from that occurring poleward or
equatorward (cf. Corbel 1959, Menard 1961, Pardé 1947). This line
of thought immediately recalls Peltier's development of the concept
of morphogenetic regions, but it is still not certain whether each of
these areas displays the landform features which are typical of a morphogenetic region or of a transitional zone between adjacent morphogenetic regions. Support for the morphogenetic-region concept and

[1] The term *mixed slopes* was used to describe the declining and retreating slopes
found together in South Alberta, in an article on 'The Geomorphology of the
Medicine Hat Area', *Geographical Bulletin*, No. 18, 1962, pp. 86–107.

the foregoing observations of distinctiveness comes from the writings of Schumm and Hadley (1957) on their semi-arid cycle of erosion. Unfortunately, fluvial processes alone have so far been considered

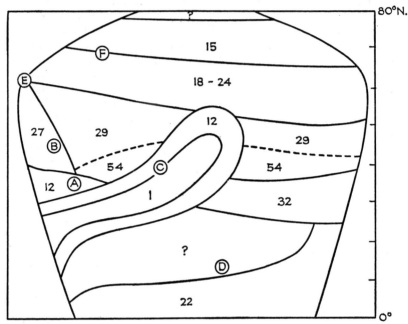

Fig. 7(*a*). A comparison of denudation rates by fluvial action (in mm per 1000 years) in different climates, depicted on an idealized distribution diagram for the Northern Hemisphere.

(The base diagram is that employed in Finch and Trewartha's 'Elements of Geography', McGraw Hill, New York 1949, p. 131 and the superimposed figures are those collected by Corbel.) Inset capital letters are for mountainous terrain as follows:

A. Circum Mediterranean Mts. with rates 100–450.
B. Alpine series with rates *c*. 200.
C. Southwest U.S.A. with rates of 170–200.
D. Brazil with rate of 92.
E. Alaska with rates *c*. 800.
F. Norway with rates *c*. 600.

in this new cycle, and it still remains to be seen how observations on slope development will compare to those just described. In contrast to these views, Smith and Ruhe (1955) make no qualification of their belief that in the prairie lands pedimentation takes place. Thus although the distinctive appearance of one of these areas is agreed, dissension exists about mode of origin. The relative importance of slope failure in these areas will therefore require careful attention in future work. Controversy over the development of valley-side slopes in humid landscapes has already distracted attention sufficiently from the importance of weathering and slope failure, for as Mulcahy so aptly states, 'The introduction of the concept of the variation in stability of slopes implies that landscapes do not develop by continuous backwasting or downwasting, but that the development of any given slope will proceed while it is unstable and cease when it becomes stable' (Mulcahy 1961).

Peltier, it will be recalled, begins his article by pointing out that seven morphogenetic regions have been recognized, and suggests that the boreal and west coast marine climates should also be distinctive enough to produce characteristic geomorphic features. Surprisingly, though, his subsequent remarks on polygenetic topography appear to consider the effect of climatic fluctuations only on a relatively long-term basis. Corbel's recent figures on solution rates of rocks in different environments indicate that some reappraisal is now needed on rates of chemical weathering in the morphogenetic regions described. It could also be argued that under ideal conditions distinctive climatic regimes should produce unique combinations of landforms that would be matched with particular types of soil and vegetation. In fact it is more customary in physical geography to find a type locality, where the total environment shows an approximation to ideal conditions, about which variation and then transition occur. The morphological significance of marked seasonal contrasts or short-term cycles of climates must be enhanced in these transitional zones.

When the climatic data which appear to be geomorphologically important are considered separately and collectively on world maps, the pattern of morphogenetic regions which emerges is generally far from simple (Fig. 7). Thus Peltier's treatment of the concept of morphogenetic regions now seems oversimplified and overgeneralized, yet it has the merit of acknowledging realities. It remains to be seen how further observations will influence future ideas on this concept.

The data on rates of fluvial erosion also pose the question of why geomorphologists are slow to recognize massive mountainous areas as distinctive entities, as the climatologists and biogeographers acknowledge them. Massifs generally record rates of erosion far exceeding those of adjacent areas and, because of their special environments, the effectiveness and combination of subaerial processes vary within them. That conditions are especially favourable for the increased incidence of slope failure is demonstrated by Band's observations on the frequency of avalanches on Kachenjunga (Band 1956),

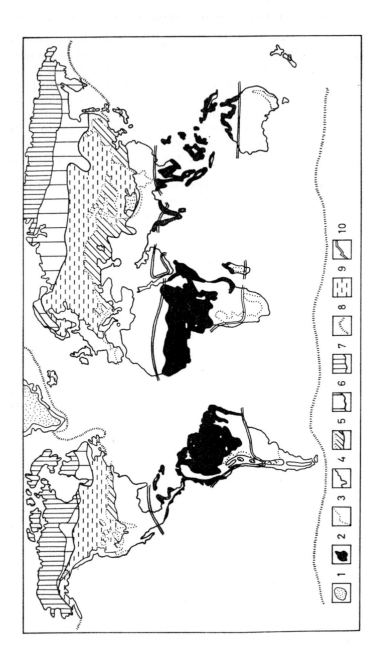

or Rapp's recent suggestion (1959) that avalanche erosion is probably an important morphological process in mountainous terrain. Even from the low mountains of Britain there is sufficient evidence to indicate that the continuous action of solifluction and creep, with sporadic transfers of deposits by slumps and slides, is considerable (Galloway 1961, Hopkins and Wahrhaftig 1960). But in spite of information available on amounts of material involved in the failures of today, the role of slope failure in moulding landforms and providing debris to the Tertiary landscape, for redistribution during the Quaternary glaciation, can only be guessed. This consideration is relevant to views on relic features of Tertiary origin in the present scene and to ideas on the role of ice-sheets, which in places scoured pre-existing landforms but nearby exerted only a passive or even a protective influence.

Periglacial activity, change in sea-level, and postglacial climatic change have all left their mark in the slope deformations occurring in these islands, but on a scale that has still to be evaluated. In Northern Ireland, for example, the strong out-facing slopes which begin at Binevenagh (Derry) and end near White Mountain (above Lisburn, Co. Antrim) are obviously younger than and genetically different from those lying on the lavas inland. Although this semi-circular wall is breached by a number of valleys and glens it possesses steep free faces, below which the surface slope changes markedly. The lower slopes in some cases suggest stability in their smooth and gentle outlines, contrasting sharply with those highly irregular slopes which result from landslips, slides or slumps of considerable proportions (cf. also Charlesworth 1953, pp. 236–7, and Stephens 1958).

---

Fig.7(b). Temperature data which appear to be important to the geomorphologist,

(1) Average actual temps. below 32°F all the year.
(2) Average actual temps. above 70°F all the year.
(3) Poleward limit of average actual 70°F isotherm.
(4) Equatorward limit of average actual 32°F isotherm.
(5) Zone of overlap between 32° and 70° isotherms.
(6) Approximate position of average actual 32° isotherm in April and October.
(7) Approximate limit of general permafrost.
(8) Approximate limit of pack ice.
(9) Extensive microthermal zone particular to the Northern Hemisphere.
(10) Land areas where diurnal range of temperature greater than annual range.

Note how in the Northern Hemisphere the length of the frost period or the range of average actual temperatures must be morphologically significant over considerable areas. The intertropical area where diurnal ranges are important extends over much of the land area in the Southern Hemisphere.

Fig. 7(c). Precipitation regime data which appear to be important to the geomorphologist.

(1) Areas essentially outside temperate and tropical storm tracks.
(2) Thunderstorm zones of importance.
(3) Areas with monsoon type of climate.
(4) Areas with at least 2" of precipitation in Jan., April, July and Oct.
(5) Areas with less than 5" precipitation per year.
(6) General equatorward limit of snowfall.

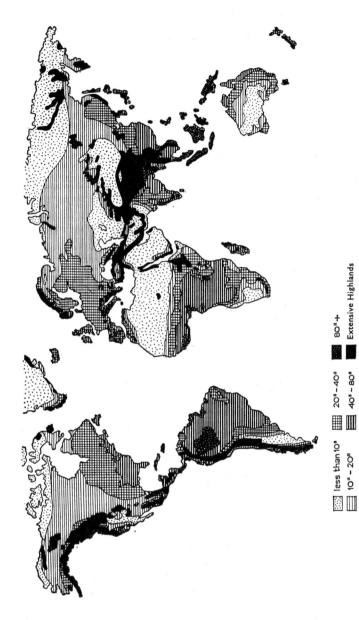

Fig. 7(*d*). Average total precipitation and distribution of the Highland Massifs.

Detachment of blocks from the free face has produced rock pinnacles in some places, but elsewhere the scale of the process has been
so great that miniature fault blocks have been displaced. The latter
seem comparable to the landslips about Fernhurst, Sussex, described
by Wooldridge (1950). On account of slope failure and rapid recession
of a scarp, many minor streams have undergone a marked change
of habit. As observed in Alberta, the reduction of large displaced
masses by secondary slips and slides, as well as by running water
and weathering, is taking place.

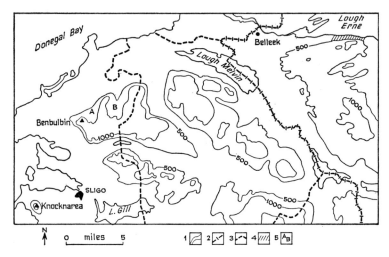

Fig. 8. (1) Contours at 500′ and 1000′ a.s.l. (2) Eire boundary, (3) County
boundary, (4) Area of recurrent slope failure affecting loughside road, (5) Large
amphitheatre recesses of debatable origin.

(N.B. For Antrim coast diagrams see Stephens, p. 390, *Adv. of Science*, 56,
1958.)

Another fine escarpment on Carboniferous Limestone rocks, running through Fermanagh, Leitrim and Sligo, displays many features
similar to those just described on the lavas. This rockwall has also
been broken by a number of valleys; its slopes contrast to those
lying further south, and once more a striking free face surmounts
a gentler, lower slope along its length. Slope failure and scarp retreat
southwards seem to progress more slowly than in Antrim. The general
outlines of this high ground appear to be most exotic when viewed
from the northwest and this impression is strengthened by the
detached mesa of Knocknarea, beyond Sligo. Just as the Scottish

views of Quinag, Canisp, Suilven and Stac Polly from the west suggest inselbergs, so too this scene is suggestive of a relic African savanna landscape (Fig. 8).

Near its eastern end fresh scars indicate that slope failure still occurs, while in its middle reaches rock pinnacles on detached blocks, below the free face, again are present. The major problem at the western end of the scarp centres on the origin of the two large amphi-

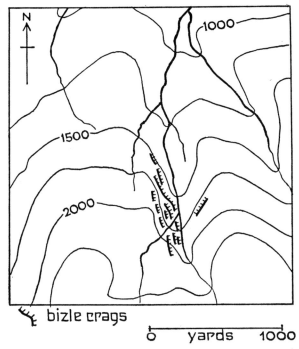

Fig. 9. The Bizle, on the north face of Cheviot, Northumberland. Another large rock recess of debatable origin.

theatre recesses near Benbulbin. It would be easy to consider these features as low-level corries which developed on the weather side of the British Isles when the snow line was lower. A comparable recess of debatable origin at Sallagh Braes, in Antrim, which is currently being investigated by Stephens, suggests that some qualification may be necessary, however. It therefore seems possible that scars formed by slumping during interglacial periods could have provided favourable nuclei for cirque or cirque-like development during a subsequent glacial period, along lines similar to those proposed by Thorarinsson in his study of cirques in the Icelandic plateau basalts (Thorarinsson and others 1959).

Without doubt there must be many other 'corries' of doubtful origin in the British Isles where the possibility of rock walls being the steep slip faces of large landslides has never been fairly considered. 'The Bizle' on the north side of Cheviot is a case in point. This rock recess lies between 1500 and 2000 ft and possesses both the super- ficial appearance and correct location of a corrie. Especially im- pressive are the stepped rockwall, which extends for about one third of a mile along its west side, and the debris piled upon its floor. The debris takes the form of older, large tumbled blocks bounded by younger and smaller scree material. It is doubtful if local conditions in the Quaternary era could give rise to a true corrie. Again, the Bizle Burn in its present tract looks incompetent to destroy any original headwall and lip forms, if the Bizle had been a corrie. On the other hand the collection of rock debris within the feature could certainly represent the product of rock falls and slides. These floor deposits indicate that the rate of accumulation has exceeded that of removal for some considerable time, and if this relationship persists, the growing protective cover will eventually lead to modifications in the outline of the whole feature. This challenge is similar to views recently expressed by Watson (1961) on the origin of certain features in the Tal-y-llyn valley, Wales: 'Where valley sides have been truly oversteepened by glacial erosion they are unstable and masses may slump down into the valley leaving a scar above the cluster of hum- mocks which may resemble a glacial cirque with moraines in front; at Tal-y-llyn the great scar formed by the Graig Goch occurs directly above the moraine-like mounds which form the bar.' The recognition of this landslip by Watson also radically alters the interpretation of the lake at Tal-y-llyn. C. A. Sinker, of the Preston Montford Field Centre, has supplied to the author useful notes on several similar features in the Welsh Border country. Craig Gamhyll at Moelfre, west of Oswestry, is a landslip cwm where debris from a glacially- oversteepened valley side has ponded up a lake. Lesser examples include Craig-y-rhiw, nearer to Oswestry, and Craig Pen-y-buarth at the head of the Tanat valley, by Llangynog.

As for parallels among the larger scale features in the British Isles, it seems reasonable to suggest that slope failure and scarp retreat, like those occurring at and near the Antrim coast, must affect simi- larly located areas elsewhere in these islands (Savigear 1952; Steers 1946). It also seems possible for these processes to be relatively important in those parts of Britain which have inherited suitable landforms from the Tertiary-Quaternary landscape. A willingness at least to check these views may eventually afford an explanation for some of our more puzzling landforms.

To complete this essay, several practical aspects of the topic deserve to be included. In Calgary, for example, the present spread of building prudently avoids the steep valley sides of the local rivers and

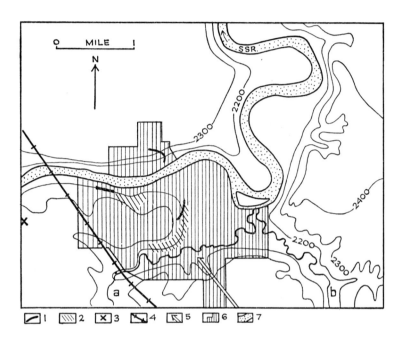

Fig. 10(a). Slope failure in Medicine Hat: (1) Sections of road affected by contemporaneous slope failure, (2) Areas where property is susceptible to slope failure, (3) Locality where slumping and gullying threaten city reservoir, (4) Trans-Canada Highway, (5) Line of the former trunk road safely using gully tract down from Prairie surface, (6) Urban area, (7) S.S.R. South Saskatchewan River. a. Sevenpersons Creek, b. Ross Creek.

coulees where slope failure is possible. The continuing demand for building space accordingly poses a serious problem for city planners. Nearby at Medicine Hat, somewhat similar but more urgent problems have to be faced, for the value and safety of property are already adversely affected by slumps and slides in several parts of the town. Attempts to stop the movements have so far relied upon planting trees and bushes, but this has not proved very effective. Farther north, at Edmonton, slope failures on the North Saskatchewan River draw attention to hazards concerned with transportation. Observations here, as elsewhere, suggest that recurrent or likely failures near river crossings make it costly and occasionally useless to drive roads

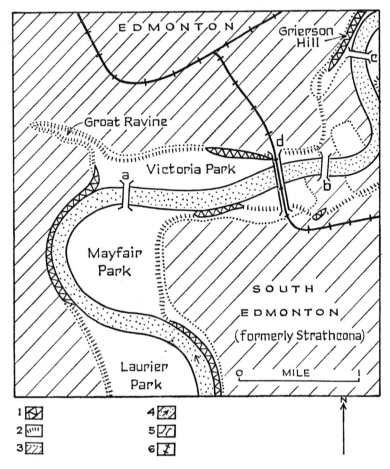

Fig. 10(b). Slope failures at Edmonton: (1) Steep faces susceptible to slope failures, (2) Valley bluffs, ranging in height from c. 2050′–2150′ a.s.l. (3) General limits of built up area, (4) Flow of N. Saskatchewan river, (5) Bridges: a. Groat Bridge (road) b. Fifth Street Bridge (road), c. Low Level bridge (road), d. High Level bridge (road and railway), (6) Railway.

(N.B. Maps and diagrams on the South Saskatchewan Project are available in the Report of the Royal Commission on the S.S.R. project. Queen's Printer, Ottawa 1952, pp. 180–1.)

obliquely up susceptible slopes—e.g. on Grierson Hill. Better by far first to instal training and conservation aids along a convenient tributary creek or gully and then to lay a road along it, roughly parallel to the thalweg, as in the Groat Ravine, Edmonton. In the absence of suitable tributary gullies, appropriately graded cut-and-fill sections with short bridges can often be safely employed, rather than long high-level bridges, as on the Trans-Canada Highway where it crosses the South Saskatchewan River and Sevenpersons Creek west of Medicine Hat. Problems of yet another type can be illustrated in Saskatchewan, and from the locality where the new hydrological installations are being prepared for the South Saskatchewan Project. It is particularly unfortunate that the valley sides should carry slumped earth masses between Elbow and Outlook, for this is the key area in the Project. One cannot help but wonder how slope failure processes will influence the future of the earthdam being constructed at Coteau Creek or the effective volume of the lake which will be impounded upstream. These few examples illustrate the general circumstance that, where Prairie streams are incised by 100 or 200 ft, river-side settlements and farmland usually encounter difficulties from unstable slopes (Fig. 10).

Property, installations and lines of transportation in Greece are widely affected, not only by similar slope failures and accelerated rates of erosion but also by catastrophic failures due to earth tremors. The loss of productive land and damage to cultural features are more important in Greece than in the Prairie Provinces, however, since prevailing economic conditions place a far heavier burden upon the land resources (see for example, Common 1958, Margaropoulos 1952). Field evidence near Salonika and historical writings on Greece suggest that accelerated rates of erosion began in c. 400 B.C. Although 0·6 million hectares of the mountain and hill pastures are estimated already to have lost 75 per cent of their topsoil, some constructive conservation work is in hand. This work is currently limited in its scope and extent by more urgent priorities of the basic national problems of overpopulation, underemployment and shortage of capital.

Reports in the Press testify to the frequency and nuisance value of slope failures in the British Isles, from natural or man-made causes. Examination of property in any extensive mining area will usually prove the existence there of subsidence (i.e. an anthropogenic form). Unrecorded though are the problems frequently occurring on building sites, similar to those experienced in 1954 on a new housing scheme at Drumry, near Glasgow, where susceptible drumlins began slumping after bulldozers had removed earth from their bases. The patient efforts required to protect or repair installations are just as likely to be overlooked. The continual breaking up of the surface on a four-mile stretch of the Belleek-Enniskillen road, near Lough Erne, illustrates the effect of persistent slope instability upon lines of transportation. It would appear that this road has long been troublesome, causing bother even prior to 1927 when the present surveyor arrived. Since 1927 special allocations of money (to the order of £300 annually) have been granted for maintaining this stretch of road. Movements are troublesome throughout the whole year, but accelerate in response to wet weather. Some attempts have been made to drain and buttress the slide-prone area, but these have so far failed to halt the movement either of material down on to the road or of parts of the road towards the lakeside. Only on three occasions in the last thirty years, however, has the road been closed to traffic, twice on account of material coming down on to the road surface and once because of the carriageway collapsing. A measure of success in dealing with the problem has apparently been achieved, by infilling sections of the undulating road surface and realigning the road above a persistent slip surface.[1] Yet these and other reminders are continually ignored, apparently because of their familiarity or local interest.

## Conclusion

It will now be clear that there is still ample scope for further work on the allied topics of slope failure, rates of erosion and regional differences in the combination of erosional processes. At this time when the tendency for professional specialization becomes increasingly emphatic, these topics are timely reminders that insight into some research problems comes only from a breadth of interest.

## References

Band, G., 1956. 'Kanchenjunga climbed.' *Geog. Mag.*, 28 (9), 422–38.
Baver, L. D., 1956. *Soil Physics*. J. Wiley & Sons, Inc., N.Y. (3rd ed.) Chaps 5 and 12.
Bayrock, L. A., 1958. in *The Glacial Geology of the Alliance-Brownfield District of Alberta*, comments on the importance of slumping in valley modification and notes that the valley of the Battle river has been widened by as much as one mile by this process.
Bjerrum, L., 1955. 'The stability of natural slopes in quick clay.' *Proc. Europ. Conf. on the Stability of Earthslopes. Geotechnique* 5 (1).
Bjerrum, L., and Eide, O., 1955. 'The slide at Bekkelaget.' '7th Oct. 1953.' *ibid.*

[1] Information kindly supplied by Mr McClure, County Surveyor, Fermanagh.

Bower, M., 1960a. 'Peat erosion in the Pennines.' *Adv. Sci.*, 16 (64), 323–31.

Bower, M., 1960b. 'The erosion of blanket peat in the S. Pennines.' *The East Midland Geographer*, B, 22–33.

Bowes, D. R., 1960. 'A bog burst in the Isle of Lewis.' *Scottish Geog. Mag.*, 76 (1), 21–3.

Bull, A. J., 1950. 'Gravitational sliding.' *Proc. Geol. Assoc.*, 61, pp. 198–201.

Charlesworth, J. K., 1953. *The Geology of Ireland.* Oliver and Boyd, Edinburgh (pp. 236–7).

Cholley, A., 1957. *Récherches morphologiques.* Lib. Armand Colin, Paris, pp. 5–19.

Christiansen, E. A., 1959. 'The glacial geology of the Swift Current area, Saskatchewan.' *Dept. of Mineral Resources Report 32*, Regina.

Common, R., 1953. 'A report on the Lochaber, Appin and Benderloch floods.' *Scot. Geog. Mag.*, 70 (1), 6–20.

Common, R., 1958. 'Some recent developments in Greece.' *Tijdschrift voor Econ. en Soc. Geografie*, 48 (12), 256–9.

Common, R., 1962. 'The geomorphology of the Medicine Hat area.' *Geographical Bulletin* 18, 86–107.

Corbel, J., 1959. 'Vitesse de l'erosion.' *Annals of Geomorphology*, 3 (1), 1–28.

Cotton, C. A., 1961. 'The theory of savanna planation.' *Geography*, 46 (2), 89–101.

Cumberland, K., 1947. *Soil erosion in New Zealand.* Whitcombe and Tombs, Christchurch, New Zealand.

Dettmann, M. G., 1958. 'Water uptake by pure clays and soil crumbs.' *Journ. Soil Science*, 9 (2), 306–14.

Fraser, F. J., and others, 1935. 'Geology of S. Saskatchewan,' G.S.C. Memoir 176, King's Printer, Ottawa.

Galloway, R. W., 1961. 'Solifluction in Scotland.' *Scot. Geog. Mag.* 77 (2), 75–85.

Gifford, J., 1953. 'Landslides on Exmoor.' *Geography*, 38 (1), p. 11.

Gravenor, C. P., and others, 1960. 'Air photographs of Alberta.' Research Council of Alberta Bulletin 5, Queen's Printer, Edmonton (see particularly pp. 15, 18, 19 and 31).

Hays, T., 1942. 'Physiographic notes from Lakeland.' *Geog. Journ.*, 100 (1), p. 168.

Hills, E. Sherborn, 1943. *Outlines of Structural Geology.* Methuen, London. (2nd ed.) Chap 1.

Hopkins, D. M., and Wahrhaftig, C., 1960. 'Annotated bibliography of English language papers on the evolution of slopes under periglacial climates.' *Annals Geomorph., Supplementary Volume* 1, 1–8.

Horton, R. F., 1945. 'Erosional development of streams and their drainage basins.' *Bull. Geol. Soc. America*, 56, 326–9.

Jarnefors, B., 1958. 'Determination of slip surfaces in the landslides at Surte on the Göta river.' *Geol. Foren. I. Stockholm Förh.*, 80 (1), 97–101.

King, L. C., 1951. *South African Scenery.* Oliver & Boyd, Edinburgh. (2nd ed.)

Krynine, D., and Judd, W., 1957. *Principles of Engineering Geology and Geotechnics.* McGraw Hill, New York.

Mackay, J. R., 1959. 'Glacier ice-thrust features of the Yukon coast.' *Geographical Bulletin*, 13, 5–21.

Mackay, J. R., 1960. 'Crevasse fillings and ablation slide moraines, Stop-over Lake area, N.W.T.' *Geographical Bulletin*, 14, 89–99.

Margaropoulos, P., 1952. 'Mountain range management and improvement in Greece.' *Journ. Range Management*, 5 (4), 200–6.

Menard, H., 1961. 'Some rates of regional erosion.' *Journ. Geol*, 69 (2), 154–61.

Mollard, J. D., 1960. *Air Photo Analysis and Interpretation.* 616 McCallum Building, Regina (see especially Plates 27, 31, 32, 33 and 34).

Mulcahy, M. J., 1961. 'Soil distribution in relation to landscape development.' *Annals Geomorph.*, 5 (3), p. 218.

Odenstad, S., 1958. 'Landslide at Göta, 7th June, 1957.' *Geologiska Foreningens I. Stockholm Förh.*, 80 (1), 76–86.

Parde, M., 1947. *Fleuves et Rivières.* Collection Armand Collin, Paris (Chap 10).

Parizek, E. J., and Woodruff, J. F., 1957. 'A clarification of the definition and classification of soil creep.' *Journ. Geol.*, 65, 653–6.

Peltier, L. C., 1950. 'The geographical cycle in periglacial regions as it is related to climatic geomorphology.' *Annals Assoc. Amer. Geographers*, 40, 214–36.

Praeger, R. L., 1950. *Natural History of Ireland.* Collins, London (pp. 96–7).

Rapp, A., 1959. 'Avalanche boulder tongues in Lappland.' *Geografiska Annaler*, 41 (1), 34–8.

Rapp, A., 1960. 'Literature on slope denudation in Finland, Iceland, Norway, Spitzbergen and Sweden.' *Annals Geomorph.*, Supplementary Vol. 1, 40–1.

Research Council of Alberta, 1958. *Preliminary Report 57–2*, Queen's Printer, Edmonton.

Rudberg, S., 1958. 'Some observations concerning mass movement on slopes in Sweden.' *Geol. Foren. I. Stock. Förh.*, 80 (1), 114–25.

Russell, L. S., and others, 1940. 'Geology of the Southern Albertan Plains.' G.S.C. Memoir 221, King's Printer, Ottawa.

Sandegren, E., 1960. 'The landslide on the Kyrkviken, Feb. 1959.' *Geol. Foren. I. Stock. Förh.*, 82 (3), 382–96.

Savigear, R., 1952. 'Some observations on slope development in South Wales.' *Trans. I.B.G.* (18), 31–51.

Schumm, S. A., and Hadley, R. F., 1957. 'Arroyos and the semi-arid cycle of erosion.' *American Journal of Science*, 255, 161–74.

Sharpe, C. F., 1938. *Landslides and Related Phenomena.* Columbia Univ. Press, New York.

Sjors, H., 1961. 'Surface patterns in Boreal peatlands.' *Endeavour*, 20, p. 220.

Smith, G. D., and Ruhe, R. V., 1955. 'How water shaped the face of the land,' in 'Water', *Yearbook of Agriculture*, U.S. Dept. of Agric., Washington D.C. (pp. 121–5 and diagram on p. 141).

Steers, J. A., 1946. *The Coastline of England and Wales*. Camb. Univ. Press (pp. 67–9, 264–8, 278–9, 298–9, 311–12, 332, 373–4, 468).

Stephens, N., 1958. 'The evolution of the coastline of North East Ireland.' *Adv. Sci.* 56, 389–91.

Taylor, D. W., 1948. *Fundamentals of Soil Mechanics*. J. Wiley & Sons Inc., N.Y.

Terzaghi, K., 1958. 'Mechanics of landslides' in the Berkey Volume, *The Application of Geology to Engineering Practice*. Geol. Soc. of America, N.Y. (pp. 83–124).

Thomas, T. M., 1959. *The Geomorphology of Brecknock*, p. 147.

Thorarinsson, S., and others, 1959. 'On the geology and geomorphology of Iceland.' *Geografiska Annaler*, 41 (2–3), 165–7.

Ward, H. 1945. 'The stability of natural slopes.' *Geog. Journ.*, 105, 1945, 170–96.

Watson, E., 1961. *Excursion guide to the Tal-y-llyn valley, Merionethshire*. Dept. of Geography, Univ. College of Wales, Aberystwyth, p. 5. (The author is grateful to Professor E. Estyn Evans for bringing this publication to his notice.)

Weischet, W., 1960. 'Geographische Auswirkungen des Erdebens vom. 22 Mai 1960 im Kleinen Süden Chiles.' *Erdkunde*, 14 (4), 273–88.

Williams, M. Y., and others, 1930. 'Geology of S. Alberta and S.W. Saskatchewan.' G.S.C. Memoir 163, King's Printer, Ottawa.

Williams, P. J., 1957. 'The direct recording of solifluction movements.' *Amer. Journ. Sci.*, 255, 705–14.

Wooldridge, S. W., 1950. 'Some features in the structure and geomorphology around Fernhurst, Sussex.' *Proc. Geol. Assoc.*, 61, 165–90.

# Landforms of the Western Macdonnell Ranges

## A study of inheritance and periodicity in the geomorphology of arid central Australia

### J. A. MABBUTT

### Introduction

Australia is the world's driest continent, with almost three-quarters of its extent classed as semi-arid or arid (Meigs 1952). Much of the dry part is accessible and has extensive air-photo cover. A good deal of reconnaissance has already been carried out by geologists, geomorphologists, and soil scientists, but arid Australia remains little studied from the viewpoint of climatic geomorphology.

As a preliminary, it is necessary to distinguish inherited landforms produced under past conditions from those expressive of the present climate—particularly so because, in the structurally stable environments of central Australia, landforms have tended to persist through a long history of sub-aerial erosion. Relict weathered profiles, truncated river systems, and sand-dunes now vegetated and stabilized, testify to important climatic change. It remains to establish the sequence of such change by relating it to stages of land-surface development.

Normal difficulties of interpretation are enhanced in the Australian arid zone by the absence of large through-going rivers—which might record climatic changes in detail—by isolation from the effects of sea-level changes, and by the paucity of correlative sediments with fossils or artefacts. Nevertheless, the zone offers a worthwhile challenge to the climatic geomorphologist, partly because of its great latitudinal extent and its potential linkage of climatic changes of the humid tropics with those of the humid mid-latitudes, and partly because of its situation in the palaeoclimatologically little-known Southern Hemisphere.

Investigation of the effects of climatic change, mainly restricted so far to relatively young land surfaces on the south and east fringes of

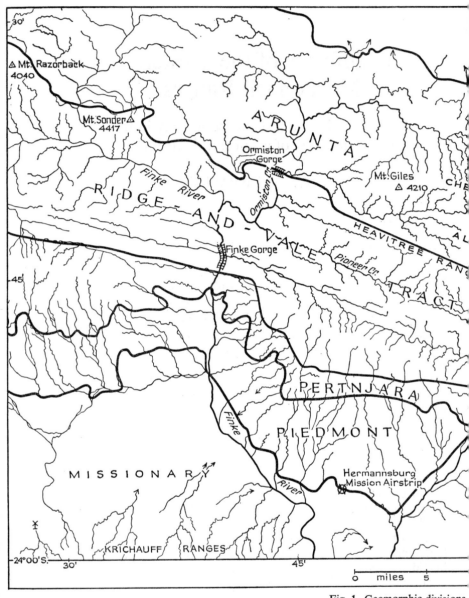

Fig. 1. Geomorphic divisions

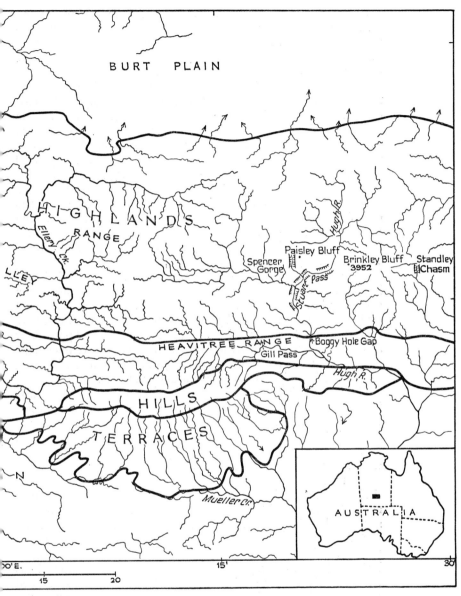

Macdonnell Ranges.

the Australian arid zone, have revealed alternations of wetter and drier phases, presumably related to Pleistocene and Recent fluctuations elsewhere (cf. Jessup 1960). These studies are not yet collated into a general sequence, nor is it certain how far the findings in the fringe areas apply to the whole arid zone.

The present study, of an area in the heart of central Australia, has the object of establishing a regional geomorphic history on the basis of its inherited landforms, and of interpreting these landforms in terms of periodic climatic change. The area chosen is the western Macdonnell Ranges (Fig. 1), which extend for about 150 miles west of Alice Springs in a continuous belt of rugged mountains, parallel ridges, and dissected hills rising in spectacular fashion from the monotonous plains of 'The Centre'. The Ranges form the watershed between drainage towards Lake Eyre on the one hand, and a less organized system of dry rivers going into the plains on the north and northwest on the other. The divide runs near the north margin of the Ranges, most of the area draining southwards to the Finke River across the east–west grain of structure and relief.

The area is a strategic one for two reasons. Firstly, it is in the highest part of central Australia, with a history of sub-aerial erosion extending back into the Palaeozoic, so that ancient landforms and drainage lineaments might be expected to survive on its extensive resistant rocks. Secondly, it is an area of strong relief and potentially active morphogenesis, likely to contain areas so sensitive to climatic fluctuations that even short-lived changes in the balance of erosion and deposition might produce significant landforms.

The western Macdonnells were geologically explored about seventy-five years ago, but the stratigraphic succession was first established by Madigan (1932). The stratigraphic nomenclature used here, and set out in Table I, is that proposed by Prichard and Quinlan (1962), who made a regional geological survey in 1956 for the Commonwealth Bureau of Mineral Resources.

After an aerial reconnaissance in 1928 and a car journey through the Ranges to the Finke in 1930, Madigan published the first detailed account of the physiography (Madigan 1931). He claimed that the southward drainage has persisted since early Palaeozoic times, and that the rivers are antecedent to the fold structures which they traverse. This southward drainage had earlier been remarked upon by Ward (1925), who regarded the even crests of the Macdonnells as remnants of a former erosion surface of late Mesozoic age, graded to an emerged depositional surface in the Lake Eyre Basin. On this view, the south-going drainage is partly inherited and partly superimposed. In an account of Australian land surfaces, King (1950)

TABLE I

## STRATIGRAPHY OF THE WESTERN MACDONNELL RANGES*

| | | | |
|---|---|---|---|
| | | Siltstone and pebbly sandstone (lateritized) | (?) Cretaceous |
| | | Unconformity | |
| | Pertnjara Formation | About 20,000 ft of calcareous conglomerate, calcareous greywacke, and sandstone | (?) Devonian |
| | | Regional Unconformity | |
| | Mereenie | 900–1300 ft of red quartz sandstone | (?) Ordovician |
| | | Regional Unconformity | |
| Larapinta Group | Stokes Formation | About 1000 ft of siltstone and silty greywacke | Ordovician |
| | Stairway Greywacke | 1000–1400 ft of quartz greywacke and quartz sandstone | |
| | Horn Valley Formation | 400 ft of siltstone with thin limestone beds, thickening westwards to 1000 ft | |
| | Pacoota Sandstone | 2700 ft of silicified quartz sandstone | |
| Pertaoorrta Group | Goyder Formation | 1600 ft of quartz greywacke and quartz sandstone with interbedded limestone | Cambrian |
| | Jay Creek Limestone | 200 ft and above of dolomitic limestone with thin shale beds | |
| | Hugh River Shale | 1600 ft of shale with some siltstone and dolomitic limestone | |
| | Arumbera Greywacke | 800 ft and above of feldspathic and micaceous quartz greywacke with interbedded siltstone; thickens westwards | Upper Proterozoic or Cambrian |
| | Pertatataka Formation | About 2000 ft of siltstone with minor limestone and quartz greywacke | |
| | Areyonga Formation | 1300 ft of tillitic siltstone and quartz greywacke | |
| | Bitter Springs Limestone | 2500 ft of well bedded dolomitic limestone, limestone and shale | Upper Proterozoic |
| | Heavitree Quartzite | 500–1500 ft of quartzite and quartz greywacke with quartz siltstone | |
| | | Major Unconformity | |
| | Arunta Complex | Gneiss, granite, and schist | Archaeozoic |

* From Prichard and Quinlan (1962). Rock thicknesses are mainly based on a measured section at Ellery Creek.

identified the sub-Cretaceous surface of central Australia with his supra-continental Gondwanaland surface. He inferred a former planation in the Macdonnell Ranges from the transverse drainage, and suggested an upwarp of the Gondwanaland surface to produce the observed relief. Mabbutt (1962), describing an upland surface of subdued relief, took it as part of an extensive deeply-weathered land surface. Later investigations have shown this upland surface to be the complex product of more than one period of erosion.

**Physiographic Description**

The term *western Macdonnell Ranges* is somewhat loosely applied to a complex of country bounded by the Burt Plain on the north and by the Missionary Plain on the south, and containing the following subdivisions, all of which are aligned from east to west (see Fig. 2), clearly reflecting the geological sequence set out in Table I.

*Arunta Highlands*

This northern area of rather confused relief is cut in the Archean basement—schist, gneiss, and granite of the Arunta Complex, and resistant metaquartzites. It consists mostly of rugged peaks and short ridges, prominent east–west quartzite ranges, and restricted intermont plains. Although the Highlands lack the impressive continuity of the ranges to the south, they include the highest summits, and several peaks exceed 4000 ft above sea-level. A low hilly or plain tract, the Alice Valley, occupies an anticlinal zone in the south.

*Ridge-and-Vale Tract*

This tract borders the Arunta Highlands on the south. It is carved in a sequence of 30,000 to 40,000 ft of sedimentary rocks ranging in age from Upper Proterozoic to Ordovician. They rest unconformably on the Arunta Complex and dip very steeply southwards, approaching the vertical and indeed achieving some overturning at the base. There are three main ridges and two strike vales; the ridge crests are at about 2500 ft above sea-level, increasing in height westwards and attaining 3000 ft in the Heavitree Range, while the vale floors are mainly between 2000 and 2200 ft.

*Heavitree Range.* The prominent northernmost ridge is formed on the reddish silicified sandstone and quartz greywacke of the Heavitree Quartzite. Mainly between 500 and 1000 ft high, it is broken only by narrow drainage gaps. The northern face is commonly a sheer cliff above a steep concave slope eroded on Arunta schist, while the steep southern slope consists of rocky quartzite buttresses. The ridge is triplicated by faulting in its higher western part.

*Glen Helen Vale.* This intermont lowland is about 1½ miles wide and is drained in different parts to the Hugh River, Ellery Creek and the Finke River. Its northern half is underlain by thinly-bedded

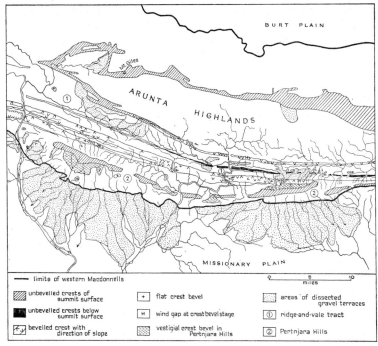

| | | |
|---|---|---|
| ▨ unbevelled crests of summit surface | ⊞ flat crest bevel | ▦ areas of dissected gravel terraces |
| ■ unbevelled crests below summit surface | H wind gap at crest bevel stage | ① ridge-and-vale tract |
| ▨ bevelled crest with direction of slope | ▦ vestigial crest bevel in Pertnjara Hills | ② Pertnjara Hills |

—— limits of western Macdonnells

Fig. 2. Summit surfaces and terraces in part of the western Macdonnell Ranges.

dolomitic limestone and shale of the Bitter Springs Limestone Formation, which forms a zone of rounded foothills to the Heavitree Range. The southern portion consists mainly of an alluviated lowland on siltstone of the Pertatataka Formation, with discontinuous low ridges of quartz greywacke. Prominent gravel terraces form secondary divides between elements of strike drainage.

*Arumbera Ridge.* This narrow-crested, discontinuous central ridge is distinguished by the deep red colour and bizarre weathering-forms of the Arumbera Greywacke. It increases in dimensions westwards, but remains lower and narrower than the strike ridges to the north and south.

*Southern Vale.* South of the Arumbera Ridge is a lowland between half a mile and one mile wide, underlain mainly by siltstone and limestone of the Pertaoorrta Group. It is traversed by broken low strike ridges, particularly in the south. Strike drainage is less developed than in Glen Helen Vale, except in the west where the Arumbera Ridge makes an effective barrier against transverse streams.

*Larapinta Ridges.* The complex southern range begins in the east as a single flattish-crested ridge about half a mile wide, but west of Ellery Creek widens and splits into three ridges separated by very narrow strike valleys. The highest and most massive ridge is the northern one, of silicified Pacoota Sandstone. The strike valleys are formed on limestone and siltstone, while the ridge country extends on to the outcrop of Mereenie Sandstone. The bevelled crests of the Larapinta Ridges are generally 100 to 500 ft lower than that of the Heavitree Range.

## Pertnjara Hills

These are a complex of short ridges and subconical hills contrasting strongly with the ordered arrangement of ridges to the north. They are cut in massive and very thick calcareous conglomerates of the Pertnjara Formation. Sub-parallel transverse streams pass across the hill belt, which is closely dissected by pinnate tributary systems. Although not spectacular in relief, the Pertnjara Hills form an important secondary divide above the level of the Larapinta Ridges east of the Finke, and constitute the main watershed further west.

## Piedmont Terraces

A belt of dissected terraces occupies a zone between 5 and 8 miles wide at the south foot of the Ranges, in the north part of the Missionary Plain. The terraces consist of partly calcreted gravels overlying surfaces planed across Pertnjara greywacke.

## The Summit Surface of the Western Macdonnells

Even and continuous strike ridges in the western Macdonnells give an exaggerated first impression of accordant crests. There is, however, no simple summit-plane to indicate complete former planation, but the smooth profiles of the crests and upper slopes, and the flatness on many ridge crests, contrast with the rugged steepened slopes below and justify grouping as a summit surface.

Remnants of the summit surface in the ridge-and-vale tract lie mainly on the Heavitree and Larapinta ridges, for except in the extreme west the Arumbera Ridge is either below the level of the summit surface or is narrow-crested. Two elements in the summit surface are recognizable, namely crest bevels and upper slopes. Crest bevels may be flat, or sloping up to 10 per cent, or slightly convex in cross-section, but invariably truncate planes of bedding. Fairly abrupt rounded junctions link them with the smooth upper slopes, which are mainly convex above and rectilinear below, where they may exceed 30 per cent. Although influenced by structure, these slopes are mainly smooth across the bedding planes and relate to a former period of crest rounding.

The crest of the Heavitree Range is extensively bevelled east of Ellery Creek, mainly at altitudes of between 2400 and 2600 ft. The slope on the bevel rarely exceeds 5 per cent, and with minor exceptions, as at Boggy Hole Gap, is directed southwards from the top of the prominent north face. An amplitude of relief of 100 ft along the bevelled crest is common. The bevel descends laterally towards drainage gaps, near to which it is most perfectly formed, with slopes as low as 2 per cent. Broad sags in the bevelled quartzite surface mark abandoned transverse valleys.

In the higher part of the Heavitree Range, west of Ellery Creek, the bevel is steep and unimpressive, except within half a mile of drainage gaps. Mid-way between Ellery Creek and the Finke it is replaced by a smooth asymmetrical crest above 2800 ft and continuous with the upper slope. The multiple ridges farther west are narrow-crested and carry no bevel.

The Larapinta Ridges, despite their bulk, are almost completely bevelled, and extremely even in long-profile. This circumstance may relate to the lesser resistance of weakly silicified sandstones. Bevelled crest slopes are gentler than on the Heavitree Range, with most gradients less than 5 per cent. The bevels here in the east are some 100 ft lower than those on the Heavitree Range opposite, and are 200 ft and more lower west of Ellery Creek. In contrast with the Heavitree Range, the Larapinta Ridges display bevels sloping both to north and to south. Some are juxtaposed in faceted crests, but south-descending bevels alone occur near the passages of the main south-going channels. Where a secondary divide occurs on the Pertnjara Hills, the bevels are entirely north-sloping.

Smooth upper slopes are developed only on the south side of the Heavitree Range, where some extend to the tops of unbevelled ridges. Many descend to within 150 ft of the vale floor, either giving place abruptly to steep lower slopes, or slackening to form sloping narrow benches which descend laterally towards drainage-breaches. Corresponding slopes are better-developed on the Larapinta Ridges, mainly on the north face where they owe their smoothness to the relatively low resistance offered by the Pacoota Sandstone. They also descend into the narrow strike valleys tributary to the Finke gorge. Narrow benches occur at the foot of the upper slopes on the north side of the Larapinta Ridges, particularly in the west near Ellery Creek and the Finke gorge, where on the southern sandstone ridges they attain the dimension of lower bevels distinct from, and at least 300 ft lower than, the main crest bevel to the north.

The massive Pertnjara conglomerates appear to have been less conducive to the formation or preservation of summit surfaces than the quartzites, but vestiges of a summit bevel, mapped in Fig. 2, survive as restricted flattish ridge-and-spur-crests between 2400 and 2600 ft above sea-level. They probably once formed part of undulating lowlands sloping north and south from higher hills. No landform-equivalent of the upper ridge slopes can be distinguished in this closely-dissected area, but there are signs of relict weathering in surface reddening restricted to certain slopes below the vestigial summit level. This reddening might relate such slopes to the second stage of the summit surface.

In the Arunta Highlands, true summit-surface remnants are restricted to the prominent ridges and summits of metaquartzite, which are characteristically smooth. Upland levels can be recognized on the massive igneous rocks only as closely-accordant low hilltops above rocky plains, indicating that older erosion-surfaces once existed, but have since been irregularly stripped. A former partial planation may be reflected in local accordance of summits at 4200 ft on Mt Giles, and more extensively in a regional similarity of crestal altitudes on the higher ranges, with a gradual westward rise from about 4000 ft at Brinkley and Paisley Bluffs to 4400 ft at Mt Sonder. Such a planation level would be distinctly higher, and presumably older, than the crest bevels of the ridge-and-vale tract. If the gneissic summits at about 3500 ft north of Brinkley Bluff are accepted as an extension of the postulated older surface, the Chewings Range must already have formed higher ground above it.

The most extensive upland level on the Archaeozoic rocks is that which slopes northwards from the Chewings Range at about 2800 ft to about 2600 ft above the Burt Plain. Into this, the east–west upper course of Ellery Creek is shallowly incised. The corresponding surface south of the Chewings Range appears to be the crudely-bevelled divide between Ellery Creek and Finke drainage at the west end of the Alice Valley; this in turn appears to correlate with the slightly lower crest bevels in the ridge-and-vale tract further south.

The smooth slopes of the quartzite ranges and summits are well exemplified on Mt Giles and Mt Sonder, whence they descend steeply to within 250 ft of nearby valley plains. Although higher-lying than the second, or upper slope stage of the summit surface of the ridge-and-vale tract, they appear to be its equivalent.

### Interpretation of the Summit Surface

The two elements of the summit surface are interpreted as successive stages in the formation of an old landscape—the first of partial planation, and the second of valley formation at a lower level.

At the crest-bevel stage, the Heavitree Quartzite formed an asymmetrical strike ridge, low and discontinuous in the east and increasingly prominent west of Ellery Creek. The Larapinta Ridges were more subdued, forming either a low rounded rise with broad drainage-gaps, or a sloping bench below the Pertnjara Hills. The crest-bevel surface in the ridge-and-vale tract was not a continuous southerly slope, for extrapolation of the Heavitree ridge bevels carries them well below the bevels on the Larapinta Ridges opposite. A broad shallow strike vale must already have existed when the bevels were cut, with its north-bounding ridge 100 to 200 ft higher than the ridges to the south. Similarly, the multiple fault ridges of Heavitree Quartzite near Ormiston Gorge already existed.

Within the area shown in Fig. 2, the crest-bevels in the ridge-and-vale tract rise regionally westwards from 2400 ft to more than 3000 ft on the Heavitree Range and from 2300 to 2800 ft on the Larapinta Ridges. Altitudes on the reconstructed vale floors can only be estimated from a few surviving bevels, as on the Bitter Springs Limestone southeast of Ormiston Gorge, but here again a westward rise seems to apply. Either, therefore, drainage ran eastwards at some time during the crest-bevel stage, or else the west of the Ranges has later been uplifted relative to the east.

North of the ridge-and-vale tract, the east–west orographic axis through Chewings Range to Mt Giles and Mt Sonder already existed as a line of broad summits. The slopes of the Heavitree ridge bevels and the height of the remnants on the Arunta rocks south of the Chewings Range suggest that lowland stretched from east to west on the line of the present Alice Valley. The secondary divide on the Pertnjara Hills already existed as discontinuous uplands rising about 200 ft above imperfectly-planed surfaces sloping away to north and south. The bevelled remnants are sufficiently extensive, and their forms sufficiently well preserved, to indicate that local, as apart from regional differences in altitude reflect relief on the crest-bevel surface, not the effects of later earth-movement.

With the formation of the upper slopes, the relief of the area assumed its present pattern. These slopes generally extend to within 200 ft of the present vale floors, delimiting minor valleys between multiple ridges. The secondary divides between strike drainage in the ridge-and-vale tract had also reached something like their present positions, as shown by variations in the height of hillside benches on the Heavitree Range. The lowlands of the Alice Valley and the Missionary Plain were already defined north and south of the ridge-and-vale tract, and the broad crest through the Arunta Highlands had been reduced to the narrow strike ridge of the Chewings Range and to monadnock peaks.

Incision of valleys was greater on the south than on the north of the main divide, and greater in the west than in the east of the Ranges. Asymmetry of rejuvenation is consistent with the relative downwarping to the south and east which may be assumed from Cretaceous structures in the Lake Eyre Basin.

Both elements of the summit surface are planed smoothly over all but the most resistant rocks, even where upper ridge slopes exceed 50 per cent. Well-formed crest bevels on the Heavitree ridge near Boggy Hole Gap show less than 2 ft of microrelief, with joint-broken bands of more silicified sandstone standing only slightly higher than bands of less cohesive rock. The upper ridge slopes exhibit the waxing slopes characteristic of an environment more humid than the present, while the sharply incised present-day gullies are usually located in the rounded re-entrants of the former hillslopes. A general smoothness of slope contrasts markedly with the ruggedness of lower facets.

The summit surface also displays evidence of a degree of weathering irreconcilable with the present semi-arid climate. Considerable differential movement of silica seems to have occurred formerly. Spheroidally-weathering bossy outcrops of quartzite indicate zones of secondary silicification, whilst desilicification has elsewhere penetrated to considerable depths, as in the soft pipe rocks of the Pacoota Sandstone. Kaolinization of quartz greywackes has been observed locally. In addition, deep iron staining and limonite fillings occur in the crevices of joints. Former weathering is naturally shallow on the indurated quartzites, but some sandstones have been altered to depths of more than 50 ft. Many rocks are fragmented, with cores of little-weathered rock surrounded by weathered material; elsewhere, core stones survive the removal of their weathered surround. Such features are typical of the lower part of a poorly-developed weathered profile, possibly of lateritic type. The evidence points to the stripping of a former shallow regolith mantle from the summit surface.

The degree of weathering is, as stated, wholly discordant with the present climate. The stripped weathered rock-surfaces and core stones are now undergoing slow angular fragmentation, mainly as a result of superficial physico-chemical weathering. Slopes formed by erosion of the summit surface exhibit little chemical weathering, are rugged instead of smooth, and are intricately controlled in their form by structure. The summit surface is therefore a relict land surface formed under a more humid climate than the present, and still bearing the remnants of an ancient weathering-profile.

## Age of the Summit Surface

The complex summit surface has been identified as part of an extensive old weathered land surface in central Australia (Mabbutt 1962). Its relationships to planation-levels beyond the Macdonnell Ranges are best shown east of Alice Springs, where the hillslope bench on the Heavitree Range grades laterally into the silcrete cappings of mesas up to 200 ft high. Similar landforms occur further east along the Todd River plains. The silcrete duricrust is seen as part of a dissected surface which, extending far to the southeast, planates soft Palaeozoic and Cretaceous rocks and is characterized by deep weathering with thick pallid zones. Where this silicified former plain abuts against the James and Krichauff Ranges, south of the Macdonnells, it is again separated from an extensive plateau-like crest bevel by smooth upper slopes, although the difference in height between plain and bevel is less here than in the western Macdonnells. The upper slopes are accordingly taken as corresponding to an extensive erosional surface which, known to transect rocks of Lower Cretaceous age, must be younger than these.

In the north of the Arunta Highlands, the upland surface identified with the crest bevel is distinctly higher and older than the erosional Burt Plain. This is a piedmont plain characterized by selective shallow lateritization, and regarded as part of the weathered land surface (Mabbutt 1962). The Burt Plain must therefore be equated with the upper-slope stage of the Macdonnells, and so with the silicified land surface to the southeast.

The nearest proved Mesozoic rocks are Lower Cretaceous marine radiolarites. These occur near the base of a deep valley fill about 5 miles north of the Ranges (Crespin, unpublished data), and are truncated by the Burt Plain. The fill, mainly argillaceous, ranges from 1700 to 2300 ft above sea-level. Weathered siltstone, occurring in low silcrete-capped mesas near the Finke–Derwent Creek divide in the western extension of Glen Helen vale, is also regarded as Cretaceous by Quinlan and Prichard (*op. cit.*) on the basis of lithology, occurrence, and absence of folding. The vale fills are thought to be terrestrial, formed marginally to the marine Cretaceous of the Burt Plain. The base of the siltstone is near the level of the present vale floor, at 2200 ft above sea-level.

Clearly, vale erosion to the depth of the present valley floors occurred in the upper valley of Derwent Creek before the siltstone was deposited. The fill here occurs below facets of the upper-slope stage, but the weathered state of the siltstone and the slopes of its siliceous capping indicate that the upper slopes passed across this rock. The geomorphic setting is therefore not inconsistent with a Lower Cretaceous age for the siltstone. Corresponding deep erosion did not penetrate the strike vales in the heart of the western Macdonnell Ranges, as represented by the area mapped in Fig. 2, for there is no evidence of prior deep cutting below the upper slopes.

If the siltstone within the western Macdonnells is Lower Cretaceous[1], and if it marks the approximate upper limit of Cretaceous deposition, then the crest bevels must be pre-Cretaceous, resulting from sub-aerial erosion possibly continuous since Silurian time. Strong pre-Cretaceous erosion dissociates the crest bevel from the sub-Cretaceous surface, with which it was placed by King (1950). The accordant summits tentatively recognized above the crest bevels in the Arunta Highlands may mark a still older planation.

### Terraces and Flood-plains

The vales and piedmont lowlands of the western Macdonnells are extremely varied. Erosional landforms consist mainly of foothills, pediments being very restricted; the remaining areas consist largely of gravel terraces and alluvial flood-plains. Intermont terraces are best developed in Glen Helen Vale—on the Ellery Creek–Finke divide and westwards along Pioneer Creek. They are less extensive near the Ellery Creek–Hugh River divide. Piedmont terraces, as mapped in Fig. 2, form lobes extending into the Missionary Plain (a third lobe lies west of the Finke River). Despite variations in detail, there is sufficient consistence in the sequence of alluvial deposits throughout the area to allow discussion under the categories of high terrace, middle terrace, low terrace, colluvial aprons, and flood-plains.

[1] Investigations since this essay went to press now indicate a likely unspecified 'Tertiary' age for the older valley fills of the western Macdonnells, and mid-Tertiary for the lower stage of the weathered land surface. Hence the crest bevel may be pre-Tertiary or even Lower Tertiary, but it remains probable that it was never covered by Cretaceous deposits and that it began to be fashioned in the Palaeozoic.

## The High Terrace

*Intermont High Terrace.* The gravel of the highest terrace and the underlying bed rock are both weathered. Form, weathered profiles, and relationship to the summit surface are best observed on the secondary divide between Ellery Creek and the Finke in Glen Helen Vale. Dissected terraces occupying a length of six miles of vale here slope from the Heavitree Range almost to the foot of the Arumbera Ridge. In the Ellery Creek catchment the terrace spurs range from 75 ft above flood-plain levels at their distal ends to 135 ft near the Heavitree Range. Corresponding heights are about 50 ft greater at the head of Pioneer Creek, because of extra incision by the Finke drainage. The terrace spurs have slopes of 1·5–3 per cent, steepening rapidly to 10 per cent and greater within 200 yd of the Heavitree Range, where the terrace surface grades smoothly into the hillslope bench. The high terrace is thus associated with the second stage of formation of the summit surface. Longitudinal gradients of 1 per cent were measured along the terrace surface westwards towards the Finke and eastwards to Ellery Creek.

The terrace gravel thins irregularly towards the axis of the vale, from about 30 ft near the Heavitree Range to less than 5 ft locally. Its upper half is unconsolidated, and is mixed with red sand and ferruginous pisoliths. The lower half is generally, though not everywhere, iron-cemented. Locally, near the Heavitree Range, the gravel is underlain by current-bedded sand and coarse grit with gravel lenses.

The rock beneath the gravels is almost everywhere weathered, depth and degree of weathering varying with rock-type and site. The Bitter Springs Limestone Formation is selectively weathered, the shales being kaolinized in depth and the limestones considerably iron-stained. A calcreted breccia usually separates the gravels from the limestone beds. The Areyonga and Pertatataka siltstones possess deep pallid zones, while the greywackes are kaolinized to depths as great as 100 ft. Differences due to lithology aside, weathering is especially pronounced near the foot of the Heavitree Range, affecting siltstones within the Heavitree Quartzite as well as those at the base of the Bitter Springs Limestone Formation.

The terrace gravels consist of quartzite and sandstone apparently derived from the Heavitree Range; the unusual development of strike drainage within the quartzite, where the ridge is triplicated by strike faulting, may have favoured an exceptionally large supply of gravel. The deposits range from cobble to boulder gravels. Rather large boulders tend to be concentrated at the surface, probably because of selective weathering-out of smaller pieces. The coarse surface mantle is much weathered; its boulders are typically desilicified on the outside, and many are fragmented. Iron pisoliths and strongly ferruginized pebbles are common in the loose surface layer.

Many of the cobbles are sub-angular rather than sub-rounded near the Heavitree Range, where the terrace material seems part fluvial and part colluvial. The proportion of colluvium generally increases upwards in the section. Colluvial fragments increase markedly in bulk close to the ridge, but are generally not larger than cobble size except where the capping locally continues on to the hillslope bench. The bulk of the gravel elsewhere is sub-rounded and apparently fluviatile, and poorly sorted and bedded. There also occurs a small fraction of exceptionally well-rounded gravel, particularly of the boulder size, which seems inexplicable as a first-cycle deposit between 2 and 5 miles from its source. It may have been reincorporated from still higher former terraces which no longer survive, and may have come originally from the Pertnjara conglomerate (in which well-rounded boulders are typical) during an early period of filling by north-going drainage. With these exceptions, the gravels can be considered as primary deposits derived from the ridge to the north.

The weathered profiles are essentially lateritic, although with thin ferruginous zones and with restricted mottled zones. The depth and degree of weathering are remarkable in view of the intermont situation, and of moderately steep slopes vulnerable to erosion. The profiles may be in part compound, and the kaolinized pallid horizon in part older than the iron-cemented gravels above. Local irregularities in the depth of weathered rock below the gravel support such a view. Since a lowland already existed here at the crest-bevel stage, rock rotting may have penetrated it deeply. Possibly, also, the cutting of the upper slopes was complex, sub-stages of relative stability and deep weathering being interrupted by erosion and deposition. Nevertheless, the high terrace grades laterally to the summit surface and it must also be grouped with that surface on the basis of weathering status, as all younger landscape-elements are relatively little-weathered. Together, the high terrace and the summit surface form part of a deeply-weathered landscape.

The high terrace remnants further east, on the divide between Ellery Creek and the Hugh River, exhibit similar profiles and surface relationships to those described in the foregoing, although they stand at lesser heights above present flood-plains. These eastern gravels, deposited by drainage going north through the Larapinta Ridges, are derived mainly from the Pertnjara conglomerate and are markedly rounded. However, quartzite and sandstone alone survive from the mixed assemblage of the parent conglomerate.

It is apparent from the slopes on terrace remnants that the exact position of the initial divide was determined by chance divergence of distributary channels on the terrace surface. However, the divide must have accorded approximately with the watershed on the sub-gravel surface, for the thickness of gravels remains fairly constant down-valley. Slight shifts of divide followed from headwater piracy, itself reflecting unequal speed of downcutting; the Finke has extended its catchment at the expense of Ellery Creek, which in turn has encroached on the catchment of the Hugh. Both derangements are to the advantage of the catchment on the west.

*Piedmont High Terrace.* Transverse and longitudinal slopes on the terrance remnants make it difficult to subclassify the piedmont terraces, since they involve marked variations in height with distance from hills, or from one entrenched flood-plain to the next.

Remnants have been identified, in the main, near the hill front, and near drainage exits which form the apices of gravel fans. The remnants survive as narrow ridges less than ½ mile wide and up to 3 miles long, with deeply indented margins. Maximum heights above adjacent flood-plains are normally between 125 and 150 ft, but one fragment near the southern exit of the Finke gorge is at 190 ft. Slopes from the hills are between 0·25 per cent and 2 per cent; since the terrace surface converges on the present flood-plains down-valley, it may be as low as 75 ft near the distal ends of long spurs.

The high terrace consists of unconsolidated weathered quartzite gravel, generally decreasing in thickness down-slope from 40 ft near the hills to less than 15 ft. The gravel is underlain by up to 5 ft of calcreted rubble, beneath which a weathered calcareous greywacke, kaolinized to a light grey colour, passes into relatively fresh purplish rock at a depth of 20 to 50 ft. The weathered rock shows in distinctive white patches on dissected terrace margins.

The rounded gravels come from the Pertnjara conglomerate in the hills to the north. They display many of the surface characteristics already described for the intermont high terrace—such as the superficial layer of weathered boulders, above average size at 8–12 in. diameter, and the characteristic red sand and ferruginous concretions between the boulders.

In the absence of any landform equivalent of the upper ridge-slopes on the south side of the Pertnjara Hills, the relationship of the piedmont high terrace and the summit surface is not readily established. However, the terrace-hill junction is separated by apparently-weathered slopes from the vestigial plane attributed to the crest-bevel stage. The strongest evidence for equating piedmont and intermont high terraces occurs near the exit of the Finke gorge, where lateral accordance links a sloping bevel on the southernmost Larapinta ridge—the equivalent of the hillslope benches of Glen Helen Vale—with a nearby mesa of high terrace.

*The High Terrace in the Arunta Highlands.* Existing flood-plains show that the gneiss and schist of the Arunta Complex yield little gravel, which in any event is susceptible to destruction by weathering. Random counts north of Boggy Hole Gap gave 2–5 per cent of schist cobbles for flood-plain gravels, and 0·5–1 per cent for the lower terrace. No schist was found in an adjacent piece of middle terrace. It seems, therefore, that high terraces in the Arunta Highlands survive only where quartzite ranges have supplied quartzite gravels. The original gravel fans here were much smaller than to the south, where the Pertnjara conglomerates formed a ready source of gravel.

High terrace remnants 180 ft above river-level occur on the south flank of the Chewings Range near Standley Chasm. They comprise 50 ft of quartzite colluvium, an unstratified, unsorted deposit ranging from pebbles to blocks 2 ft in diameter. The lower part is slightly indurated, with a ferruginous cement, while the underlying schist is weathered to a depth of more than 50 ft. The terrace descends at a slope of 2 per cent to 10 per cent, standing but 75 ft above river-level at a distance of 2 miles from the Chewings Range.

High terraces further west have been identified on air photographs, on the south of the Chewings Range, and on the southwest flank of Mt Giles. Narrowly dissected, they slope steeply from the mountain flanks to less than 100 ft above present flood-plains within a mile of the mountain front. High terraces on the south flank of the Sonder-Razorback ridge are cut through to depths of 300 ft near the high ground. In the plains to the south, which are formed on Archaeozoic schist, mesas more than 200 ft high bear a cap of silcrete 20 ft thick above deeply-weathered, somewhat arkosic and lightly-indurated sands which have been mapped as Mesozoic. No quartzite gravel has carried the distance of 3 miles from Mt Sonder.

Lateral continuity between the high terrace surface of the Arunta Highlands and the upper slopes on the quartzite summits is impressively clear on Mts Sonder and Giles, confirming the equivalence of the high terrace here with that further south.

### Landform Inheritance from the High Terrace Cycle

In the ridge-and-vale tract the high terrace is now restricted to secondary divides in Glen Helen Vale, or to spurs flanking Pioneer Creek. Even less remains in the Arunta Highlands. The stage in which the terrace was formed, however, widely influences the landforms in both areas, partly through that planation which preceded deposition of gravel, and partly through associated deep weathering.

The small range in thickness of gravel shows that the striking lack of residual relief on the high terrace results from planation rather than from depositional levelling. Strike drainage like that of today planed off the terrain between the main sandstone ridges. The Arumbera Ridge stood above the intermont lowland in the west of the area, but east of Ellery Creek was in many parts destroyed or buried. The surviving remnants of terrace indicate planation for much of the Alice Valley. The plain, now exhumed from its gravel cover, survives extensively on resistant rocks in the vales, particularly as accordant, rounded foothill summits up to 100 ft high on Bitter Springs Limestone, and also on thin sandstone ridges of Goyder Formation in the Southern Vale. Exhumation is in progress in the middle sector of Pioneer Creek, where the stripped ridge crests are about 30 ft below high terrace nearby.

On deeply-weathered rocks, the planed-off surface has largely been destroyed by subsequent erosion, with selective etching of soft bands by the removal of saprolite. On newly-stripped surfaces, minor facets and joint-blocks appear to correspond directly with irregularities of the old weathering-front (Mabbutt 1961a) or to the exhumation of core stones. Some of the fantastic weathering forms on lower slopes of the Arumbera Ridge nearby may have originated similarly, for present-day weathering tends slowly to reduce and to remove perched blocks and vulnerable projections, all of which suffer granular disintegration.

In the Alice Valley, the importance of selective etching can best be gauged from where high terrace remains on the north margin, as near Standley Chasm. Although the remnants indicate almost complete bevelling of the Alice Valley, and associated widespread deep weathering when the high terrace was formed, there is no trace either of summit bevels or of weathered mantles in the rugged lowlands to the south. However, the rocky plain stretching eastwards to Alice Springs is traversed by numerous schistose or dyke ridges, and is studded with tors and low domes of more massive rock, with a remarkably consistent range of height of between 50 and 100 ft. The ridges pass northwards beneath surviving remnants of high terrace. Despite the lack of summit bevels—due perhaps to lithology—it appears that the high terrace planation set a limit to present relief in the Alice Valley.

The crests of many of the low dyke ridges are deeply ferruginized, while the tors on many gneissic hills exhibit core stones similar to those known where stripping has occurred (Mabbutt 1961b). What has been adduced of the regional geomorphic history is quite consistent with a view that selective weathering and partial etch-planation formed the present Alice Valley lowland.

Lithological differences apart, weathering below the high-terrace plane was particularly strong at the foot of the main ridges in a manner which has strongly influenced the course of later erosion. Strike dissection is generally advanced near the ridge-foot, and almost every terrace spur is separated from the nearby hillslope benches by a deep narrow valley. A high rate of infiltration, where runoff from the steep slope was checked at the junction with the plain, may possibly account for excessive weathering at the ridge-foot. Moreover, the resistant ridge-building rocks are generally more compact and less pervious than those of the piedmont, so that sub-surface contributions of water may be expected to have influenced piedmont weathering. Again, the water table fluctuates more widely in the piedmont than on the ridges. The hillfoot zone is then especially liable to weakening through weathering, as well as being especially subject to erosional and depositional regrading by virtue of its position. It is accordingly very sensitive to climatically-induced changes of morphogenesis. Comparison of profile between the terrace and the present plain indicates an erosional adjustment from the concave hillfoot profile of a humid environment to the angular hill-and-plain junction of a more arid landscape. Because little deepening of valleys has taken place since the high terrace stage, most subsequent erosion and deposition have occurred in the piedmont zone. Cyclic subsurface weathering has similarly been invoked as a cause of steepened margins of granite inselbergs in South Australia (Twidale 1962).

## The Middle Terrace

*Intermont Middle Terrace.* This terrace generally occurs about 60 ft below the high terrace, or at heights of between 20 and 75 ft above present flood-plains. Its development varies with the degree of dissection of the high terrace: where the latter is narrowly dissected, as on the Ellery Creek–Finke divide, the middle terrace forms sloping valley-side benches at between 30 and 50 ft above river-level and with little gravel, passing into discontinuous river terraces less than $\frac{1}{4}$ mile wide; where the high terrace has been extensively destroyed, as along the Hugh River, the middle terrace may form extensive fans, or terraces as much as a mile wide flanking the larger channels downvalley.

In contrast to the high terrace, however, the middle terrace in the vales is overtopped by considerable rising ground, for the erosional phase of the middle-terrace cycle involved selective erosion rather than widespread planation. Accordingly, the middle terrace is compartmented in tributary valleys and varies a good deal in height. Its form is strongly affected by residual relief; there are marked cross-slopes from local hills, while ridge barriers at transverse drainage gaps have aided its development locally.

Longitudinal gradients are typically less than on the high terrace, being mainly below 0·25 per cent. The high and middle terraces converge on each other down-valley, while the middle terrace itself converges, although less markedly, on the present flood-plains.

The middle terrace gravels consist of weathered cobbles and boulders of quartzite and sandstone. They are rounded only where derived from the Pertnjara conglomerates; elsewhere, sub-angular or sub-rounded cobbles predominate. The gravels are unconsolidated, with a stony cover of red earth soil on extensive flats, and with a little red sand on bare, stripped margins. The gravels contain derived iron pisoliths; near Boggy Hole Gap are cobbles derived from silicified limestone in weathered high terrace nearby. On stripped surfaces is a weathering-concentrate of larger boulders, some weathered and fragmented, although less markedly so than with the high terrace.

The gravel is typically less than 15 ft thick, and tends to thin down-valley. Thinning away from the hill-base is less marked and less regular than in the high terrace, for the gravel of the middle terrace rests on a slightly uneven surface cut in part in fresh rock. Where weathered rock underlies the gravel, it can be explained as a truncated weathered high-terrace profile, with the gravels of the middle terrace overlying but not genetically associated with it.

*Piedmont Middle Terrace.* The middle terrace of the piedmont forms tongues stretching outwards from river-exits of the Pertnjara Hills, between dissected spurs of high terrace. These tongues are narrower and shorter than intact lobes of high terrace. Longitudinal gradients are smaller, but transverse gradients probably greater, on the middle than on the high terrace of the piedmont; transverse gradients commonly attain 2 per cent. It is difficult to separate the terraces in distal sites, because of these differences of slope. The identity of the middle terrace is most clear near the hills, where it generally occurs about 60 ft below adjacent patches of high terrace and 80 ft above valley floors. At its distal end, the middle terrace stands between 20 and 40 ft above the flood-plains. In the western lobe shown in Fig. 2 it is however overlapped by younger deposits along the Finke River, passing beneath them without a dissection rim. Unlike the high terrace, the middle terrace does not occur outside the discontinuous drainage-arcs of the Finke River and Rudall, Jerrimah, and Mueller Creeks. Since these drainage-arcs coincide with the intersection of an undissected middle-terrace surface with the present flood-plains, they probably mark the approximate original periphery of the middle-terrace lobe. This peripheral drainage is incised as much as 40 ft below the high terrace, so that dissection of the high terrace here may have resulted in part from regional rejuvenation of drainage. In contrast, dissection of the middle terrace is explicable by adjustment of river-gradients within the gravel lobes.

The middle terrace is extensive only alongside the larger elements of drainage from the Pertnjara Hills. Minor elements dissecting the high terrace possess but meagre spreads of middle terrace, which is most typically associated with irregular rounded spurs 20 to 40 ft below the high terrace.

The contrast between an originally unbroken panfan of high terrace, and a middle terrace confined between dissected remnants of high terrace, also holds good in the piedmont zone. For instance, near the southeastern margin of the eastern lobe shown in Fig. 2 the high terrace caps low interfluves of Pertnjara greywacke, while little-dissected tongues of middle terrace occupy broad shallow valleys 30 ft below.

The middle-terrace gravel of the piedmont is typically less than 10 ft thick, and underlain by calcreted rubble less than 5 ft thick. The underlying calcareous greywacke is less weathered than beneath the high terrace. The sub-gravel surface may disappear beneath younger deposits in distal sites. The gravel near the surface of the middle terrace is smaller in median diameter than that of the high terrace, with a larger proportion of cobbles. Bare gravel is confined principally to stripped margins and rises, and a stony red earth soil, commonly with a calcareous sub-soil, is usually present (Litchfield 1962).

The middle terrace of the piedmont tract increases in extent eastwards, relative to the high terrace, as a result of increasing planation between the two respective stages. In the west of Missionary Plain, Rudall Creek is narrowly entrenched and the middle terrace occupies valleys between spurs of high terrace. East of the Finke River, however, the middle terrace forms broad lobes such as that on which the Hermannsburg Mission airstrip is located.

## The Low Terrace

A lower terrace is present as discontinuous alluvial flats in lower tributary valleys. It flanks some main channels in the ridge-and-vale tract, and constitutes flood-plain terraces and undissected older flood-plains in the southern piedmont. In the Ranges it is generally between 5 and 15 ft above the present drainage, attaining 25 ft near large channels such as Ellery Creek; in the piedmont it is less than 5 ft above present drainage, except locally in areas of strong dissection. Its longitudinal gradients are generally only slightly greater than those of the present flood-plains, while its transverse slopes are variable.

Even where it stands very little above the flood-plain it is distinguished by red soils, in contrast to the red-brown or grey-brown soils on younger alluvia. An erosional unconformity separates the low terrace and the flood-plains. In tributary valleys and in the extreme west of the piedmont, sub-alluvial surfaces cut unevenly on relatively fresh rocks may occur slightly above flood-plain level, whereas the base of the present flood-plain deposits is rarely exposed.

The low terrace is predominantly of sandy alluvium with gravels restricted to seams a few feet thick. Only in tributary valleys are gravels exposed at the surface: normally they are covered by as much as 5 ft of alluvial red earth. The gravel layers in tributary valleys consist of little-sorted, sub-angular to sub-rounded cobbles, varying in size near the main channels. The gravels are usually calcreted, with lime abundant at depth in alluvial sections, but except near outcrops of limestone the upper alluvium is non-calcareous, consisting of well-structured red earth. Geomorphologically and in weathering status, the alluvial red earth plains in the Alice Valley appear to be equivalent to the low terrace.

## Colluvial Landforms

The terrace gravels, particularly those of the high terrace, commonly have marginal colluvial facies which have already been described. The colluvial deposits now to be discussed are aprons distinct from river terraces. They are most widespread on the north front of the Heavitree Range.

As is well shown near Boggy Hole Gap and Gill Pass, the colluvial slopes head near the base of prominent quartzite cliffs and rest on a rectilinear slope of about 35 per cent cut in Arunta schist. This rock base is locally and unevenly weathered, as though an older irregular weathering-profile had been truncated. The colluvial slopes are steeply concave. The long upper sectors, at 30 per cent to 35 per cent, consist of thin scree mantles narrowing upwards, and of rock in place. The scree passes rather abruptly at the base to fan-like tongues of mixed colluvial-alluvial deposits which extend up to 200 yd from the ridge with average slopes of 10 per cent.

The colluvium consists mainly of angular cobbles and small boulders, weathering to sub-angular, with a minor content of larger blocks. It is somewhat weathered and ferruginized, has a red sandy earth matrix, and is sufficiently indurated to stand in steep short slopes where gullied. Its weathering status is certainly equivalent to that of the middle or low terrace. Similar, but more indurated, limonitized slope mantles have been described from the Rumbalara Hills in the southeast of the Northern Territory (Sullivan and Opik 1951). The aprons have smooth stable surfaces consistent with their internal weathering, and there is little doubt that these are inherited landforms. Few cobbles, such as form the mass of the colluvium, are being added today. Present-day weathering of the quartzite face yields large joint-blocks, which lie sparsely scattered across the older colluvium, but are not incorporated with it. They contrast with the older deposits in their size and in their light-coloured weathering surfaces. The old colluvial forms are now being destroyed by gullying, particularly in their upper parts.

Aside from dissection now in progress, the aprons have undergone prior erosion which has deeply embayed them. It seems likely that the relevant episode of cutting took place when the aprons were formed, as the smooth slopes and weathered profiles continue into the old re-entrants.

The colluvial fans may pass smoothly downslope into or beneath the alluvial red earths which here floor the Alice Valley. Locally, however, they are trimmed by through-going drainage and interfinger with terraces, and their place in the terrace sequence can be ascertained. At Boggy Hole Gap, the colluvium passes beneath upper flood-plain alluvium and has been trimmed by channels at the upper flood-plain level. Also, the colluvium here incorporates middle-terrace gravels, while the colluvial surfaces continue to a level below that of the adjacent low terrace. On this evidence, the colluvial slopes are older than the flood-plains, but may be younger than the low terrace and are certainly not older than it. Such a relationship, consistent with the degree of weathering of the colluvium, is confirmed from the Southern Vale, where the low terrace at the heads of tributaries of Pioneer Creek is locally overlapped by colluvium. Dating should, however, probably allow for a certain range in time of origin, for the red earths which overlap and therefore partly post-date the colluvium have also been equated with the low terrace.

### Flood-plains and River Channels

Detailed description of the flood-plains and their deposits is beyond the scope of this essay. However, they provide a useful picture of river action in the present climate, and a standard of comparison with fluvial features inherited from older morphogenetic systems.

The main drainage is everywhere aggrading. Outcrops of rock are extremely rare in the flood-plains and channels, even at traverses through the Ranges. The main channels are flanked by flood-plains up to ½ mile wide, which extend for long distances up the main tributaries. In general, an upper and a lower flood-plain can be distinguished, the former being the more extensive, particularly along the large rivers. The two flood-plain elements are normally separated by a distinct step about 5 ft high, but the vertical separation may increase to 10 ft along main channels and to 15 ft in constrictions of the valley.

The upper flood-plain is generally at or near high flood levels, as marked by debris lines, but its surface is apparently fairly stable. It is characteristically formed of calcareous grey-brown alluvium, with gravel seams which may be calcreted, particularly in limestone areas. The lower flood-plain is much less regular. It is traversed by the channel or braids of the main river, and by numerous minor flood channels. Low sand-bars, alluvial flats, and gravel mounds and spreads make up its surface.

The main channels are up to 200 yd wide, typically braided, trench-like in cross-section, and with steep banks up to 10 ft high. The beds are flattish and sandy except where subject to scour, which produces irregular minor channels with deep holes and intervening bars of unsorted boulder gravel.

The depth of alluvial fill in the flood-plains and channels is remarkable. More than 60 ft of sand and gravel overlie the rock bed beneath the Todd River at Heavitree Gap, south of Alice Springs, at a site which may be typical of the area. Rivers of the arid zone are subject to deep scour and mobilization of bed deposits during flood flow, but such depths of fill must indicate an aggradation after deep down-cutting.

## Interpretation of Terraces and Related Deposits

Terraces as described here are not confined to the Macdonnells. They form aureoles about most of the quartzite ranges of central Australia, including such outlying eminences as Mt Liebig which have not been affected by regional rejuvenation of drainage. In all areas the sequence is similar: a weathered high terrace, a middle terrace, and a complex of low terrace and flood-plains. The terraces draw together with increasing distance from the mountain-front. In the western Macdonnells, regional down-cutting separates the high and middle terraces, but west of the Finke catchment, as north of Mt Liebig, the whole terrace sequence may pass beneath younger aggradational surfaces. The thickness of terrace gravels is everywhere comparable, and everywhere decreases away from the upland; the gravels are consistently sub-angular or sub-rounded except where they are derived from Pertnjara conglomerates, while a colluvial marginal facies is normally present. If the lobate terrace-margins of the middle terrace south of the Macdonnell Ranges be taken as an original limit, then the terraces were fan-like products of minor streams, and through-going major rivers remained competent to remove material fed into them.

Phases of planation and deposition have alternated with a general or recurrent down-cutting. Since the relevant cycles are so widely recorded in terrace suites, recurrent earth-movement is less likely to explain them than is climatic change. The hypothesis of climatically induced periodic instability of slope, with related changes in the load/discharge balance of streams, is in keeping with the outward convergence and thinning of terraces. Oscillations of climate, with similar effects, have already been postulated from the borders of dry Australia, mainly on the evidence of soils (Butler 1959), but not previously for the central part of the arid zone.

The periodicity indicated by the terraces includes planation, deposition, weathering, and cutting. The suggested interpretation requires conditions wetter than those of today, in which weathering-mantles formed on hillslopes, themselves stable under a vegetation closer than the present. Weathering of lowland surfaces would be expected with increased wetness, but this at the same time would promote incision. The resultant lowering of water table might favour the deepening of weathering profiles. A trend to drier conditions could first express itself in stream behaviour, with a change from incision to planation. With further increase in aridity the weathered slope-mantle would become unstable, and slope-wash and minor streamflow would spread it at the hill foot.

Such climatic shifts from wetter to drier seem to have been superimposed on a general trend to desiccation, indicated by increasingly shallow weathering. Morphologically, and in weathering status, the high terrace forms part of a weathered land surface (Mabbutt 1962) characterized by deep lateritic weathering on lowlands and by formation of regolith on the hard rocks of uplands. Successive cycles have achieved successively less weathering. Judged by catchment area, the high terrace corresponds to the removal of between 10 and 50 ft of regolith from hillslopes; the middle terrace represents between 5 and 25 ft without any allowance for the incorporation of reworked material from the high terrace. The core stones and the selectively weathered rocks on the summit surface in the Macdonnells are taken as the residuals of former regoliths, stripped almost to the irregular weathering front. Lateritic weathering of the high terrace was followed by formation of red earth on the middle and low terraces, and by the formation of the lithosols of the flood-plains and newly-eroded rock surfaces. Abundant evidence elsewhere in central Australia—e.g. the onset of interior drainage and the growth of sand dunes— indicates desiccation proper as a cause of reduced weathering, not merely a decreasing time-scale.

Any attempt to estimate the magnitude of climatic fluctuation from the magnitude of terracing must allow not only for the secular trend towards aridity, but also for the complication that achievement in any one cycle is preconditioned and limited by events in the cycle preceding. For instance, prior weathering influences not only the supply of colluvium in the subsequent phase of instability, but also the nature and rate of erosion of lowland areas in the next cycle of cutting. The effects of inheritance and desiccation are not unrelated: reduced prior weathering becomes progressively more limiting on subsequent erosion.

Hillslope weathering has been negligible during the flood-plain cycles. Colluvial yield has accordingly been reduced, so that aggradation has been increasingly restricted to the larger river catchments and their margins. The last significant colluvial deposits are the stable aprons correlated with the lower terrace. Present-day colluvium includes fallen blocks, and the grit and sand of slopewash. The change is reflected in the decreasing fraction of gravel in the later parts of the terrace sequence.

The ages of the terraces are unknown. No attempt will be made here to correlate postulated climatic fluctuations with sequences established in distant areas. Available evidence calls for lateritic weathering persisting into middle or late Tertiary time in much of Australia; the onset of such weathering may have been remote, even on the geological scale. There is perhaps a geological prejudice against asserting a Tertiary age for little-consolidated gravels, and the possibility of an unconformity between the high terrace capping and its saprolitic base is a real one. Nevertheless, the capping itself has undergone lateritic weathering, and in this sense must belong with the weathered land surface.

Periodicity in morphogenesis, probably due to climatic fluctuations, appears to have been a feature of the Macdonnells since the time of deep weathering. One is tempted to suggest that the older fluctuations may be connected with world-wide Pleistocene changes of climate, but immature soils suggest that the flood-plain cycles are recent. Climatic fluctuations in the heart of the arid zone accord with the idea that pluvial and interpluvial rhythms have resulted from changes in the circulation-pattern of the atmosphere—specifically, in the strength of the tropical cells of high pressure, rather than in mere zonal shifts.

Extreme aridity, as indicated by movement of wind-borne sand and by the initiation of sand-plains and dunes in the south of the Missionary Plain, certainly post-dates the high terrace. Fluvially-dissected remnants of this now stand in sandy plains devoid of surface drainage. Aeolian sand nowhere transgresses the middle terrace, while the low terrace with its red-earth soils must be grouped palaeoclimatically with the older terraces rather than with the flood-plains. On the other hand, the flood-plains breach or delimit the main areas of aeolian sand, although younger dunes also occur on them. Maximum aridity seems to have followed the low-terrace cycle, marking the climax of the long-continued secular trend towards dryness. Some recovery is suggested by the resumption of fluvial deposition, and by the fact that the sand surfaces are now naturally stable. Since older and younger dunes occur, one may assume that the short-term cycles of erosion and deposition by streams included phases of marked aeolian activity as maximum secular desiccation approached. Stream action, however, did not apparently cease altogether in the piedmont and intermont tracts.

The idea of an Australian arid period (Crocker and Wood 1947) is widely current, and is commonly associated with the thermal maximum or Climatic Optimum of about 5000 B.P. (Gentilli 1961). Geomorphic evidence in central Australia suggests an earlier date for the inception of dune-fields in relation to later erosion by the lower Finke (Mabbutt 1962). The concept of periodic events is valuable in allowing for more than one period of extreme aridity and in extending the term of aeolian activity.

## Development of the Drainage-Pattern

No pattern of drainage so remarkably discordant with structure as that of the western Macdonnells can be omitted from a study of the geomorphology of the Ranges. The possibilities are fourfold: that the drainage is antecedent, that it is superimposed, that it has been inherited directly from an erosional surface without superimposition, and that it has evolved by regressive erosion and derangement through capture. Published hypotheses appeal to one or another of the first three of these possibilities.

Antecedence was invoked by Madigan (1931) on the evidence of a northerly provenance of the Pertnjara conglomerate prior to the main folding of the Macdonnells. On this view, the drainage-pattern is of Silurian or greater age. Both inheritance and superposition were suggested by Ward (1925)—inheritance in the north and superposition from a Mesozoic cover in the south. Inheritance was emphasized in a brief reference to the area made by King (1950), who used the pattern of drainage as evidence for the former existence of a high-level erosional plain in the Ranges. In an earlier, generalized account, the present writer (Mabbutt 1962) stated that partial planation of the Ranges was achieved in the formation of a (?) Tertiary weathered land surface on which elements of the transverse drainage already existed. These several hypotheses will now be examined in relation to the geomorphic stages indicated by the inherited landforms of the western Macdonnells.

With minor exceptions, the area is drained southwards by the Finke system. Each of three main elements—the Hugh River, Ellery Creek, and the Finke—traverses the Ranges by a main channel. The main divide lies a minimum of 5 miles north of the orographic axis, which runs east–west through the Chewings Range to Mt Giles and Mt Sonder.

The drainage patterns show an east–west zonation reflecting geology and relief. The Arunta Highlands are characterized by complex rectangular drainage-patterns; the ridge-and-vale tract has trellised drainage; the outcrop of Pertnjara conglomerates forms a secondary divide, with transverse or radial drainage. Transverse drainage occurs throughout, involving channels of a wide range of drainage-order.

*Hypotheses of Evolution of Drainage*

*Antecedence.* The mere fact that drainage can be suggested as antecedent to Lower Palaeozoic folding is a salutary reminder of the duration, and possible complexity, of geomorphic evolution in central Australia. Since Madigan (1931) made the suggestion, detailed work on the stratigraphy of the Pertnjara Formation by Prichard and Quinlan (1962) has improved the basis of reconstruction.

Three main depositional cycles are recognized within the Pertnjara Formation. The first cycle is represented by a basal sandstone 1000 ft thick, which passes into a sandstone-pebble conglomerate east of Ellery Creek. In the second cycle, 8000 ft of conglomerate were laid down. The pebble sequence of the conglomerate shows a reverse stratigraphic order of source-rocks, indicating the successive removal of Palaeozoic and Proterozoic rocks farther north and the eventual exposure of the Arunta Complex. The third cycle of deposition is marked by a second conglomerate, also about 8000 ft thick, which passes westwards along the strike into 3000 ft of pebbly greywacke. Prichard and Quinlan concluded that the distribution of coarser sediments in each cycle indicates a source to the north and northeast, and that successive cycles are probably related to phased uplift in this direction.

The Pertnjara Formation is almost conformable with the Mereenie Sandstone west of Ellery Creek, but is unconformable further east. The erosional unconformity progressively truncates the Larapinta Group eastwards and passes on to the Jay Creek Limestone. Prichard and Quinlan (*op. cit.*), assuming that the conglomerates were littoral, suggest that the strandline lay near the line of Ellery Creek during the first and second cycles of deposition, and that during the third cycle it had moved east of the area shown in Fig. 1. The basal unconformity is accordingly a plane of marine erosion. The Pertnjara Formation was later folded with the older rocks beneath.

The correspondence between postulated Silurian geography and that of today is not close. Whereas the higher ground then lay north and east of the Missionary Plain, in a pattern apparently reinforced by Pertnjara movements, it is now rather north and west, and the earlier southwesterly drainage has been replaced by one heading south or south-southwest.[1] Further, the sea had encroached over the whole south part of the area by the close of Pertnjara deposition.

Only in the sense that an upland area formed on Archaeozoic rocks existed north of the Missionary Plain syncline can any element of the present landscape be regarded as antecedent to the post-Ordovician fold movements of the western Macdonnells. There is no trace in the Arunta Highlands of an ancestral southwesterly drainage responsible for Pertnjara sedimentation, of which drainage that south and west of the Silurian shoreline might be considered an extension.

*Superposition from a Cover.* The hypothesis of superposition, if used in complete explanation of the discordant drainage of the western Macdonnells, must imply a former cover above the present crest-bevel. Neither Pertnjara nor postulated Mesozoic deposition is adequate in this respect.

The Pertnjara Formation has shared most of the folding of the older sedimentary rocks and its basal unconformity is vertical or nearly vertical, so that its erosion can have produced little shift of the outcrop. Accordingly, the idea of antecedence having been rejected, no drainage north of the Pertnjara Hills can have originated on a Pertnjara cover. Apart from this geological argument, the Pertnjara Hills themselves form a secondary divide of north-going drainage with many transverse elements: such elements must post-date any major shift of outcrop.

Mesozoic and correlated deposits in and near the Ranges have been

[1] The patterns of Cretaceous deposition suggest that this replacement occurred before the Lower Cretaceous.

discussed above, where it was concluded that the vales must have been eroded before the Lower Cretaceous and that it was unlikely that the Cretaceous fill extended to the crest level. Accordingly, no superposition of drainage across the main ridges could have occurred on this fill.

*Inheritance.* This topic requires an examination of the relationships between drainage gaps and the summit surface. Fig. 3 shows generalized profiles of a number of drainage gaps through the Heavitree and Larapinta ridges, typical of the main channels and their larger tributaries in the ridge-and-vale tract. With the exception of a few small gaps, bevelled and unbevelled ridge crests slope towards the gaps, outlining the broad shallow valleys of upper gaps. Bevelled crests generally descend at less than 5 per cent, and bevels are particularly smooth near the gaps. Only on the east side of Boggy Hole Gap is the slope of the crest-bevel opposed to the (southerly) direction of drainage. The bevelled crest normally meets the gap at between 200 and 300 ft above the river bed, while the equivalent junction on unbevelled ridges occurs at greater and more varied heights. Below the junction with the crest-bevel, the gaps have smooth upper slopes which commonly attain 50 per cent. These slopes may be rectilinear, giving a V-shaped upper profile to the gap, or convex or faceted, suggesting two sub-stages of formation. They usually end at between 50 and 150 ft above the river bed. The mid-ranges of gaps are the profile equivalents of the smooth upper ridge-slopes. At Ellery Creek gorge through the Larapinta Ridges the mid-stage of gap-cutting is marked by a bench—a narrow valley floor later trenched through. The hillslope benches, sloping towards the gaps, are graded to the middle-gap features, as is the high terrace.

The lower parts of the gaps are generally narrow gorges, occupied wholly by river channels. The heights of the gorges increase westwards with the heights of the ridges, from 50 ft at Boggy Hole Gap to more than 150 ft west of Ellery Creek (Fig. 3). Rocky walls of gorges contrast with smooth slopes above: the latest stage of downcutting clearly followed the period of deep weathering. In the ridge-and-vale tract, rock floors are confined to a few small gaps; normally there is a channel fill.

The three stages of gap-formation correspond to the stages in the formation of the strike ridges. The major transverse drainage of the ridge-and-vale tract must already have existed when the crest-bevels were cut, and the main outlets were then, as now, to the south. Rivers crossed the quartzite barriers in open valleys, between which were narrow ridges with rounded asymmetrical crests up to 100 ft high in the east but exceeding 300 ft in the west. The meandering gorge of

Ellery Creek is incised in an early shallow winding valley, which belongs to the first stage of development of gaps. The drainage passages were fewer where the ridges were most massive or highest; the soft sandstone of the well-planed Larapinta Ridges was crossed by more channels than was the more resistant Heavitree Quartzite.

Once formed, the gaps have survived and have developed with increasing relief. They have been fixed points in subsequently-evolving drainage, although a few shallow dry gaps in crest-bevels indicate some elimination of transverse drainage during the second stage of formation of the summit surface.

Proof of the great age of the transverse drainage in the ridge-and-vale tract, if not complete evidence for inheritance, is at least con-

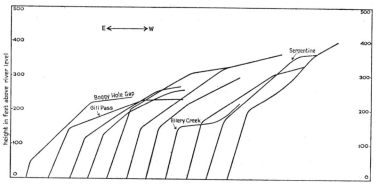

Fig. 3. Characteristic river gap profiles in the ridge-and-vale tract. Note the increasing relief from east to west.

sistent with it. The major elements of the drainage existed, even if they did not originate, in conditions of low relief, and they have declined rather than increased in number with increasing relief. The distribution of gaps shows sufficient *general* influence by geological controls, as expressed in the massiveness and resistance of the ridge-building rocks, to indicate a degree of adaptation such as might be expected from former sub-aerial planation.

Superposition and antecedence having been rejected, additional evidence for inherited drainage in the ridge-and-vale tract is provided by the alignment of its main drainage gaps, which indicates that they formed along pre-existing transverse rivers. Alignment would be unlikely if the gaps had formed successively by river capture, nor is there evidence of widespread exploitation of structural weaknesses in detail in the formation of gaps here, as might be expected where regressive erosion and capture had occurred. Figure 2 illustrates the straight course of the Finke through this part of the Ranges, and the Ellery

Creek gaps are also well-aligned, although the channel swings westwards to cross the Pertnjara Hills, where a secondary divide has been shown to have existed on the summit surface. East of the area shown in Fig. 2, the Hugh River receives important tributaries south of the ridge-and-vale tract, and each has its series of aligned gaps.

Apart from the regional transection of geological structure, there are notable local examples of discordance which, in the absence of superposition, provide strong further argument for inheritance. Among the larger relevant examples are the incised meanders of Ellery Creek through the Larapinta Ridges, even though these are poorly-developed in comparison with the incised meanders of the Finke through the plateau-like James Range south of the Missionary Plain. But caution must be exercised in interpreting discordant pseudo-meanders, which may have originated by back-cutting along intersecting structural planes. This may be the explanation of some apparently very marked discordances in the Arunta Highlands, where crest-bevelling did not occur. For instance, the small meanders of Ellery Creek across a low quartzite ridge above its passage through the Chewings Range are sited on faults, while the more spectacular course of Ormiston Creek across the syntaxis of the Chewings and Heavitree Ranges can also be explained by structural guidance.

Inheritance as envisaged for the crest-bevel stage is now proceeding in the upper catchment of the Palmer River, a right-bank tributary of the Finke in the south of the Krichauff Range, southwest of the Missionary Plain. In this relatively stable area, the bevelled summit surface is undergoing incipient etching by drainage inherited from the summit bevel, and many channels maintain their southeasterly courses through low ridges formed by exhumed sandstone strata.

However, it is not implied that all inherited drainage in the ridge-and-vale tract dates from the crest-bevel. Transverse drainage occurs in high and low orders of channels, and many minor gaps must have been inherited from valley plains below the summit bevel. The multiple crossings and recrossings of Larapinta Ridges by small tributaries of the Finke in the west of the area are in narrow gorges cut below accordant ridge bevels which here represent the high terrace stage: the crossings are presumably inherited from strike vales on the weathered land surface.

Inheritance, although plausible in the ridge-and-vale tract, cannot explain all transverse drainage of the western Macdonnells, for such drainage in the Arunta Highlands crosses former watersheds devoid of signs of prior planation. Still higher and older erosion surfaces would be required for drainage initiation. As already described, the altitudinal grouping of summits in this area may be taken as slight

ESSAYS IN GEOMORPHOLOGY

evidence of such a surface, but indications are that even at that stage the orographic axis would have lain near its present position, so that inheritance cannot provide an explanation of drainage across it. Furthermore, the gaps through the Chewings Range appear to be younger, not older, than those farther south; they fail to record the stadial development which marks gaps in the ridge-and-vale tract, and their gorge walls can extend directly to the rounded summits of ridges. An alternative hypothesis is accordingly considered for this part of the western Macdonnells.

*Regressive Erosion and River-Capture.* The hypothesis of regression and capture relies on the asymmetry of the main divide in the Arunta Highlands, and on its position north of the orographic axis. It envisages the breaching by capture of a former east–west watershed on resistant quartzites in the Arunta Highlands. The greater energy of south-going drainage derives from the difference in altitude between the plains north and south of the Ranges: the Burt Plains are about 2300 ft above sea-level, whereas the east of Missionary Plain is between 1900 and 2000 ft. The inequality of level may have resulted from earth-movements of several dates. It appears significant that the main watershed, here lying in the north of the Ranges but passing into the south of them further west, is in each case displaced away from a basin of Cretaceous marine deposition and of possible relative downwarping. Basining may thus provide a cause of rejuvenation and of extension of drainage.

The Arunta Complex has a pronounced east–west structural grain, reflected in the trend of the Alice Valley lowland and in the uppermost courses of Ellery Creek and the Finke. The headstreams occupy, and are shallowly incised into, a broad east–west depression in the crest-bevel surface which descends northwards from the Chewings Range, and which was accordingly formed when the Chewings Range was a divide.

Where the main rivers swing southwards to cross the Chewings Range, they begin to be cut progressively deeper below the upland surface, which slopes in the opposite direction. The gaps were evidently made after the crest-bevels had been cut, and can only have resulted from regressive erosion and capture by drainage on the south of the former divide, during the two periods of rejuvenation before and after the high terrace stage. The considerable erosion indicates a long history, as does the absence of nickpoints. The transverse sectors possess continuous steep grades which bring channels down from about 2500 ft north of the Chewings Range to 2300 ft above sea-level on the south side.

Regressive breaching of the Chewings Range is visibly in progress in the upper catchment of the Hugh River. Here, Spencer Gorge and Standley Chasm are narrow, joint-guided clefts, within tens of yards of a break-through. Considerable derangement will eventually occur because of the difference in base-level between the two sides of the Range. Marked structural control characterizes all gaps or near-gaps in the Chewings Range, as is well exemplified by Stuarts Pass along Ellery Creek.

River capture has operated on a smaller scale in the ridge-and-vale tract, where lesser gaps have formed or grown in association with capture and with unequal competition between elements of strike drainage. The fall of the main rivers through the ridges is appreciable, and local base-levels on either side of a strike ridge may differ by more than 50 ft. Small-scale piracy has led to the proliferation of minor gaps through narrow ridges, as elbows of capture and barbed tributary-patterns within the Hugh catchment indicate for some of the gaps in the east of the Arumbera Ridge. The possibilities are manifold, since repeated reversal may have affected a single gap, in association with alternating changes in the relative advantages o$^c$ competing streams. The relevant circumstances are well exemplified in a gap west of Gill Pass in the Heavitree Range. Much of the Alice Valley formerly drained south through this, as shown by the slopes on the red-earth plains to the north, but the drainage has been largely tapped by an east-going channel on the north side, wherein a small nickpoint is now less than 100 yd from the gap entrance. See-saw local changes between transverse and longitudinal drainage naturally hinge on the gaps, which handicap their tributary catchments in proportion to their resistance to down-cutting. These changes must be envisaged as deviations from that trend in favour of south-going drainage which the regional advantage in base-level confers.

### Inheritance and Periodicity in Drainage-evolution

To the complex geomorphic history revealed by the inherited landforms of the western Macdonnells corresponds a complex record of the evolution of drainage. There has been no single cause of discordance, nor a single period of initiation. Inheritance and regressive erosion each appear to have operated, affecting different parts of the Ranges, both before and after the cutting of the crest-bevels. Transverse drainage is, after all, inevitable where down-warping, as in the Lake Eyre Basin, draws streams across the geological grain, and where strike-controlled relief is fixed by near-vertical dips.

Inheritance cannot have been a simple process, for the form of the summit surface indicates that only partial planation of the

E

ridge-and-vale tract was achieved when the crests were bevelled, and that relief was never sufficiently subdued for rivers to have swung freely across the quartzite outcrops. It is probable that much of the evolution of transverse drainage has been achieved through periodic planation, deposition, weathering, and erosion, as revealed in the terrace sequence. The effect of the high-terrace cycle on drainage patterns is clearly demonstrated in Glen Helen Vale. On the Ellery Creek–Hugh River divide the high terrace at several points overlaps the low and broken Arumbera Ridge from the south: the northeast drainage consequent on the terrace surface has been rejuvenated from the Hugh River on the north side of the Ridge, and has maintained itself during down-cutting. Existing gaps have been deepened and new ones initiated. On the Ellery Creek–Finke divide, the high terrace, descending from the north, buries low ridges of Areyonga sandstone, and minor channels are in all stages of incision across structure. The evolution has been aided by prior weathering and subsequent rapid selective excavation of saprolite, leaving the sandstones upstanding. There is little doubt that most of the discordant drainage of the Alice Valley has had a similar origin, for the consequent drainage on high terrace remnants is continued as transverse, southeasterly courses through the stripped low hill lands to the south.

This reconstruction combines inheritance with limited superposition, taking the surface on which the streams were emplaced primarily as a product of earlier planation, and the final levelling as the result of gravel deposition. The imposed patterns are those of the distributary drainage responsible for gravel deposition. The high-terrace cycle was merely a substage in the formation of the weathered land surface, and many such cycles may have run their course in a subaerial history of 300 million years.

## Acknowledgements

The writer gratefully acknowledges helpful criticism of the original manuscript by Professor G. H. Dury, Mr J. N. Jennings, and Dr C. R. Twidale. Permission was kindly granted by the Director, Commonwealth Bureau of Mineral Resources, Geology and Geophysics, to make use of unpublished records. Mr R. T. Kelson assisted in fieldwork in the area during 1961.

## References

Butler, B. E., 1960. 'Periodic phenomena in landscapes as a basis for soil studies.' *C.S.I.R.O. Aust. Soil Publcn.* No. 14, 1959.

Crespin, I., 1950. 'Report of micropalaeontological examination of samples from the 16 mile Government Bore, West of Alice Springs, Northern Territory.' Aust. B.M.R. Unpubl. Record No. 1950/48.

Crocker, R. L., and Wood, J. G., 1947. 'Some historical influences on the development of South Australian vegetation communities.' *Trans. Roy. Soc. S. Aust.*, 71, 91–136.

Gentilli, J., 1961. 'Quaternary climates of the Australian region.' *Ann. N.Y. Acad. Sci.*, 95, 465–501.

Jessup, R. W., 1960. 'An introduction to the soils of the south-eastern portion of the Australian arid zone.' *J. Soil Sci.*, 11, 92–105.

King, L. C., 1950. 'The cyclic land surfaces of Australia.' *Proc. Roy. Soc. Vict.*, 62, 79–95.

Litchfield, W. H., 1962. 'Soils of the Alice Springs area.' in *C.S.I.R.O. Aust. Land Res. Ser. No. 6.*

Mabbutt, J. A., 1961a. ' "Basal Surface" or "Weathering Front".' *Proc. Geol. Assn.*, 72, 357–8.

Mabbutt, J. A., 1961b. 'A stripped land surface in Western Australia.' *Trans. Inst. Brit. Geog.*, 101–14.

Mabbutt, J. A., 1962. 'Geomorphology of the Alice Springs area' in *C.S.I.R.O. Aust. Land Res. Ser. No. 6.*

Madigan, C. T., 1931. 'The physiography of the Western Macdonnell Ranges.' *Geog. Journ.*, 78, 417–31.

Madigan, C. T., 1932. 'The geology of the Western Macdonnell Ranges.' *Q.J. Geol. Soc. London*, 88, 672–711.

Meigs, P., 1952. 'World distribution of arid and semi-arid homoclimates.' *UNESCO Review of Research on Arid Zone Hydrology*, 1, 203–10.

Prichard, C. E., and Quinlan, T., 1962. 'The geology of the southern part of the Hermannsburg 1:250,000 Sheet.' *Aust. B.M.R. Report No. 61.*

Sullivan, C. J., and Opik, A. A., 1951. 'Ochre deposits, Rumbalara, Northern Territory.' *Aust. B.M.R. Bull. No. 8.*

Twidale, C. R., 1962. 'Steepened margins of inselbergs from north-western Eyre Peninsula, South Australia.' *Zeit. f. Geomorph.*, 6, 51–69.

Ward, L. K., 1925. 'Notes on the geological structure of Central Australia.' *Trans. Roy. Soc. S. Aust.*, 49, 61–84.

# The Landforms of Low Latitudes

## J. C. PUGH

The continental areas of the humid tropics include greatly extensive exposures of crystalline basement rocks. Where these occur, and on the poleward margins of the tropical zone where there is a marked dry season, the typical landscape is one of wide plains studded with inselbergs, to account for which a variety of cyclic processes have been invoked. Cotton (1947) set out the relevant hypotheses in some detail, and has more recently (1961) reappraised the evidence. Initially he recognized a landscape in which the residual hills rose abruptly from flat plains, as described by Passarge (1928) and by Falconer (1911). This type of landscape, while it may exist in certain localities, is not as widespread as these authorities averred: one of Falconer's type areas was the Kilba Hills in Northern Nigeria (also referred to by Davis 1930) where the present writer found, surrounding all those parts of the hill mass which he visited, pediments measuring up to 6 degrees of slope and frequently trenched by marginal depressions (Pugh 1956); pediments also exist round one of Passarge's type areas, the Alantika Mountains of Adamawa. Crickmay (1933), describing flat plains about residuals in other parts of Africa, advanced his hypothesis of panplanation to account for the type of terrain which he identified. The most widespread feature of the more humid savanna areas is, however, the pediment, which may be found surrounding virtually all residuals. The writer (*op. cit.* 1956) has recorded pediments, round the Lapai Hills of Northern Nigeria, which slope away from the hill mass at $2\frac{1}{2}$ degrees for at least half a mile, effecting a drop in height of nearly 120 ft and precluding any extension of the pediment-head by action of the rivers on the plains; in the sandstone areas of the Benue Valley in northern Adamawa, pediments but 30 ft wide surround small residual hills. Cotton (*op. cit.* 1947), drawing on accounts by Thorbecke (1927) and Holmes (1919), originally identifying an additional type of inselberg landscape in which marginal depressions surround residuals, considered this type to be characteristic of the more humid areas; but the marginal depressions have now been described by Clayton (1956) for the dry zone of Ghana, and by Pugh (*op. cit.* 1956) for Northern Nigeria. Cotton's later paper (*op. cit.* 1961) recognizes that the correlation of such depressions with greater rainfall cannot be substantiated.

The different hypotheses advanced to explain these varying forms are not mutually exclusive. The variety of form can be accepted because of the increasing use in the description of landscape of quantitative observations which were not made at the beginning of the century. Clearly no single 'cycle of erosion' can explain all the forms observed. Processes can be taken to vary with lithology and with past and present conditions of temperature and rainfall, with time as an important factor. In the humid tropics, the combination of all the factors largely determines, for example, the depth to which bedrock is decomposed. Material rotted *in situ* may extend to depths of hundreds of feet, or may be totally absent; the 'basal surface' between decomposed and unaltered bedrock is now recognized as of considerable importance. To take but a few examples, Ruxton and Berry (1957, 1961) have made comparative studies of decomposition in Hong Kong and Africa; Cotton's later paper invokes Büdel's work, and Birot (1960) stresses the importance of deep decomposition and of its variations. These studies throw light on the development of humid tropical landforms of large and small scale alike.

On the large scale, the recognition of deeply rotted material over wide areas does not, by itself, explain either the great plains or the residual forms standing above them. It does, however, reduce the time factor in the development over a wide area of landforms resulting from a change in base-level. As Dixey (1955) has stressed, a new cycle initiated by a change in base-level advances rapidly inland from the coast, up the major rivers and their larger tributaries (Plate 13). Valley floors are widened at an early stage by retreat of the bounding valley side, broad floors constituting extensions of the new cyclic plains developing in the coastal margins. The rapid inland fingering of the new cycle results in roughing-out of the landscape into compartments, which will shrink by progressive retreat of the scarps and valley sides and will be further subdivided by stream incision as the new cycle extends up smaller tributaries. In the final stages the smaller residual areas will be reduced by general downwearing (Plates 14–15). This pattern accords closely with King's views (1948) on the development of bornhardts. Structure will clearly play an important part, the spacing of joints or other lines of weakness being a determinant of the frequency of major streams and therefore also of the size of the initial blocks of terrain isolated by the new cyclic development.

It cannot be stressed too strongly that the back-wearing of scarps and of valley sides results from processes of vertical downwearing. Backwearing and downwearing are not mutually exclusive: the former is the manifestation of the latter in localized form. Water acts under the influence of gravity, whether flowing in a stream channel, moving as sheetflow across the surface, lubricating soil, or percolating downwards to the watertable. The relative importance of these several actions depends on a variety of factors, including lithology, and location with respect to the cyclic advance. In that part of a valley downstream from a cyclic nickpoint, vertical downcutting by the stream will usually be at a maximum, surface wash and soil creep are accelerated on the steep slopes initiated by incision, and erosive effects are greater than in the stretches upstream, where the new cycle has not yet arrived, or than downstream, where the new cycle has been longer established, where incision is much reduced, and where slopes are more gentle. In addition, incision by the stream may lead to mechanical failure of the slopes, again resulting in downward movement of material. There is thus a concentration of downwearing in a zone behind the advancing cyclic front, and as this front progresses across country, the zone follows, giving the effect of lateral backwearing of the margin of the older surface. In the extreme case of very resistant rock, the nickpoint advances very slowly indeed; and the other downwearing processes may keep pace with it, so that the stream descends from the upper to the lower surface by way of a high fall over a scarp. Recession of the scarp between major streams is similar to the recession of valley sides below the nickpoint, resulting from slope failure and accelerated soil creep, assisted by gullying and basal spring-sapping in appropriate circumstances. (See Plates 13, 14 and 15.)

The gullying of the scarp face deserves special mention. One point of King's pediplanation hypothesis was the contrast in type of waterflow between the steep slopes and the pediment. The latter, he argued, experienced non-erosive laminar flow, while the former experienced turbulent flow, highly erosive in character. This contrast in type of water-flow emphasizes the zoning of processes in the savanna landscape, active downwearing being largely restricted to the scarp or to the corresponding scarp zone. The change in flow appears to be the result, and not the cause, of the contrast in slope. Examination of a savanna scarp will usually reveal a large number of gullies which are, to a greater or lesser extent, incised into the scarp face but which are not continued across the pediment. Admittedly the larger incisions are extended across the low-angle slopes, carrying either seasonal or perennial streams, but the smaller gullies usually end at the foot of the steep slope. The intermittent water-flows which they carry off the scarp appear to fan out at the pediment-head, to form sheet-flow over the lower-angled slope. In some cases the fanning-out of flow results from the accumulation of a debris fan, but in other cases either there is no fan, or else the convexity of surface form is so slight that it cannot be distinguished by eye. The spreading-out of channelled flow into a sheet can be readily appreciated if the change occurs beneath the accumulated talus of a debris slope or fan, but it seems to occur with equal ease where debris is missing altogether and the scarp-foot nick between hill-slope and pediment is well marked. If a fan is present and develops to moderate size, it is liable to deflect water laterally, and to lead to the incision into the pediment-head of a marginal depression (Pugh, *op. cit.* 1956).

Under savanna conditions, the change in mode of flow may result in part from the difference in depth of weathered material on the steep slopes and on the pediment. On the former, the percentage of surface run-off is high, on the latter it is low, for the savanna pediment, unlike its true desert counterpart, may have a considerable depth of weathered material and permit much percolation: even the pediment-head usually carries an appreciable soil cover. It is significant that under humid tropical conditions, the depth of decomposition may be great even on the steep slopes, which then carry not only a soil mantle but frequently quite thick vegetation; the sharp break of slope between hill-side and pediment then gives place to a continuous concave curve, and the contrast in type of surface flow is less distinct.

The recession of scarps and the shrinking of residual blocks is not of course restricted to inter-tropical areas, but operates anywhere under suitable conditions. It was admirably described by Davis (1932) as follows:

> The old-age processes of peneplanation continue their action unchanged in the early stages of the new cycle of erosion introduced by the upheaval; hence the central peneplain shows no significant change of form, except that it becomes an older and older peneplain, in spite of being now in the infantile stage of the new cycle instead of in the senile stage of the former cycle. So it continues until news of the upheaval is brought to it by the retrogressive erosion of peripheral streams; then it is more or less sharply dissected.

This was truly observed: Davis's error lay in his assumption that other processes should be regarded as operating.

The most common landscape of the savanna areas is, then, one of wide old-age plains separated by scarps or by zones of active downwearing, which recede steadily, encroaching upon the upper plains and extending the lower plains. Provided that this action takes place in deeply weathered material above the unweathered basal surface, there are no complications. Residuals isolated from the upper plain will have a comparatively short life unless protected by some form of duricrust capping, their period of survival after the advent of the new cycle depending on their position relative to the major rivers. In sedimentary areas with a lateritic surface crust, the typical residual is usually a flat-topped mesa, shrinkage of which is slowed by the hard layer at or just below the surface. The crust is often relatively soft towards the centre of the mesa, but is appreciably harder towards the residual edge as a result of improved drainage and increased aeration. Hardening occurs also in the scarp zone, where it leads to uniformity of slope-angle below the duricrust edge and to narrow canyon-like valley heads below the nickpoints. Recession of the duricrust edges normally involves the breaking off of fragments which are left unsupported by removal of the softer underlying material.

In areas of partly unweathered rock, particularly on outcrops of basement material, the forms are different. Residual hills commonly form bornhardts and kopjes, but the plains themselves include areas of bare rock standing little if at all above the general level. Such areas represent upward projections of the basal surface. The perfection of plains cut without distinction across weathered and unweathered material implies considerable efficiency of erosional processes. The exposures of bare rock at plain-level frequently display exfoliation-jointing, which lies parallel to the plain surface in the central parts of exposures but, in the writer's experience, not infrequently dips towards the edges of the exposures. The thickness of the exfoliating sheets ranges from a fraction of an inch to many feet. The very thin sheets could conceivably result from diurnal variation of temperature, for temperatures of the exposed rock surfaces can range under clear-sky conditions from about 160°F in early afternoon to as little as 40°F ten or twelve hours later. However, most sheeting is clearly due to some other factor than diurnal change of temperature, which is not appreciable at depths of some feet below the surface: the major joints which separate the sheets are almost certainly due to relief of load, although they are possibly developed further by some kind of weathering. King (op. cit. 1948) has stressed that bornhardts are formed in areas of plutonic rock, and that the curved exfoliation-jointing results from relief of pressure by erosion of overlying material, with major joints extending downwards below surface level at the margins of each bornhardt. The surface exposures just mentioned would seem to represent, in effect, the tops of bornhardts which will be left standing in the next cycle. King, referring to the sub-rectangular jointing system of many plutonic masses, argues that, with the onset of a new cycle, selection by streams of lines of weakness will lead to the rapid dissection of a residual mass into compartments of varying size, depending on the spacing of the major joints. The larger compartments are thought to develop into bornhardts, and the smaller into kopjes.

It is, however, possible to find kopjes which in profile resemble bornhardts: although a kopje may be made up of characteristic large boulders, the outline of the boulder mass can unquestionably retain the smoothly-curved, dome-like profile which typifies bornhardts. These circumstances leave little doubt that a bornhardt can, in suitable conditions, deteriorate into a kopje. The controlling factor is the jointing of the rock mass and the relative importance of the curved exfoliation-joints and of the sub-rectangular joints: the former exercise dominant control in the early stages of exposure, but mastery passes to the latter as sub-aerial weathering etches them out (Pugh, in preparation).

Not all kopjes are formed from bornhardts by deterioration in this manner. In some cases, as King's paper implies, the frequency of the sub-rectangular jointing permits the onset of a new cycle to produce so complete a sub-division into compartments that residuals may assume kopje form from the beginning. In other cases, as demonstrated by Alexander (1950) in Singapore and by Berry and Ruxton (op. cit. 1957) in Hong Kong, weathering along closely-spaced joints proceeds below the surface in a matrix of weathered material, so that the onset of a new cycle, in which weathering-products were stripped away, would leave piled corestones in kopje form. In this respect, the origin of some kopjes would seem to be analogous to tor formation as proposed by Linton (1955). Lithology probably determines which of the three methods of formation is most likely to occur in any locality.

The frequency of bornhardts and kopjes decreases away from the scarp or scarp zone, as would be expected with the localized downward erosion already described. The general level of the plain above a scarp is frequently continued as a summit-plane across massed bornhardts beyond the scarp edge; it can sometimes be traced for considerable distances over scattered residuals. Summit planes need however to be identified with caution, for domes shrinking by recession of their sides must inevitably undergo rapid reduction of summit-altitude in the final stages of destruction. In some places, however—usually on a residual less regular in form than a domed bornhardt—the summit can be confidently identified as a clear relic of an old surface, particularly if it carries a remnant of a shallow stream-course truncated at both ends. Such a remnant may be no more than a few acres in extent.

Multi-cycle bornhardts can also be found in the form of dome-on-dome residuals (Pugh 1954). At the base of the upper dome are repeated the features normally encountered where the main dome meets the plain—that is, the sharp junction between the exfoliating free face on the one hand, and the pediment-head on the other, although this junction is sometimes masked with talus. The higher junction is not associated with a true pediment, but the equivalent of a pediment is clearly exhibited as the flattened top surface of the lower dome and of the small valley-heads working back into the upper residual at the junction level. Superimposed profiles of typical inselberg country frequently show a marked correlation of the bevels

Fig. 1. Dome-on-dome bornhardt south of Iseyin, Western Nigeria.

at the base of an upper dome with summit-planes which, tangential to simple domes, are referable to the erosion-surface above the nearest scarp (Fig. 3). Some bevels of this kind are very well developed; others involve no more than a change of angle in the bornhardt face, depending on the resistance and the jointing of the rock. The significance of a change of angle in the free face can sometimes be clearly seen when the residual changes slightly in form or lithology along its length. The Addo Rock, south of Iseyin in Western Nigeria, is a bornhardt where clear bevels at the northern end become reduced to changes in steepness of slope at the southern. During the wet season, the resemblance of kind between the two ends is clearly marked by lichens, which form a thin and almost continuous green line along the bevel. Presumably they can hold to the rock at this level, but cannot maintain themselves on the steeper faces above and below. Addo is also an excellent example of the lake-bearing type of bornhardt which appears to be not uncommon in West Africa: it carries two ponds below the top level, one of which never dries out although lying less than 50 ft from the steep west face. This permanence of water suggests absence of joints in the vicinity, which is of particular interest in view of the general convexity of the bare surface. Where such permanent water exists the bornhardts were ideal refuges for early settlement; the movement of the village of Addo from the top to the bottom of the hill is comparatively recent.

The degree to which multi-cyclic bevelling is displayed varies widely; as has been stated, it may vary even on one residual. On very resistant rock, bevels may be barely recognizable even as changes in the angle of the rock face; in places the dome-on-dome form is magnificently clear, but elsewhere, and particularly on small residuals, the upper dome can have started to disintegrate to kopje form, producing a kopje on top of a low whale-backed bornhardt (Plate 16). In large and complex residuals or residual masses, bevels can be so extensive as to constitute small tablelands (Pugh 1955). Western Nigeria provides many examples of such minor tablelands, the bevel which forms the general level being largely ringed round by higher domes reaching upwards to the higher summit-planes of the region. Here again, the residual masses formed excellent sites for early settlement, and still support a number of small towns such as Shaki and Oke Iho, built on fairly level ground and defended by difficult access up the rocky valleys and defiles of the edge (Fig. 2). This mode of association between settlement and landform extends well into the humid tropical areas of West Africa. The largest example known to the writer is that of the Idanre Hills of Western Nigeria, which rise to over 3000 feet, and where the modern town is on the first tableland above a steep climb of some hundreds of feet; the old town was on the bevel above this, ringed round by still higher summits (Fig. 4).

The origin of the bevels is clearly identical with that of the summit-planes. The identity of form of the base of any upper dome with the form of the foot of a residual on the plains of the current cycle suggests that identical processes have led to the formation of upper and lower domes. Probably the mechanism of formation is that shown in Fig. 5. An initial surface may be planed across a large part of the landscape, cutting, if time permits, both across weathered and across unweathered rock. This latter is occasionally exposed at the surface, possibly with exfoliating sheets of the type already described; the former underlies most of the landscape, with the basal surface of unweathered material at varying depth. Onset of a new cycle will lead to progressive upstream incision, accompanied by recession of valley sides. Where rotted material extends to considerable depths, the new cycle can be expected to extend rapidly across country. Where rock is unweathered, the new cycle will sweep round it to continue in the general inland direction, leaving the residual as a bornhardt; where rock is partly weathered into corestones, a kopje will form. Small domes thus exposed shrink steadily: exfoliation along curved joints, and weathering along sub-rectangular joints, assisted by increased

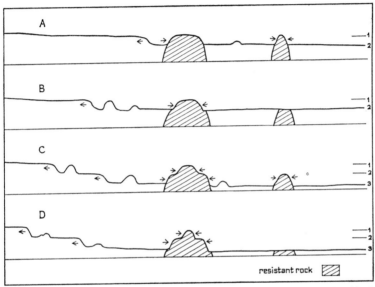

Fig. 5. Mechanism of inselberg bevelling by scarp retreat. Three types of residual are shown.

acidity of water where patches of vegetation are present, may reduce small residuals rapidly to the point of extinction, re-establishing the situation of rock-exposures at plain-level. On larger residuals, the retreat of the hillsides will be slow compared with recession of the cyclic scarp across the weathered rock of most of the country, and isolated bornhardts will slowly shrink, not only under the processes already listed, but also under stream-action, gullying, and slope failure, so that the feet of large residuals slowly retire inwards from the petrological boundary. On very resistant rock, retreat may be very slight. A whole range of combination is therefore possible— residuals where petrological differences have no topographical expression (small residuals having been reduced to plain-level); residuals which have no petrological difference from the plain (hills isolated by the receding scarp and due for early obliteration); residuals with close agreement between the petrological and topographical boundaries (on very resistant rock); and residuals where the topographical boundary lies some distance inside the petrological boundary (possibly the normal case).

The onset of a second new cycle leads to the temporary reappearance of residuals in the small localized areas of unweathered rock. It also leads to the temporary appearance of a new series of residuals formed of country rock, in that youthful zone of active downwearing which, immediately following the headward extension of the new cycle, maintains itself in any given belt of country for but a short time. On very resistant rock, the scarp of the second cycle approaches and merges with the earlier scarp, which may have made no impression in the period intervening between the two cyclic advances, or which may have undergone no more than a slight flattening at its base. In the latter event, a change in angle of slope is significant; in the former, the residual is similar in type to that envisaged by Bailey Willis, growing steadily in size with successive cycles and relatively indestructible. But when a new scarp is temporarily checked at a petrological boundary from which an earlier scarp has receded slightly, a bevel is established, to constitute a feature of cyclic significance. The two scarps continue subsequently to work inwards towards complete reduction of the residual.

If these possible sequences be accepted—and it is difficult to envisage alternative hypotheses capable of explaining all the features encountered—then several points are worthy of emphasis. To accept an upper dome as having been longer exposed than a lower dome tends to confirm the hypothesis of degeneration of bornhardts into kopjes under certain conditions. The example illustrated in Plate 16, between Zaria and Kaduna in Northern Nigeria, shows a kopje standing on a dome as the upper part of a multi-cycle residual. There is unlikely to be much difference in the original jointing of the upper and lower sections of the residual. If the kopje form here had resulted from the subterranean survival of corestones before exposure by the first new cycle, rotting underground ought surely to have affected also the lower portion, which is now exposed as a dome, in the intercycle interval. As the lower dome is still largely intact, the inference is that the kopje form is a direct result of longer exposure, with resultant increased weathering along sub-rectangular joints.

Curving of exfoliation-sheets on the lower dome suggests that fracturing due to relief of load does not take place until late in the unloading process. Continuation of curved exfoliation-joints below ground-level, adduced in some instances by King, would help to explain the sharpness of the nick at the base of the free face, either at plain-level or above a cyclic bevel, and might also explain the not infrequent presence of a gully head between a free face and the next bevel below it. There would be, in effect, a marginal depression of a type not hitherto described; although it has as yet been noted by the writer only on the bevels of multi-cycle forms (Plate 17), it could equally be expected at the foot of any exfoliating residual where a stream has worked headward to encounter the underground exfoliation-joints. The general normality of exfoliation-joints on the lower dome therefore suggests that relief-of-load fracturing does not occur until the removal of at most the last few hundred feet of overlying rock, corresponding to the minimal interval between major surfaces: the curved joints of the lower dome must post-date—or at the least be coincident with—the recession of the upper dome to provide the bevel.

Marginal depressions have been twice mentioned above. In the writer's view, these can probably form in a variety of ways, corresponding broadly to the variety of origins suggested for bornhardts. Cotton's original hypothesis (*op. cit.* 1947) that such depressions are typical of humid tropical areas is, as stated, inadequate in view of widespread distribution, for the features occur even in the drier margins of the savanna. Clayton (*op. cit.* 1956) suggests that they result from headward extension of streams in areas of decomposed rock; Pugh (*op. cit.* 1956) argues that they can be expected in the normal sequence of erosion, round residual masses of a certain size. It has also been suggested above that they may be associated with the extension below ground-level of exfoliation-jointing at the feet of residuals. To combine these possible settings and origins with the range of bornhardt types described would suggest that depressions as described by Clayton are marginal to bornhardts on small unweathered outcrops, to large residuals at the plain-level, and to the receding scarp and its outliers, while depressions of the type described by the writer are restricted to the scarp zone and to the larger residual masses; depressions of either type, assisted in their formation by underground extension of exfoliation-jointing, would then be restricted to bornhardts, large or small, on unweathered exposures of plutonic rock.

Clayton stresses the importance of the relationship between the scarpfoot nick and the watertable. Knowledge of the form of the latter within the residual is scanty. Where domes carry permanent ponds on the surface, it must be doubtful whether a groundwatertable in the strict sense exists at all. But where jointing is well developed, or where weathering along the joint planes is well advanced, water in quantity must be held within the hill. Clayton refers to an example where the scarpfoot nick acts as a springline after a period of heavy rain, and argues for the rotting effect of frequent rises and falls of the watertable in the relevant zone. A number of writers have looked to accumulated debris to assist in chemical weathering at the scarpfoot: moist conditions would undoubtedly persist longer into the dry season if debris were present than if it were not, although probably not for very much longer unless the watertable were very close to the surface. It appears that weathering effects may be achieved with little or no reduction of efficiency without having recourse to debris: where the scarpfoot nick is clear of debris—as frequently occurs—this circumstance is well demonstrated. The marked overhang which is sometimes seen, resulting from recession of the scarpfoot faster than the free face above, may well be associated with the effects of a fluctuating, inclined watertable in the lower part of the residual.

Towards the humid margins of the tropical areas, noticeable changes occur in surface form: sharp breaks of slope tend to disappear. The scarpfoot nick so characteristic of savanna areas is not typical of humid equatorial regions, possibly because, with no true dry season there, saturation-level is more constant. The effects of seasonal fluctuation of the watertable are diminished but may still be considerable: although no month is necessarily completely dry, a rise in monthly average totals from, for example, 4 inches to 20 inches, must inevitably affect the saturation-level. A significant fact may well be not the absolute fluctuation between highest and lowest levels of saturation at any one point, but comparative values of fluctuation over relatively short distances. In the drier savanna areas, the scarpfoot nick may owe its origin, at least in part, to the effect of fluctuating saturation which, occurring close to the surface at the nick, rarely affects the surface lower down the pediment or higher up the hill-side. Variations of saturation in humid areas may be felt both on steeper and on flatter slopes; maximum effect is less strongly localized. In consequence, not only does the scarpfoot nick disappear, but the upper slopes may be more gentle and the lower slopes steeper than in drier areas. The pediment, judging from observations in a number of widely scattered localities, becomes straighter in long-profile with greater rainfall, and also steeper as rainfall totals increase: Pugh (*op. cit.* 1956), Fair (1947, 1948), King (1951), and Pallister (1956) cite pediment-slopes ranging from $2\frac{1}{2}$ degrees in the semi-arid Karroo and round the Lapai Hills of Northern Nigeria, through 3 degrees in Southern Rhodesia and in eastern Uganda, to 5 degrees in sub-humid Natal: the present writer has measured slopes of

$5\frac{1}{2}$ degrees around Ibadan in southwestern Nigeria, and Pallister mentions slopes of 7 degrees in Buganda. The modification of form follows principally from the thickening of the soil mantle, even on steep slopes, under humid tropical conditions, involving the presence of extra moisture, and with lubricated soil-creep under gravity becoming of greater importance than sheetwash. It may be assumed that differences in rock can cause differences in angle of slope in accordance with variations in type of detritus supplied, but where deep weathering is general and little distinction can be made between soil types, the lower slopes may be of fairly uniform inclination over considerable areas, irrespective of original differences in bedrock. It is possible, moreover, to cite slope-values for pediments which appear to contradict the suggestion that angle steepens with increased rainfall. Pallister refers to occasional pediments of 13 to 15 degrees in East Africa, but his diagrams suggest that these are, in fact, lower hillslopes rather than true pediment-heads; Mabbutt (1955) cites pediments in Namaqualand as being 6 to 8 degrees at their heads—evidence apparently directly opposed to the hypothesis now in question, unless these steeper slopes are not true wash-pediments but are due to accumulation of transported material on the pediment-head in the form of a fan of barely perceptible convexity. Accumulation in this manner has been mentioned earlier. The writer has found in Northern Nigeria that steep pediment-heads up to 10 degrees can be identified as accumulation-fans, when they are surveyed in cross-profile and tested by augering.

The percentage of convexity in the landscape tends to increase with totals of rainfall. Pallister argues that with increasing wetness, steepening of the pediment and rise of the debris-slope lead to obliteration of the free face or of a duricrust edge. Dixey, while maintaining that the area affected by flattening is much enlarged in humid areas, stresses that climate and structure are alike involved in determining whether there is pedimentation and scarp retreat or whether there is more general lowering of the surface into flowing landscape-forms. Both sets of processes, he thinks, may proceed side by side simultaneously, or both may have left their trace as a result of climatic changes involving superimposition of one set of conditions upon another. The smoothing of landscape-forms can be (but is not always) so pronounced that Derruau (1956) remarked:

> On peut se demander si le schéma davisien de la pénéplaine, malgré la lenteur du recul des rapides, ne s'applique pas au climat équatorial mieux qu'au climat tempéré, qui n'a jamais duré assez longtemps pour que la maturité soit dépassée.

This quotation, however, ignores a number of significant points of difference between the humid temperate and humid tropical forms. Firstly, deep weathering has already been mentioned. Secondly, the vegetative pattern must be considered: vegetation in the humid tropics takes hold everywhere except on the very steepest slopes, and by helping to develop soil and in raising the acidity of water running over the surface, contributes directly to the production of landform. Thirdly, landslides increase in importance into the humid tropics, although they are less common than might perhaps be expected: Birot stresses that on slopes greater than 48 degrees landslides are rare, as the soil there is too thin. For all that, landslip gravure is of sufficient importance in some areas (Wentworth 1943) to dominate the erosive processes, and to produce landforms which have little of a subdued davisian character, sharp-edged ridges between landslide gullies being typical. It is, of course, possible to find extensive landslide forms in higher latitudes also, lithology appearing to be the dominant control in low and in middle latitudes alike. Fourthly, the quality of material reaching the streams differs greatly from humid temperate lands to humid tropics, Birot notes for the humid tropics the absence from streambeds of large fragments and of coarse material generally: fragments decompose in their journey over the hill-slopes towards the streams. Rapid decomposition of blocks below about 1 ft in diameter, which yield sand, is very characteristic. One result of the absence of coarse material is that the streams are reduced in cutting power; Birot accordingly suggests that one cardinal point of difference between the humid tropical and humid temperate regions is that in the latter the long-profiles of streams are graded earlier than are the valley-sides, whereas in the former the converse applies. Stream erosion in the humid tropics is less efficient than transport across slopes, which in turn is less efficient than decomposition.

Lithology is, as always, of great importance. Where rocks resist decomposition, they may in the humid tropics form sugarloaf residuals if isolated by erosion in a new cycle, but as King (1962) has indicated, these are largely similar in form to savanna bornhardts and extra-tropical bare-rock domes, and are not specifically characteristic of humid tropical conditions. Lithology is also important in the case of massive limestone, giving such forms as those described by Sweeting (1956) in Jamaica. It has been suggested that under high temperatures and with a concentration of carbon dioxide from decaying organic material of the forest cover, the solvent power of water on limestone is about four times greater in humid tropical than in humid temperate regions. The cockpit country of Jamaica and Puerto Rico, for example, has been classed as exemplifying a mode of karstic development which, resulting directly from this accelerated tropical solution, has no parallel in humid temperate limestone regions. The tower karst of these areas has been called a second characteristic assemblage of forms. However, complete agreement does not prevail on these matters, for some workers prefer to regard cockpit country and tower karst as typical of karst in general, holding that in the past too much emphasis has been placed on solution and on associated collapse of passages, and too little on surface features of solution which are not restricted to tropical regions. Tropical karst therefore appears to vary from the karst of humid temperate regions, less in terms of landform than of vegetation: the limestone forest of the humid tropics—anything from scrub to fairly dense forest with a 60 ft canopy—appears unlike the vegetation of temperate karst lands, but man has interfered considerably with vegetation in Europe, and the original natural vegetation of some of the limestone areas in Britain was fairly thick woodland.

It is difficult to determine the precise extent to which man has modified the tropical landscape. His direct interference has been slight, but his indirect effect considerable. On the fringes of the high forest country, the customary clearing and burning of farms has resulted in steady encroachment of savanna grasses on the forest zone. Extension of induced savanna has had several effects: it has lowered evapotranspiration, has increased soil temperature, and has decreased the humus content of soils. It has also tended to accelerate soil-erosion, by exposing the soil between grass tussocks to the action of heavy rain, and by increasing direct runoff at the expense of percolation beneath the forest cover. These factors tend to an increase in soil erosion. Buildings on pediments (the obvious low-angled and well-drained locations for settlement) have frequently disturbed the smooth laminar sheet-flow, concentrating surface runoff between buildings, favouring turbulent flow, and thus promoting the development of gullies and dongas. Many of the older areas of African towns have gullies up to 40 ft deep; once gullying starts, a pediment can quickly be reduced to badland. In some areas this fact is appreciated by the local people, and terracing of stone walls on pediments as gentle as 2 degrees (Pugh and Perry 1960) forms a protection against loss of soil.

One of the more spectacular effects of man's interference is that change in the watertable that follows forest clearance. Carter (1956) has demonstrated that with human occupation of formerly empty land, and the resultant clearance of woodland, there has occurred a rise of watertable by as much as 200 ft, or even more, in the space of fifty years. These rises affected an area of sedimentary rocks of relatively low permeability, with a gradient of up to 1:75 on the surface of a watertable which declines away from the groundwater ridges which underlie streams. Reduced evapotranspiration appears to be more than balanced over most of the area by increased runoff, which results in loss of general percolation and in greater inflow to rivers, without any change in climate. In consequence, the larger streams continue to flow in the dry season longer than they formerly did; new springs have appeared, and at least one valley has been drowned by a new lake. Human action, during no more than half a century, has caused a very great increase in available surface water in the major valleys, simultaneously with a slight fall under the major watersheds. The geomorphological results of the changes have yet to be seen.

Deforestation produced rapidly by man could, alternatively, be produced slowly by climatic change. Büdel (1959) maintains that in Würm time the selva margin was nearer the poles than it now is— i.e. at about 8° rather than 6° latitude. He similarly extends polewards the margin between desert steppe and savanna, today at about 12° and in Würm time about 15° latitude. If these fluctuations in boundaries are correct, then the variation of the selva boundary in particular might have caused considerable alterations to the watertable and to the pattern of drainage. In the main valleys, reduction in flow due to increasing desiccation might be more than offset by increased flow resulting from increased runoff and from accentuation of groundwater ridges. Indeed, a slight change towards increased dryness might result locally in increased incision, although more probably the increase in material brought to the stream by surface runoff would at least counterbalance any tendency to incision.

The zone between the equator and latitude 5° has experienced humid tropical conditions for a long time, with less fluctuation than has occurred on either margin of the savanna, and with considerably less change than has affected the present humid temperate areas. Nevertheless, the older cycles identifiable in the landscapes of today may well have been initiated under very different conditions from those of the present, if one accepts any hypothesis of relative movement of continental areas and climatic zones. The landforms of low latitudes are therefore not necessarily the products of current conditions alone, but may in many cases be composite in origin.

**References**

Alexander, F. E. S., 1950. *Report on the availability of granite on Singapore and the surrounding islands*. Govt of Singapore.

Birot, P., 1960. *Le cycle d'érosion sous les différents climats*. University of Brazil.

Büdel, J., 1959. 'Climatic zones of the Pleistocene.' *Internat. Geol. Rev.*, 1, 72–79.

Carter, J. D., 1956. 'The rise in the water-table in parts of Potiskum Division, Bornu Province.' Records, Geol. Surv. Nigeria.

Clayton, R. W., 1956. 'Linear depressions (Bergsfussniederungen) in savannah landscapes.' *Geog. Studies*, 3, 102–26.

Cotton, C. A., 1947. *Climatic Accidents in Landscape Making*. Whitcombe and Tombs, Christchurch, New Zealand.

Cotton, C. A., 1961. 'The theory of savanna planation.' *Geography*, 46, 89–101.

Crickmay, C. H., 1933. 'The later stages of the cycle of erosion.' *Geol. Mag.*, 70, 337–47.

Davis, W. M., 1930. 'Rock floors in arid and in humid climates.' *Journ. Geol.*, 38, 1–27.

Davis, W. M., 1932. 'Piedmont benchlands and Primärrumpfe.' *Bull. Geol. Soc. Amer.*, 43, 399–440.

Derruau, M., 1956. *Précis de Géomorphologie*. Masson, Paris.

Dixey, F., 1955. 'Erosion surfaces in Africa: some considerations of age and origin.' *Trans. Geol. Soc. S. Africa*, 58, 265–80.

Fair, T. J. D., 1947. 'Slope form and development in the interior of Natal, South Africa.' *Trans. Geol. Soc. S. Africa*, 50, 105–18.

Fair, T. J. D., 1948. 'Hillslopes and pediments on the semi-arid Karroo.' *S. Afr. Geog. Journ.*, 30, 71–9.

Falconer, J. D., 1911. *The Geology and Geography of Northern Nigeria*. Macmillan, London.

Holmes, A., 1918. 'Rocks of the district of Mozambique.' *Quart. Journ. Geol. Soc.*, 74, 31–96.

King, L. C., 1948. 'A theory of bornhardts.' *Geog. Journ.*, 112, 83–7.

King, L. C., 1951. 'The geomorphology of the eastern and southern districts of Southern Rhodesia.' *Trans. Geol. Soc. S. Africa*, 54, 33–64.

King, L. C., 1962. *Morphology of the Earth*. Oliver and Boyd, Edinburgh.

Linton, D. L., 1955. 'The problem of tors.' *Geog. Journ.*, 121, 470–87.

Mabbutt, J. A., 1955. 'Pediment land forms in Little Namaqualand.' *Geog. Journ.*, 121, 77–83.

Pallister, J. W., 1956. 'Slope development in Buganda.' *Geog. Journ.*, 122, 80–7.

Passarge, S., 1928. *Panoramen Afrikanischer Inselberglandschaften*. Reimer, Berlin.

Pugh, J. C., 1954. 'Multi-cycle inselbergs.' *Dept. of Geog., Univ. Coll. Ibadan., Res. Notes 6.*

Pugh, J. C., 1955. 'The geomorphology of the Northern Plateau of Nigeria.' Unpubl. thesis, University of London.

Pugh, J. C., 1956. 'Fringing pediments and marginal depressions in the inselberg landscape of Nigeria.' *Trans. Inst. Brit. Geographers, Publn. No. 22*, 15–31.

Pugh, J. C., and Perry, A. E., 1960. *A Short Geography of West Africa.* Univ. of London Press, London.

Pugh, J. C., in preparation. *Phased disintegration of bornhardts to kopjes.*

Ruxton, R. P., and Berry, L., 1957. 'Weathering of granite and associated erosional features in Hong Kong.' *Bull. Geol. Soc. Amer.,* 68, 1263–91.

Ruxton, R. P., and Berry, L., 1961. 'Notes on faceted slopes, rock fans and domes on granite in the East-Central Sudan.' *Amer. Journ. Sci.,* 259, 194–206.

Sweeting, M. M., 1958. 'The karstlands of Jamaica.' *Geog. Journ.,* 124, 184–99.

Thorbecke, F., 1927. 'Der Formenschatz im periodisch trockenen Tropenklima mit überwiegender Regenzeit.' *Düsseldorfer Geogr. Vortr.,* 3, 11–17.

Wentworth, C. K., 1943. 'Soil avalanches on Oahu, Hawaii.' *Bull. Geol. Soc. Amer.,* 54, 53–64.

Willis, B., 1936. *East African Plateaus and Rift Valleys.* Carnegie Inst., Washington D.C.

# Stratigraphical Geomorphology

## A Review of some East African Landforms

## W. W. BISHOP

Stratigraphy: Study of strata, their occurrence, lithological character, fossil content, succession and mutual relations and their classification with a view to arranging them in chronological order. Also it usually includes a consideration of those palaeogeographical conditions that may explain the facts (Challinor 1961, p. 190).
Geomorphology: The science of the earth's surface features, their character, origin and evolution (Challinor 1961, p. 89).

It is unusual to find stratigraphy directly associated with geomorphology, or formally acknowledged as playing a large part in geomorphological studies. The differences in length and detail of the two quoted definitions, from a recently published *Dictionary of Geology*, might seem to reflect the present position of geomorphology in Britain. Geomorphology is normally accepted as an integral part of geographical studies, but is viewed with no little suspicion by many geologists. Nevertheless, there is a basic similarity between the two subjects: an improved definition of geomorphology, requiring little additional modification, might be obtained by substituting the words *Study of the earth's surface features* for *Study of strata* in the first definition.

In East Africa, stratigraphy and geomorphology share common ground in earth history; they are interwoven and interdependent to a considerable degree. Stratigraphical influences may be summarized under the three main heads of definition and description; dating; and deformation.

*Definition and Description.* It seems desirable to establish for East Africa, and indeed for Africa as a whole, a series of geomorphological *type areas*, for which local geographical names can be used as identifying labels, at least in the first instance; the selected areas should be those typified by particular landforms. Type areas can be used as standards of reference, as well-defined localities warranting more detailed investigation later, or as areas to be visited by workers in similar fields. The need for well-defined and adequately described

139

type areas is particularly great in relation to the recognition and correlation of surfaces which have little relief. Such surfaces have appeared in the literature on East Africa under the names peneplain, pediplain, etchplain, erosion-bevel, erosion-surface, and others; and these terms have been used to relate the features in question to the concept of flights of cyclic surfaces.

The analogy of type areas in geomorphology is with type sections in stratigraphy. These sections provide local names to define rock units which are only subsequently, when the evidence permits, grouped into broader divisions having a connotation of time. The need for such an approach in geomorphology invites reference to King's *Morphology of the Earth*, relating as this does to Africa as a morphological *type continent* which provides the basis 'for deciphering the history of continental landscapes all over the globe' (L. C. King 1962, p. 236).

The continent-wide, cyclic landscapes recognized by King under the headings *Gondwana, African*, or various Cainozoic stages, seem likely to prove the broadly correct sequence of events for many areas. The concepts invoked to explain and date the cycles involved may be perfectly valid, while the wide view of African morphology so excitingly portrayed by Professor King will be a tremendous stimulus for further work.

However, detailed geological, soil and contour maps are now available for many areas of Africa, often for the first time, in addition to good stereoscopic air-photo cover. Thus it seems desirable to return to ground for which the morphological outline has been established, and to describe that local detail which can evaluate 'the local departures from conformity, both in the effects of local structure and bedrock, and in *tectonic differences of timing*' (L. C. King, *op. cit.* 1962, p. 301). One can agree entirely with King (p. 236) that 'the face of Africa is a polygenetic and complex thing' but must differ, at least in respect of East Africa, when he suggests that 'all major problems of dating and correlation seem to be resolved'.

*Dating: Actual Age.* Opportunities of dating former landsurfaces occur in those comparatively rare situations where fossiliferous deposits resting upon them provide an upper-age limit (B. King 1958, p. 677; L. C. King 1948, 1949; Dixey 1956). Areas in which such relationships occur require detailed stratigraphical mapping if the morphology of the buried landsurface (or unconformity) is to be revealed. Mapping is also desirable to investigate the nature of the palaeontological assemblage used in dating, its relationship to the underlying surface, and the palaeoecology of sediments lying upon the buried landscape.

Investigations of the age of sub-volcanic landsurfaces have recently received considerable impetus from the preliminary application of radiometric dating by the potassium$^{40}$/argon$^{40}$ method to Tertiary and Quaternary sediments (Evernden 1959, Evernden and Curtis 1962). In East Africa it is particularly fortunate that the alkaline Tertiary volcanics have yielded, at or near their base, faunal assemblages from some fifteen localities (Bishop 1963, Fig. 1). The fauna has been termed Lower Miocene, but may possibly range from Oligocene to late Miocene or early Pliocene in at least one locality. However, this particular site (Leakey 1962, Bishop and Whyte 1962) is considerably above the unconformity of the buried surface, and well up in the volcanic sequence.

It appears probable that most of the volcanic outbursts began during the early Miocene; despite some range of time, the base of the deposits forms a very convenient datum for dating. Not only does the calcareous nature of most of the tuffs give conditions ideal for the preservation of fossils, but many of the lavas and the constituent minerals of the tuffs contain potassium and are suitable for potassium/argon dating. This technique seems likely to become of great importance in the near future in establishing ages for East African sub-volcanic surfaces, particularly as the associated faunal assemblages act as an additional control upon the new radiometric dates.

*Dating: Relative Age.* Relative dating of surfaces is based upon the principle that evidence of earlier cycles may be preserved in the form of virtually unaltered elements in the present landscape, or of facets where later erosion has not modified the morphology typical of a particular surface. If this is the case, burial and partial exhumation are not necessary to obtain a date for a particular former landsurface.

Comparative ages of successive erosion-cycles are obtained by mapping the surviving remnants and by extrapolating to their base-level of origin, which would normally be at the coast. Further, it has been suggested that the initiation and termination of any cycle must be the result of uplift relative to the coastal base-level. Alternating movement and quiescence should be marked in a series of unconformities, disconformities, or condensed sequences in the coastal marine sediments, interspersed with records of accelerated deposition (L. C. King 1962).

Thus a detailed knowledge of the Jurassic to Pleistocene stratigraphy of the marine sequences preserved along the east coast of Africa is necessary to evaluate the relative dating of surfaces in Kenya and Tanganyika east of the continental divide. To the west of the divide in Uganda and Western Tanganyika, and in the areas of internal drainage along the lines of the Gregory and Western rifts, the problem remains fundamentally stratigraphical, but is complicated by tectonic movements which have sundered river systems from time to time and have established a series of local, periodically-rejuvenated base-levels.

*Deformation.* The apparent similarity of sequence and simplicity of line of the cyclic erosion-surfaces throughout Africa, in conjunction with the hypothesis of cymatogeny (L. C. King 1962), depends upon broadly synchronous series of continent-wide earth movements. Hence it becomes necessary not only to investigate the criteria of local dating upon which the time-scale of events is based, but also to state the extent of local tectonic disturbances which have occurred during the Tertiary and Quaternary in East Africa.

Investigation of sequences in the tectonically-controlled basins of deposition associated with the rifts makes it possible broadly to date the periods of faulting responsible for truncating river systems and for forming fresh base-levels. Similarly, dating of local sedimentary sequences has made it possible in Uganda both to date and to investigate the extent of the warping and tilting which have deformed in attitude and modified in altitude many of the older surfaces since their formation. The fact that an approximate age can be given, by a study of associated deposits, for the initiation of a particular base-level or the inception of a *new* fault escarpment, means that geomorphological studies can be performed under the controlled conditions of a field laboratory.

Many aspects of the study of East African landforms are then linked with stratigraphy. The next following paragraphs, which describe the results of field work in several areas, illustrate one or more of the factors outlined above.

## 1. Classical Surfaces in Uganda

Erosion-surfaces have attracted a considerable literature since Wayland (1921) made early reference to the flat-topped hills typical of Buganda. After describing the Buganda peneplain (Wayland 1926), he designated a series of levels peneplains PI, PII (his Buganda peneplain), and PIII (Wayland 1933, 1934). Also in 1934 Wayland, followed in 1936 by Bailey Willis, introduced the term *etchplain* to refer to a surface of little relief, formed comparatively rapidly after elevation and cut across deeply-rotted country rock. Etching was said to be typical of tectonic instability in the form of relative uplift of large areas. Thornbury (1954, p. 193) refers to the concept of etchplanation, commenting that, although etching might contribute to local differential lowering of a surface 'it is difficult to visualize this process operating widely enough to produce etchplains of regional extent'. Ollier (1960) has however related the development of erosion-surfaces to differential etching-out of inselbergs in Uganda.

Five erosion-surfaces, including the Buganda Surface, were described by McConnell (1955), who assigned age-brackets to them and correlated them with sequences established in other areas by Dixey and King (Table I). Lepersonne (1956) and Ruhe (1954) extrapolate into Uganda sequences of landforms developed for adjacent areas of the Congo, while Pallister (1954, 1956a, 1956b, 1959, 1960) describes very fully the general form and distribution of the Buganda and associated surfaces in Uganda. Finally, Trendall (1962) outlines a process for the development of flat-topped interfluves capped by up to 30 feet of laterite duricrust. Such interfluves and cappings are typical elements of the Buganda Surface. Trendall's hypothesis suggests the possibility of a very recent date of development for this laterite-dominated plateau; it involves a considerable modification of form, and a lowering in height, of any pre-existing surface by the gradual settling *in situ* of the developing laterite sheet. As surface lowering of several hundred feet is involved, the concept is of far-reaching importance for the recognition, relative dating and correlation of erosion-cycles.

Table I shows some of the variations in correlation and dating that have been suggested during the last twenty years. The Buganda Surface would appear to be an easily-recognizable morphological datum, but correlations have ranged from the original Gondwana of King (1951) to his African (1962). Bishop (1958), arguing by analogy with northeast Uganda, considers that the original Buganda Surface may have been formed considerably before the Lower Miocene. At the other end of the scale, Trendall's hypothesis (1962) suggests that the surface may still be undergoing final modification at the end of a comparatively recent evolutionary process. In the absence of any evidence of actual dating within Buganda, it seems highly desirable to continue to use the local name for the feature, particularly in view of Pallister's comment (1960, p. 30) concerning 'the fragmentary nature of this surface and its remoteness from probable equivalents'.

A preliminary analysis of the *type area* for the Buganda Surface, in the district where it was first described by Wayland—on the watershed between Lakes Victoria and Kyoga, where it has suffered least erosion—is based upon the evidence shown in Figs. 1 and 2. The work supplements the broader areal descriptions of Pallister. A map to the scale of 1 : 25,000 with a contour interval of 20 ft is now

TABLE I

| Wayland 1934 | McConnell 1955 | Ollier 1960 | Pallister 1960 | King L.C. 1951 | King L.C. 1962 | Ruhe 1954 |
|---|---|---|---|---|---|---|
| PI True Peneplain —up to 6000 ft Laterite patches | 1. ANKOLE 5500+ (≡ Jurassic—Dixey, Gondwana—King) | | BUTA-BULAGA (≡ ?Cretaceous) | | GONDWANA (Jurassic) | |
| | 2. KOKI 4700–800 ft (≡ Cretaceous Dixey, Post Gondwana—King) | | | | | |
| PII Etchplain ? | 3. BUGANDA 4300–400 ft (≡ mid-Tertiary—Dixey, African—King) | ≡ Gondwana of King | BUGANDA (mid-Tertiary) | ≡ Gondwana | AFRICAN (early Cainozoic to end Oligocene) | MID-TERTIARY (4300 ft) |
| | 4. TANGANYIKA 3500–800 ft (≡ end-Tertiary—Dixey) | ≡ African of King | TANGANYIKA (end-Tertiary) | ≡ African | | END-TERTIARY (slopes down to Lake Victoria and Kyoga) |
| PIII Etchplain ? Several surfaces Pliocene. Maximum altitude 4000 ft | 5. ACHOLI 3000–500 ft (Lower Pleistocene) | | ACHOLI (Early Pleistocene) | | | |

available for the City of Kampala; it has been used to construct profiles along the ridge-crests of all the major northwest–southeast spurs crossing the main Kyoga–Victoria watershed approximately

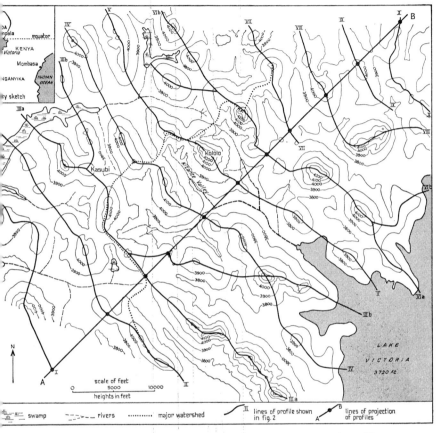

Fig. 1. The type area of the Buganda Surface, Kampala, showing location of lines of profile illustrated in Fig. 2.

at right angles (Fig. 1). The profiles, projected along the northeast–southwest line A–B, plot as shown in Fig. 2.

In the composite projected profiles, the flat-topped remnants of the Buganda Surface, capped with a thick laterite duricrust and rising to 4300 feet a.s.l., stand as isolated hills with consistent side-slopes ranging from 1 in 3 to 1 in 6. The hills rise above pronounced pediments, which have a series of negative breaks at approximately

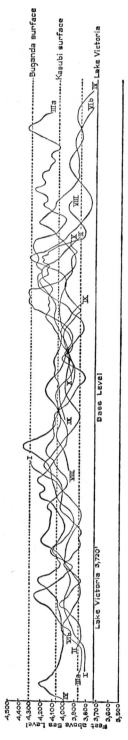

Fig. 2. Superimposed profiles of ridge crests in the Kampala area.

4060 ft a.s.l., or, for those areas draining to the south, of about 340 ft above the local base-level of Lake Victoria. Into the pediments are incized the headstreams of the Lake Kyoga and Lake Victoria drainage systems. The present-day streams flow in steep-sided, flat-bottomed valleys, as far as some 260 ft below the average level of the positive breaks of slope which delimit the pediments. That is, a pronounced dissected pediplain, consisting of pediments or of isolated gently-rounded hill tops, occurs some 240 ft below the flat hill tops which comprise the Buganda Surface. The rounded hilltops may in some cases mark intermediate stages in the progressive lowering of remnants of the Buganda Surface subsequent to removal of the protective duricrust, as outlined by Pallister (1956a and b). However, the pediments and the majority of the accordant summits represent a distinct lower surface. This is given the local term of *Kasubi Surface* by the writer, after a hill to the west of Makerere University College, Kampala, and in order to avoid any pre-judged correlation with the nomenclature of other areas (Fig. 1).

Another series of flats, comprising a third surface of little relief, but small in total area, is seen in the alluvial infillings of the swamp valleys associated with the local base-level of Victoria Nyanza (3720 ft a.s.l.), and also in the headwaters of valleys draining to Lake Kyoga (3400 ft a.s.l.).

Detailed investigation of the relations between lateritic duricrust, weathered regolith, and solid rock has been commenced in the type area as a follow-up to the preliminary investigation of spur profiles. Mapping will, it is hoped, be completed within the next few years, in addition to a complete analysis of slopes. The fact that the type area is within a city where temporary sections are continually being exposed during building operations and in cutting new roads, makes it possible to obtain a fairly complete stratigraphic background to the morphological pattern. In most of Uganda, exposures of sub-surface sections are unfortunately lacking, apart from trial-pits and auger-holes.

If Trendall's hypothesis is valid, it should be easier to establish correlations with other areas by means of the pediments of the Kasubi Surface, than by means of the Buganda Surface, associated with and dominated by laterite, and with its rather specialized mode of formation and probable progressive modification. Despite its easily recognizable morphology, the Buganda Surface may be an unreliable morphological datum for the recognition of past erosion-cycles. Detailed mapping of rock, soil, and morphology will permit Trendall's hypothesis to be reviewed against an improved background of field observation.

Hartman (1955), in seeking to account for the heavy-mineral assemblages found in Jamaican bauxites, suggests that the chemical removal of some 800 ft of limestone would be required to yield the observed mineral concentration. The limestones, from which in all probability the bauxites were developed, range from mid-Eocene to lower Miocene in age, and were not uplifted until mid-Miocene times. Findings of this description suggest that caution is needed in concluding that the various Tertiary surfaces of East Africa, which exhibit deep lateritic weathering, are unmodified. Unfortunately, the rocks here are mainly pre-Cambrian. But it remains possible that certain areas of East Africa have experienced comparatively recent modification by subsurface chemical activity and groundwater movement, in addition to the effects of recent tectonic deformation which are discussed below.

The distribution of the remnants of the Buganda and Koki Surfaces may be relevant to the chemical problem of the formation of a thick laterite duricrust. The Buganda Surface is characteristically preserved upon quartzites of the Buganda Series. It shows a general uptilt to the west, which will be discussed below, and a gentle rise from the major east–west through valleys to the less regular but generally east–west divides.

Pallister suggests that the Koki Surface is merely the Buganda Surface at a rather higher level than usual, although McConnell considers that the marked but dissected scarp feature which divides the Buganda from the Koki Surface marks both a step up in altitude and a step back in time of formation. However, as the Koki Surface is developed characteristically only on the Karagwe-Ankolean metasediments, the variation in height may arise merely from the different susceptibilities to chemical weathering of the two types of bedrock. If Trendall's hypothetical process operated on an original peneplain surface, differential erosion arising from the different chemical environments might eventually produce two surfaces at markedly different levels. In the opinion of the writer, the escarpment at the approach to Karagwe-Ankolean rocks merely separates two surfaces which were contemporaneous and continuous in origin, but which have since 'drifted apart' as it were, as the result of differential rates of weathering. But observations suggest that etching by differential erosion, as the direct result of exogenic processes, has not contributed greatly to the landscape of the Kampala area.

The verb *etch* is defined by Webster as: 'to produce as figures or designs by means of lines or strokes eaten in or corroded by means of some chemical agent'. It is not denied that deep chemical rock-rot has taken place in Buganda, as described by Ollier (1960). Penetra-

STRATIGRAPHICAL GEOMORPHOLOGY      149

tion of rotting to different depths has yielded a highly irregular 'basal surface of weathering' (Ruxton and Berry 1959). In places, the development of erosion-surfaces as peneplains or pediplains has revealed or indeed *etched-out* the details of irregularities on the surface of the fresh rock *where this rises above the local peneplain/pediplain level*. This circumstance has produced the various inselberg topographies described by Ollier (1960), particularly at distances from divides. However, there is no stripping to expose considerable areas of the basal surface of weathering as the result of differential removal of the soft rotted regolith and with accompanying formation of extensive plains. Indeed, as Ollier notes (1960, p. 44), 'the most remarkable feature of the inselbergs is that they are separated from each other by wide areas of very weathered rock'.

In the Kampala area, solid rock crops out irregularly from beneath the weathered regolith, and the 'basal surface' bears no relationship either to the Buganda or to the Kasubi Surfaces. Although detailed mapping of outcrops of the solid-rock/rotten-rock junction is not yet completed, its most typical location can be provisionally specified as associated with valley-side tors at low levels. Relevant outcrops in the Kitante valley (Fig. 1 and Plate 19), are at approximately 3840 ft a.s.l., that is, 140 to 220 ft below the Kasubi Surface. The fact that the peneplains and pediplains of Uganda are cut across deeply rotted rock which in places attains 200 ft or more in thickness, militates against the use of *etching* to describe the mode of formation of extensive areas of low relief. Little is yet known with any certainty of the detailed processes which give rise to peneplains or pediplains, but the names themselves have the virtue of being descriptive of the main features or relationships of the landforms they designate. Similar value cannot be claimed for the term *etchplain*, which seems of doubtful value in the already overburdened vocabulary of geomorphology.

Nevertheless, the general situation described by Wayland and Bailey Willis in introducing the term *etchplains*—one of recurrent and comparatively rapid uplift—undoubtedly obtains in Uganda. Periods of movement of boundary faults of the Western rift have resulted in repeated lowering of the local base-level, with consequent rejuvenation of the drainage. Similar tectonic control of base-level has been noted by Ruhe in the Congo catchment adjoining the Western rift. However, processes here involved in the formation of erosion-surfaces might well be termed *normal*, with repeated rejuvenation by tectonic action introduced as an unusual and complicating factor.

F

## 2. Buried Surfaces in Eastern Uganda and Western Kenya

Away from the coastal region, the outstanding geological characteristic of East Africa is a vast unconformity in which mid-Tertiary or later sediments overstep a variety of pre-Cambrian metasediments and crystalline basement rocks. Local exceptions to the general pattern include Karroo sediments preserved in outliers. The Karroo rocks are most extensive in Tanganyika, where evidence of the form of the sub-Karroo surface is also best preserved. McKinlay (1956, p. 81) writes 'The pre-Karroo surface (at least in South-West Tanganyika) appears to have been uneven, so that younger Karoo beds overlap older and overstep on to the pre-Cambrian crystalline rocks'; and again: 'the relative topographic relief of the area in early Karroo times was in general *somewhat similar to that at present* [W. W. B.'s italics] . . . the surface of the basin in which the lower Karroo sediments were being deposited had a considerable relief with quite steep-sided ridges and valleys of varying depths'. From 1500 to 2000 ft of Lower Karroo sediments were required to fill the deep valleys; McKinlay suggests that the considerable relief might in part be credited to early Karroo earth-movements. Peneplain-like areas associated with the more recent erosion-surfaces may not then have been fully developed in all parts of East Africa by Karroo times, or may have been tectonically disturbed, at least locally, as they are now being in some areas of East Africa.

Three small patches of Karroo beds are present in Uganda: all appear to be faulted outliers. The occurrence at Entebbe is typical of them all, occupying a graben bounded by faults trending east–west and approximately one mile apart. The Karroo sediments have been proved over 1000 ft by drilling near Entebbe, while geophysical prospecting suggests a maximum depth of about 1400 ft. These downfaulted remnants give an idea of the extent of tectonic movement in Uganda since Permian or Triassic times, and also of the extent of Mesozoic and Tertiary planation. Originally these rocks probably formed part of an extensive Karroo cover. The thickness of the sediments suggests either deep valleys, or downfaulted blocks the base of which is approximately 1750 ft below the local average height of the present-day Buganda Surface.

Apart from the patchy and tentative Karroo evidence, it is not until the outbreak of volcanic activity during mid-Tertiary times that there is an extensive stratigraphical datum to provide age criteria for East African erosion-surfaces in areas other than coastal.

## The Topography beneath the Tertiary Volcanics

Over-generalization seems to have confused the correlation and dating of many East African erosion-surfaces.

A convenient starting point in reviewing the problems involved is the reference in L. C. King (1962, p. 280) to the early Cainozoic (African) surface passing 'on Rusinga Island beneath deposits with early-Miocene vertebrate fossils, . . . *an important occurrence for dating the surface*'. In contrast, B. C. King (1958, p. 678) noted that 'Even in examples of well-dated deposits such as the sediments of Lower Miocene age in the Kavirondo Gulf, difference of opinion exists as to whether the main platform of the region passes under the sediments or truncates them (Kent 1944; Dixey 1945; and Shackleton 1951).'

Some fifteen major localities in western Kenya and eastern Uganda have yielded assemblages of mammalian fossils, which have been designated Burdigalian or Lower Miocene in age (Fig. 3). From some of these localities, faunal assemblages recovered are but small, and their evidence on dating the volcanic activity must be regarded merely as tentative. Of the ten sites yielding larger assemblages, six— Koru, Maboko, Mfwanganu, Ombo, Rusinga and Songhor—lie within, or on the flanks of, the graben structure of the Kavirondo rift valley.

Although the initial date of rifting here is open to question, considerable fault-movements have certainly taken place since the Lower Miocene. They include renewed activity along major fault-lines, and also local step- and grid-fault movements of small throw within the graben. In consequence, correlation is difficult between the well-known Lower Miocene deposits of the rift, and areas lying outside its delimiting scarps, where extensive relatively underformed erosion surfaces can be seen. Any correlation attempted must be regarded as tentative or hypothetical. The base of the lavas or of the Tertiary volcanic site can be mapped, but the lavas invariably overlie the fossiliferous deposits and may be considerably later than the faunas which they seal. Potassium/argon dating of the lavas will undoubtedly extend the number of localities at which an upper age-limit can be given to the sub-volcanic surface.

The new faunal site at Fort Ternan, within the Tinderet volcanic sequence (Fig. 3), has recently yielded a late Miocene or lower Pliocene mammalian fauna for which a $K^{40}/Ar^{40}$ age of 14 million years has been established (Leakey 1962). The Fort Ternan evidence suggests prolonged Miocene activity on the site of Tinderet of a predominantly pyroclastic cone with subsidiary flows. The main pile of

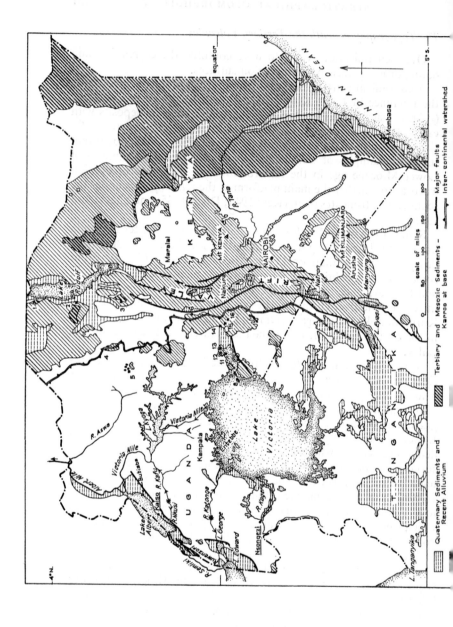

Quaternary Sediments and Recent Alluvium
Tertiary and Mesozoic Sediments – Karroo at base
Major faults
inter-continental watershed

scale of miles

INDIAN OCEAN

equator

5°S.

Mombasa

R. Tana

KENYA

Marsabit

Mt KENYA

NAIROBI

Nakuru

RIFT

VALLEY

Magadi

Naivasha

Mt KILIMANJARO

Arusha

Manyara

L. Eyasi

TANGANYIKA

Lake Victoria

Entebbe

Kampala

UGANDA

Victoria Nile

L. Kyoga

Victoria Nile

R. Aswa

R. Katonga

R. Kafu

Bukaya

Kaso

Lake Albert

L. George

Edward

R. Semliki

Kazinga

ALBERT NILE

Ruwenzori

Nsongezi

R. Kagera

R. Mara

L. Tanganyika

4°N.

lavas which forms Tinderet Mountain, underlain by flows of phono-
lite of Losuguta type which have an extensive distribution at the
eastern end of the Kavirondo rift, are thus all post-Miocene in age
(Bishop and Whyte 1962). The activity may have continued well
into the Pliocene. As these late flows frequently overlap the earlier
pyroclastics to rest on pre-Cambrian strata, the danger is apparent of
mapping the base of the Tertiary volcanics as everywhere of sub-
Miocene or pre-Miocene age.

At Maboko, and possibly also at Rusinga Island, the lavas may
also date from the Upper Miocene, while faunal evidence from some
of the sites southeast of Maralal again suggests a similar late date for
the outpourings of the Rumuruti phonolites (see below). Considerable
modification of the landsurfaces, as outlined below for Napak, could
well have taken place in the 10 million years which span the period
from sub-[Lower]Miocene to end-Miocene or early Pliocene.

This caution about the age of sub-lava surfaces can usefully be
borne in mind respecting the area north of the Kavirondo graben,
where phonolites of Losuguta and Kenya types flood an irregular
incised topography immediately north of the escarpment (Saggerson
1952). In addition, the flows seem to have spilled southwards at some
points over a pre-existing low scarp. Later faults striking principally
northeast–southwest have stepped down the flows towards the southeast. However, it seems probable that a graben with less pronounced
escarpments than those of today already existed in the Kavirondo
Gulf area, before the extrusion of the phonolites, as suggested by
Kent (in Shackleton 1951, p. 381). The form of the sub-volcanic
surface can be reconstructed accurately for the lava/pre-Cambrian
boundary. Within the Kavirondo rift, reconstruction provides little
evidence of a surface with relief slight enough to qualify as a peneplain or bevel, and to warrant correlation with the Buganda Surface.
Particularly is this true close to the Lower Miocene fossiliferous sites.

On Maboko, Mfwanganu and Rusinga Islands the sub-volcanic
surface is not exposed. It lies below the water-level of Lake Victoria,
with its morphology unknown. Pre-Cambrian rocks occur in an
isolated small outcrop on the southeast of Mfwanganu Island, on

---

Fig. 3. Generalized geological map of East Africa (after the Geological Surveys
of Kenya, Uganda and Tanganyika). Numbers indicate principal localities
yielding fossil mammals:

| | | | | |
|---|---|---|---|---|
| 1. Lokitaung | 2. Losodok | 3. Loperot | 4. Moroto | 5. Napak |
| 6. Tambach | 7. Palagalagi-Kirimon | | 8. Mfwanganu | |
| 9. Rusinga | 10. Karungu | 11. Maboko Island | 12. Mariwa | |
| 13. Ombo | 14. Songhor | 15. Koru | 16. Fort Ternan | |

Takivere Island (Whitworth 1961), and more extensively on the mainland due south of Rusinga and Mfwanganu round the former vent of Rangwa. However, in this area, the granites rise to over 5000 ft on account of local uplift of about 2000 ft 'above the *sub-Miocene peneplain*, by doming *in early Tertiary times*' (McCall 1958). Thus this area cannot be used to establish the pre-Miocene topography.

At Ombo the base of the fossiliferous grits occurs at 4390 ft a.s.l. in part of a former valley system incised into pre-Cambrian rocks. The less prolific faunal site of Mariwa (4720 ft a.s.l.) lies rather higher in the same old valley system. The fossiliferous deposits are overlain by phonolites of Losuguta type which flooded the surrounding irregular granitic topography to heights up to 5000 ft immediately north of the Ombo locality. They lap against the high residual hill mass of Maragoli (6018 ft) up to a height of over 5200 ft only 6 miles northeast of Ombo and Mariwa. Once again, the local evidence is of diversified topography rather than of a subdued and recognizable surface.

Similarly irregular relief with gneiss rising in hills more than 1000 ft high can be seen at Songhor Hill (5434 ft a.s.l.) immediately west of the main Lower Miocene sediments at Songhor (4400 to 4550 ft). Other high land occurs to the northwest in Chemill Hill (5550 ft), an extension from the Nyando escarpment. To the east and northeast the basement surface is obscured by lava and tuff, but three hill inliers of gneiss, which range from 4750 to 4800 ft, and which are associated with Lower Miocene fossil sites at 4725 ft three miles northeast of the main site, suggest that the irregular topography continues under the volcanics.

For 6 miles to the south of Songhor as far as Muhoroni, the pre-Cambrian outcrops are obscured beneath recent alluvium; but the gneisses cannot fail to lie below 4200 ft a.s.l. South of Muhoroni their renewed outcrop extends 6 miles north–south and 9 miles east–west (Binge 1961). Here the junction with the overlying phonolites is irregular, varying from 4100 to 4800 ft a.s.l. The Koru faunal site occurs at the northeast corner of this outcrop. Immediately south of the fossil site, the basement appears from beneath sediments at a height of 4600 ft. The Koru fossiliferous sediments outcrop at between 4780 and 4820 ft a.s.l. The evidence of the rocks immediately underlying them is confused, but abundant gneissose blocks may represent the sub-volcanic surface outcropping between 4770 and 4780 ft.

In view of the relief observed locally at those fossiliferous sites where the sub-volcanic topography is visible, and of the fact that the rift valley situation prevents firm correlation with areas where erosion-surfaces are well preserved, the Kavirondo region seems a dangerous one in which to attempt dating. This is particularly true if a shallow graben was already in existence prior to the Miocene.

It is unfortunate that application of the term *sub-Miocene bevel or peneplain* has been extended from this area into central Uganda. There seems to be no evidence for using in Kavirondo the term *Buganda peneplain* (Shackleton 1951), or, conversely, for suggesting on the Kavirondo evidence that the Buganda Surface (which typically is first seen 100 miles northwest of Kisumu) is of pre-Miocene age.

It is but just, however, to recall that the original correlation between this erosion-surface and an area of Lower Miocene fossiliferous sediments was made by Shackleton in 1946 with reference to land outside the graben, when the deposits at Karungu 'resting on an old lateritic ironstone and filling slight depressions in the old surface' (Shackleton 1951) were correlated with the gravels under the phonolites of the Isuria plateau and with the more widespread surface beneath the Gwasi (Kisingiri or Rangwa) volcanic deposits. All these were considered to rest on what had originally been 'one and the same evenly-planed surface which was therefore to be called the sub-Miocene peneplain' (Shackleton 1951, p. 377).

But the link between the Isuria plateau at 6000 ft, with Karungu to the northwest where the sediments outcrop between 3750 and 4100 ft (McCall 1958), involves an extrapolation of 50 miles with little evidence from the intervening area. It also calls for a relative down-warp of 2000 ft in a northwesterly direction. This may be a correct correlation, but the evidence is indeed slender for the dating of a widespread erosion-surface. In the Karungu region, Shackleton's mapping reveals a local relief of 400 ft between Nundowat and the lake.

Pulfrey (1960) has produced an excellent map showing the distribution throughout Kenya of the surface which he dates as having matured somewhat earlier than the Lower Miocene, and which he names the sub-Miocene erosion bevel. The surface, contoured at 500-ft intervals, depends for its actual dating in the west of Kenya upon areas where Lower Miocene mammalian faunas occur at or near the base of the volcanics (cf. Pulfrey 1960, Fig. 3). Difficulties of the sort noted above apply to the dating at rift localities in Kavirondo, and also to Karungu. Of the other principal fossiliferous localities mapped by Pulfrey, that near Tambach on the Elgeyo escarpment has yielded only crocodile and tortoise remains and a rhinocerotid tooth (Shackleton 1951): its Lower Miocene age is in consequence open to question. The surface of the basement gneisses, traced along the escarpment, is highly irregular, with the Tambach beds resting in deep valleys and overlain by phonolites. Exposures several thousand feet up on the scarp face and visible only in north–south section give but an extremely local picture of the sub-volcanic topography.

Beds lithologically similar to the 'Lower Miocene' Turkana grits and to the Tambach beds rest on pre-Cambrian rocks 8 to 15 miles west and southwest of Baragoi, overlain by basalts, tuffs and Rumuruti phonolites. As they have not yet yielded any fauna, their actual age is uncertain (Baker 1963). Some 80 miles south of Baragoi, in the area mapped by Shackleton (1945), near Kirimon and the Palagalagi River, a fauna occurs which was thought originally to be Lower Miocene, but further collecting has provided a larger assemblage which suggests a later, Upper Miocene age for the sediments (Leakey, personal communication). As these sediments are overlain by Rumuruti phonolites, a later date than pre-Lower Miocene or sub-Miocene is indicated for the surface on which these lavas rest. Cooke (1958, p. 17), commenting on the form of the sub-volcanic surface, notes that Shackleton himself recorded near Maralal a relief in the sub-Miocene topography of up to 500 ft.

The remaining fossiliferous Lower Miocene sites mapped by Pulfrey are those at Loperot west of the southern end of Lake Rudolf (2300 ft) in the Losodok hills north and east of Lodwar (1500 ft), and near Lokitaung west of the north end of Lake Rudolf. The fauna from this group of sites has not been published in full, but is probably Lower Miocene. However, the area has suffered considerable tectonic disturbance; Pulfrey's contour lines on the sub-Miocene surface are shown as dotted where the surface passes to the north under a continuous volcanic cover. At Loperot the fossiliferous sediments are shown as in part overlying one of the hills rising above the bevel, so that in this region also an irregular topography can be inferred.

The general map showing the distribution of the erosion bevel which has been labelled sub-Miocene, correlating the mapping of numerous individual officers of the Kenya Survey, is a welcome production. However, as suggested above, and re-stressed below, the dating of this surface in western Kenya by reference to the Lower Miocene mammalian fossil sites is open to question. The base of the Tertiary volcanics as a group is likely to be diachronous, ranging from Lower Miocene to mid-Pliocene or later.

Recent mapping of the volcanic/basement boundaries of Mts Elgon, Kadam, Moroto and Napak by officers of the Uganda Geological Survey (Trendall 1959, 1961, Fleuty in press, Macdonald 1961) provides detailed knowledge of the sub-volcanic topography in eastern Uganda. This, coupled with the recovery of a large assemblage of lower Miocene vertebrates from the Napak volcanics (Bishop 1958, 1962, Bishop and Whyte 1962) and fossils almost certainly of similar age from the base of the Moroto volcanics, gives a reliable datum in an area where the morphological relationships are clear. Some of the lavas comprising the higher and outer parts of Moroto Mountain may be later than Lower Miocene in age; $K^{40}/Ar^{40}$ dating is being undertaken. Some doming associated with the vulcanicity, similar to that noted at Rangwa, has occurred at Napak and probably also at other Ugandan centres. However, allowance has been made for this in reconstruction of the pre-volcanic landforms; relationships between the surfaces underlying the outermost cones and surfaces cut across the surrounding extensive areas of Basement Complex are quite clear.

At Napak, as at Moroto, Kadam, and Elgon, a lower surface— the Kyoga Surface—occurs beneath the volcanics; it can be mapped as virtually continuous with the Karamoja Plain to the southwest, which has been labelled 'end-Tertiary' by previous workers. The Kyoga Surface may be equivalent to the Kasubi Surface of central Buganda. Residuals of a higher surface occur at Napak, Kadam, and Moroto, inviting correlation with high-level surfaces beneath Kadam and Mt Elgon, and also with the Kitale Plateau.

At Moroto the fossiliferous sediments lie in steep-sided valleys cut some 300 ft into the basement complex and below the level of the 'Kyoga Surface' flats. These old infilled valleys, descending towards the Turkana scarp, are being re-excavated by present drainage. They seem to have headed very close to the present divide, some 4 or 5 miles west of the existing Turkana scarp. The basalt which caps the fossiliferous sediments and seals in the sites flowed towards the scarp down valleys already partly filled with sediment. These deeply-cut valleys of early or pre-Miocene age suggest that at least a low escarpment existed on the line of the present Turkana scarp by the beginning of the Miocene period. The similarity with the situation at Ombo and Mariwa, and with that at Tambach, is very close indeed, particularly as lava-flows probably equivalent in age to those overlying the Moroto fossil sites flowed down the Turkana scarp some miles north of Moroto.

Pulfrey finds it difficult to reconcile his observations in Kenya, where he has mapped the sub-Miocene bevel, with those of the writer and of Trendall in eastern Uganda. He writes (1960, p. 7) 'The contour lines Trendall indicates cannot be reconciled with any possible lines based on evidence further east, and lead to insuperable difficulties if projected further north into Turkana', and 'Bishop concludes from his work on the volcanoes of eastern Uganda that the Buganda Surface, which he correlates with the sub-Miocene bevel, is considerably pre-Miocene, the Kyoga Surface which appears to be the Uganda equivalent of the Kenya end-Tertiary surface, being slightly pre-Miocene. Such dating cannot agree with the facts east of the Uganda boundary, where none of the numerous lower Miocene deposits lie on the end-Tertiary bevel, but on the immediately preceding bevel.'

These two statements illustrate three of the major problems which beset the correlation and dating of erosion-surfaces in East Africa:

(a) They assume that there must be morphological continuity between the erosion-surfaces of Kenya and of Uganda. This seems a false premise, since a major continental divide of considerable antiquity runs north–south through western Kenya and eastern Uganda. The bulk of the Kenya drainage is eastwards to the Indian Ocean. In contrast, that of Uganda and of some parts of the western borders of Kenya runs westwards; its original control was probably an Atlantic base-level, via tributaries of the Congo River, but most of Uganda's present drainage has local base-levels in the lakes of the western rift. The date of inception of rift valley control will be discussed below.

Pulfrey (1960, Fig. 2, p. 14) reconstructs possible early Tertiary drainage in Kenya, where the Kavirondo Gulf drainage is shown as connecting eastwards with the Athi River. This suggestion is at variance with the views of other workers, while his hypothesis that the whole of the drainage of central Uganda may have been eastwards (p. 15) ignores the fact that westerly drainage via the Katonga, Kagera and Kafu systems seems to have been established at least as long ago as the early Tertiary. In the absence of any signs of a barrier between the heads of these westerly-flowing rivers and the Kavirondo Gulf, it seems reasonable to carry the Kavirondo drainage westwards also. The alternative, that of taking this drainage through a gap in the barrier of highland between Mara bridge and Narok and so across the site of the Gregory Rift into a 'Primitive Athi River', seems less attractive. The writer supports B. C. King's postulate of a lower Tertiary watershed immediately west of the Kenya rift, very near to the line of the present watershed.

Pulfrey's Fig. 3 (1960) illustrates very clearly an almost continuous barrier of 'Hills and Mountains on the sub-Miocene bevel' which virtually everywhere separates the well-defined expression of this bevel in central and eastern Kenya from any surface in

Uganda. Correlation across the barrier from east to west is further complicated by the existence of the Gregory Rift Valley a little to the east of the watershed. Extrapolation of erosion-surfaces across this area seems from Pulfrey's map to become extremely tentative, on account of the above-mentioned features, and of a rise to the rift shoulders and of extensive unbroken cover of Tertiary to Quaternary volcanics in many places.

Pulfrey's statements that the Uganda evidence cannot be 'reconciled with any possible lines based on evidence further east' or 'cannot agree with the facts east of the Uganda boundary' would be correct, if for the political boundary he substituted the physical barrier of the major continental divide. Geomorphological correlation across this feature is not to be expected. Pulfrey's sub-Miocene surface can be seen to finger out against the north–south barrier of highland which rises steeply above the back of the bevel in his Fig. 3. The divide must have existed before the surface was bevelled into it; and the area undoubtedly suffered some later general upwarping in association with rift movements.

(b) Nomenclature is confusing in which age-connotations are implicit in names given to geomorphological features. Simple geographical labels would seem preferable to the use of such names as *Miocene peneplain* or *sub-Miocene bevel*, *end-Tertiary* or *mid-Tertiary surface*. If revised dating becomes necessary, features can easily be referred to another period of origin while retaining original labels. Such apparent contradictions in terms as 'none of the numerous Lower Miocene deposits lies on the end-Tertiary bevel but on the immediately preceding bevel' would then be avoided.

Contrary to Pulfrey's statement, Bishop (1958, p. 1482) did not correlate the Buganda Surface with the sub-Miocene bevel: this had been done previously by Shackleton (1951). Bishop merely pointed out that the higher parts of the surfaces under Moroto, Napak, Kadam and Elgon had been variously equated by previous workers with a pre-Miocene, mid-Tertiary, mid-Miocene, Buganda, Uganda or Main Peneplain. The Napak faunal evidence gave for the first time an upper age-limit for the sub-volcanic surface (which is composed of two principal elements), demanding a re-dating of the generally accepted age of the surfaces and their correlatives.

(c) Finally, partly as a result of his attempt to make morphological comparisons across the barrier of the continental divide and the rift valley area, and possibly partly as the result of misapplication of the lower Miocene faunal evidence, Pulfrey finds it necessary to state that Trendall's contour lines for the sub-volcanic and adjacent landsurfaces 'cannot be reconciled with any possible lines based on evidence further east'. Yet Trendall's contours are based on detailed field mapping of the junction between the Tertiary volcanics and the Basement Complex rocks. His map portrays a buried topography which actually exists, and so *must* in some way be reconcilable with the evidence in Kenya. More detailed geomorphological mapping similar to that carried out by Trendall is badly required in East Africa. The apparent clashes of interpretation between Kenya and Uganda all disappear in the light of the fact that one would not expect to find a close correspondence across the continental divide if the two sets of drainage systems flowed to different base-levels of contrasted tectonic history.

Tertiary volcanic centres vary in their degree of post-formational erosion—with the time of cessation of activity, with the composition of the cone, and with the extent to which faulting and caldera collapse have assisted in the destruction of original volcanic piles. As has been shown above, extrusion of lavas in many areas of Kenya continued at least until the Pliocene, and in the vicinity of the Gregory Rift and in northern Tanganyika virtually until the present day. At Napak in Karamoja, however, the activity seems to have ceased comparatively early; as the cone was composed largely of pyroclastic material, breakdown of the original structure, aided by faulting and the formation of a caldera, was remarkably rapid, and no more than a skeleton remains of the original structure, after late Tertiary and Pleistocene erosion (B. King 1949, Bishop 1958, 1962).

The Napak volcano was built up from a Lower Miocene datum to a height of at least 10,000 or 12,000 ft above the plain, and then eroded to its present remnant state (Fig. 4). Trendall (in press) shows the effect of local doming of the underlying basement surface late in the history of this volcano. In addition, however, and of extreme importance in studies of erosion surfaces, post-Lower-Miocene erosion has not only removed more than 95 per cent of the volcanic cone, but has also considerably modified the flat surface of the underlying basement rocks since the protective volcanic cover was removed. The principal remnants of volcanic rocks appear to owe their preservation to resistant lava beneath the surviving pyroclastics. But, in addition, all the volcanic remnants rest upon low pedestals or plinths of basement rock (cf. Fig. 5). This circumstance implies that processes of pediplanation, acting on such gentle slopes as the sub-volcanic Kyoga Surface, have notched quite extensive pediments into the resistant metamorphic rocks. The rock step developed at the rear of the pediment notch varies from remnant to remnant at Napak

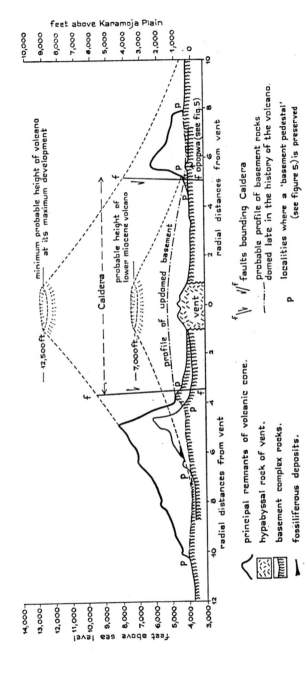

Fig. 4. Cross-sections of the dissected caldera of the volcano of Napak, Karamoja, Uganda.

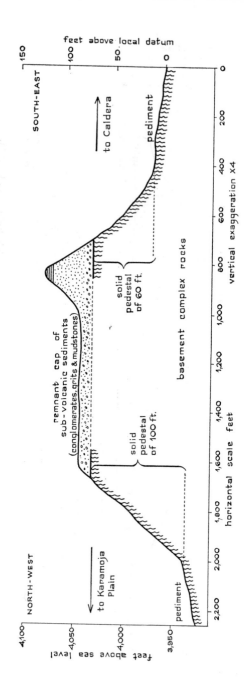

Fig. 5. Levelled profile across the hill Opopwa, near Napak, Karamoja, Uganda.

between 50 and 150 ft in height. Each step is quite distinct from the updomed basement structure, and is best developed on the outer flanks of the cone. There is no doubt that the steps relate to bevelling subsequent to the removal of the Lower Miocene volcanic cover, or that they occur round all the volcanic remnants. As outlined above, the fragments of the original cone seem to owe their survival to the presence of a resistant lava flow rather than to original hills on the sub-volcanic surface—indeed, where the original pre-volcanic relief does survive, the surfaces of some hills have been stripped of their volcanic cover. Furthermore, differential erosion of the older up-domed basement hills and of the volcanics immediately overlying them suggests different rates of recession for the slopes developed respectively on the volcanic and on the basement rocks. It would seem that the basal plinth or pedestal is a late feature which has under-cut the superimposed basal volcanic sediments, giving a continuous slope from the base to the upper part of the pedestals, as in Fig. 5.

The modern Karamoja plain, then, mirrors at a somewhat modi-fied lower level the original sub-volcanic Kyoga Surface. If modifica-tion on the required scale was possible in the interval from late Tertiary to the present time, considerable re-investigation of the processes of formation of erosion-surfaces is necessary before former surface remnants, other than those preserved as buried topographies, can be safely correlated or considered as virtually unmodified since their time of formation.

### East African Coastal Sediments

No treatment of buried surfaces in eastern Uganda and western Kenya would be complete without some discussion of the coastal sediments, which should preserve a record of successive periods of erosion, which may in places rest upon a particular surface and so provide an upper age-limit for its formation, and which provide the evidence from which by extrapolation the relative ages of inland surfaces have been obtained.

L. C. King (1962, Table VII, p. 242) gives the following sequence of deposits and events for the eastern coast of Africa from mid-Cretaceous time up to the end of the Pliocene.

| Denudation Stage | Equivalent Coastal Deposits | Age |
|---|---|---|
| Late Cainozoic Valley Phase | Sands uncomformably overlying Burdigalian | Pliocene |
| | SLIGHT UPLIFT | |
| Broad Valley-floor Pediplains | Burdigalian marine series | Miocene |
| | EPEIROGENIC UPLIFT OF A FEW HUNDRED FEET | |

| *Denudatian Stage* | *Equivalent Coastal Deposits* | *Age* |
|---|---|---|
| 'African' landscape of extreme planation | Sennonian to Eocene | Late Cretaceous to mid- Cainozoic |

## MID-CRETACEOUS DISTURBANCES

King also states (p. 239) 'Where the African cyclic landsurface (denudational or aggradational) bears covering deposits the oldest of these, continental or marine, are early Miocene (Burdigalian) in age' and (p. 270)

> 'along the whole eastern seaboard of Africa denudation in the early stages of the African planation provided the detritus for the late Cretaceous rocks, sometimes succeeded by Eocene, but by the end of the Eocene and Oligocene the smooth landscape provided little or no detritus and rock series of this age are missing. An hiatus in the offshore sedimentation therefore records the culmination of the African cycle on land. Sedimentation was resumed with coarse sandstones during the Burdigalian. . . . These sediments reflect uplift of adjacent lands by small amount and sedimentation does not continue through the middle and upper stages of the Miocene period. After this second hiatus new sands, Pliocene according to their fossil fauna (Cox 1930), record fresh uplift and erosion.'

This sequence differs somewhat for that worked out in most detail for East Africa, namely that for the Lindi area of Tanganyika described by Eames and others (1962). These workers conclude that 'the region seems to have undergone gentle overall subsidence' and that the whole sequence from Cretaceous through the Tertiary records various cycles of gentle warping. The depositional sequence from Eocene into Oligocene is one of calcareous clays and silts with impersistent reef-bands. There is apparently a break in sedimentation in the upper Oligocene, as a typical Chattian fauna is nowhere present. The lowest Miocene sediments appear to be slightly transgressive in the area south of Lindi but to the north they seem to be conformable with the Oligocene. The Lower Miocene (Aquitanian and Burdigalian) sediments commence with 15 ft of buff silty sandstones at the base but pass upwards into limestones (often of reef facies) with silts and gypsiferous clays. The sedimentary sequence from Eocene to the end of the Lower Miocene suggests an 'environment of low tectonic intensity' (Eames and others 1962, p. 63) and all these materials (p. 66) 'were probably deposited on a slowly subsiding continental shelf which was receiving little sediment'.

A major unconformity does not occur until after the end of the

Lower Miocene, when Pliocene sediments transgress the older deposits. This overstep by Pliocene deposits contrasts strongly with the consistency of strike and with the regional dip of 10° east exhibited by all the strata from Cretaceous to Burdigalian (Eames and others 1962, map on p. 65). This finding is in keeping with Dixey's observations (1948) that in the N.F.D. of Kenya the mid-Tertiary surface truncates beds carrying a Lower Miocene mammalian fauna, although it clashes with Pulfrey's mapping of his bevel in Turkana.

It seems odd to find King's Epeirogenic Uplift, which is said to have brought the African Cycle to a close and to have initiated considerable erosion below the African Surface, so poorly represented in the sedimentary record at the coast. The Uplift must presumably be placed in the Chattian Gap, if the Burdigalian deposits are indeed the equivalent of the incision of the Broad Valley Pediplains. This dating also seems at variance with the conclusions of Eames and others (1962), who find stability the dominating factor until the end of the Lower Miocene with the only major gap in sedimentation occurring in the middle and upper Miocene prior to the Pliocene transgression.

This latter break may well represent a major epeirogenic uplift which at first caused sediments to be deposited farther to the east than before, and did not permit sedimentation near the present coastline until the commencement of the Pliocene. Such an interpretation would account for the constant regional dip observed for all the deposits up to the end of the Burdigalian, by contrast with the transgressive and flat-lying relationships of the Pliocene and Quaternary deposits. It seems possible therefore that, if periods of planation inland can be correlated with deposition at the coast, the formation of an extensive surface of slight relief probably ended with the close of Lower Miocene deposition.

The Lindi area admittedly presents but a local picture. Considerable local variations in East Africa from the generalized sequence put forward by Professor King need to be signalized, in order to illustrate the nonconformist nature of the stratigraphy (and geomorphology) of many parts of Africa.

In Kenya, mapping by officers of the Geological Survey of the coastal deposits north of Mombasa reveals several later Tertiary successions. In the southern part of the area (Caswell 1956) between Mombasa and Kilifi, Upper Pliocene Magarini sands rest unconformably on Jurassic strata, but Miocene beds have been recorded in the Kilifi area (Eames and Kent 1955). Farther north, in the Malindi area, the Upper Jurassic strata are overlain unconformably by Miocene (probably Lower) Baratumu Beds, which are themselves overlain unconformably by Marafa Beds of late Pliocene or early Pleistocene age; these in turn overlap in places the Miocene sediments, to rest directly on Jurassic strata (Thompson 1956). To the north of Malindi, Lower Miocene Funda Isa limestones overlie the Jurassic and are themselves unconformably overlain by Pliocene (?)Midadoni Beds (Williams 1962).

Lithology and the details of stratigraphy vary considerably among these three adjacent areas, and the region as a whole contrasts somewhat with the evidence in the Lindi district farther south; it is closer to the sequence described by King. But apparent correlation and simplicity of sequence between area and area probably arises rather from lack of detailed knowledge than from the confirmed and well-dated operation of tectonic mainsprings on a continental scale.

### 3. Deformation of Surfaces

*The Albert–Edward Rift Valley Sedimentary Evidence*

Ruhe (1954) gives an excellent survey of the erosion-surfaces in the High Ituri Plateau of the Congo; his observations extend into central Uganda, with which he makes correlations. His paper includes a summary of the results and conclusions of previous workers in East Africa and the eastern Congo. Ruhe notes the effect of late tectonic deformation on the surfaces in the vicinity of the Western Rift Valley. He states (pp. 19–22) that three peneplains recognized by Lepersonne are in fact one and the same warped and faulted end-Tertiary surface. However, Ruhe's dating of this surface in relation to the evolution of the Western Rift Valley seems to require some revision in the light of present knowledge of the stratigraphy within the rift.

His comment (p. 6) that the comparative dating method employed by King, involving the period of termination of each cycle at the coast, is valid only 'if the cycle of erosion is initiated or terminated at the coast', is particularly relevant in Uganda, where the bulk of the drainage ceased to be sea-controlled or coast-controlled from the moment when the headwaters of the Congo drainage were severed by the inception of the Western Rift Valley. The Aswa drainage in northern Uganda provides an exception, reacting directly to a Nile-Mediterranean base-level. Here may be the reason for McConnell's low-level Acholi surface in northern Uganda. The remainder of the drainage of Uganda has been subject to tectonic controls by rifting rather than by influences operating on the continental margin.

Ruhe observes that the 'end-Tertiary surface' (to accept for the

present this label for the feature) in Uganda extends westwards to
the top of the Lake Albert escarpment at Butiaba. Concluding
(pp. 33–6, Fig. 7) that the ancestors of the present day Nkusi/Kafu,
Katonga and Kagera rivers drained westwards *on the end-Tertiary
surface* across the present location of the Albert–Semliki–Edward Rift
Valley to the ancestral Congo river, he suggests that Plio-Pleistocene
warping of the surface ensued, culminating in rifting. On this view,
the end-Tertiary surface in Uganda was downthrown relative to the
Ituri surface, which was in its turn upwarped relative to the end-
Tertiary surface of the Congo basin. Such an interpretation allows
for the asymmetry of the two walls of the rift with the 'end-Tertiary'
surface rising to 7000 ft a.s.l. west of the rift but to no more than
4000 ft a.s.l. to the east in Uganda. The present writer would agree
with these correlations, and also with the scheme of events which
culminated in the beheading of the Congo drainage by rifting. However, the date of this beheading and rifting event as Plio-Pleistocene
or 'end-Tertiary' is open to question: it must in fact have been much
earlier.

The date of initiation of faulting seems to relate to the suggestion
that the Kaiso-Kisegi Beds (for the fauna of which a Plio-Pleistocene
age is suggested) *rest on the downthrown end-Tertiary surface* within
the rift, and also that the Muzizi Valley, which hangs above the
southeast wall of the Albertine rift, is floored with *Kisegi sediments
of the same age as the earliest rift accumulations*, suggesting that these
beds were formed before the main rifting. Ruhe (p. 17) concludes
that 'the Plio-Pleistocene date of rifting is firmly established'. But
these conclusions are incorrect: so much is seen from the stratigraphy
of the Western Rift.

(a) Near Kaiso on Lake Albert occur the oldest deposits within the
Albertine Rift of which the age can be considered firmly established.
Mammalian fauna from sediments outcropping between lake-level
and about 300 ft above is of Lower Villafranchian or lowest
Pleistocene age (Bishop, in press). Unfortunately no boreholes
have been sunk on the Kaiso spit itself, to prove the depth of pre-
Pleistocene sediments below the Kaiso Series at this point. However, there is no irregularity in the Bouguer contours for this part
of the geophysical survey of the Lake Albert Basin, so that Lower
Villafranchian sediments seem not to rest on, or only to overlie at
shallow depth, the pre-Cambrian basement rocks.

(b) In the Lake Edward Basin, rocks of identical lithology but yielding a smaller mammalian assemblage than those at Kaiso, are also
of Lower Pleistocene age. They outcrop above lake-level for some

10 miles south of the Kazinga Channel. Bouguer contours seem here again to imply considerable depth of Pre-Pleistocene sediments, although by contrast the geophysical evidence suggests a thin veneer of Quaternary deposits in the Lake George basin.

(c) In the Lake Albert Rift, a borehole near Butiaba penetrated more than 4000 ft of sediment before running into the crystalline rocks of the rift wall (Harris and others 1956). There was no suggestion that rocks of the Kaiso Series, equivalent to those outcropping at lake-level only 30 miles to the southwest, occurred at or near the base of this hole. Indeed, the Geological Survey noted that lithology suggested assignment of the first 1700 ft at most of the record to the Kaiso Series and younger strata. The preceding 1600 ft would then be equivalent to the Kisegi Series, and the bottom 700 ft would belong to (?)Miocene.

(d) Although the Butiaba hole ran into the rift wall at 4000 ft it served as an excellent density control for the geophysical observations. Recorded gravity anomalies imply a thickness of some 8000 or 9000 ft of sediment in the axial region of the rift (Brown 1956). The beds penetrated near the escarpment seem unlikely to thicken lakeward; a great thickness of pre-Pleistocene sediment (much of it possibly Miocene, or older) is presumably implied by these observations.

(e) Borehole evidence at the south end of Lake Albert, where the rift sediments lap on to the fault block of the northern nose of Ruwenzori, shows at least 1132 ft of Kisegi Beds underlying typical Kaiso deposits of presumed Lower Villafranchian age (Harris and others 1956, p. 9). Additional boreholes nearby, commencing in typical Kaiso Series at the surface, penetrated as much as 1900 ft of sediments without striking the underlying pre-Cambrian rocks.

(f) It is presumably in this area at the northern nose of the Ruwenzori block that Kaiso-Kisegi Beds (thought to be of Plio-Pleistocene age) are considered to rest on an erosion-surface downfaulted within the rift. But in this unbalanced region, the graben of the Albertine rift changes its form within a few miles, to become the major horst-like uptilted structure of Ruwenzori. In such an area, interplay of uplift and downfaulting has in all probability resulted in local nonsequence and unconformity with alternating transgression. A fully-preserved depositional sequence is most unlikely. The fact that deposits of the Kisegi Series, or even locally of the Kaiso Series, rest in this area on Pre-Cambrian crystalline rocks need not mean that they come at the base of the whole sequence within the graben, or that they were the earliest deposits formed after the initiation of rifting. The palaeontological, geophysical and borehole evidence within the rift suggests that much older deposits of considerable thickness occur in the graben, farther from the consistently upward-thrusting nose of Ruwenzori.

(g) Mammalian fossils which recall those of the Kenya Lower Miocene have been found in the eastern Congo section of the rift some 20 miles west of Lake Albert (Hopwood and Lepersonne 1953). The deposits which include the fauna consist of some 250 ft of sandstones, grits and conglomerates, resting on a basal lateritic formation which has been correlated tentatively with the mid-Tertiary peneplain. In addition, Lepersonne describes a local occurrence of sedimentary rocks beneath the basal laterite. These sediments have been provisionally assigned to the Karroo on grounds of lithology, and similar sediments in the deeper parts of the Uganda section of the rift may also be as old as Karroo. Lepersonne observes that there must be a distinct time-break between these Congo Miocene deposits and the overlying Kaiso Series, while de Heinzelin (personal communication), in a recent survey in the Congo section of the Lower Semliki Valley, found fossils suggestive of a Mio/Pliocene age in deposits lithologically similar to the Kisegi Series.

(h) Despite the correlation of Ruhe, there is in fact no evidence of the age of the Muzizi sandstones, or of similar deposits occurring in identical situations in the Nkusi and Katonga through-valleys. Although a tentative correlation with the Kisegi Series has been suggested, other geologists have considered them possibly as old as Karroo.

(j) Lepersonne suggests on the Congo evidence that at least four periods of faulting have affected the western rift, namely, post-Semliki-Series, post-Kaiso and pre-Semliki-Series, ( ?)pre-Kaiso, pre-Miocene. The faulting mainly responsible for the graben he considers to be pre-Kaiso in age, but there is no evidence to show whether it is also pre-Miocene.

(k) The lithology of the Kaiso Series, as compared with the later Semliki Series, leads Bishop (1962 and in press) to suggest that during the deposition of the Kaiso Series the level of Lake Albert probably coincided with the 'hanging base line' of Wayland (1925). If so, the amount of throw in post-Kaiso times was small compared to the total inferred displacement of approximately 10,000 feet measured against the top of the Uganda rift wall (Fig. 6).

Considerably more sediment is represented in the downfault block of the graben than the 1000 ft estimated by Bailey Willis (1936).

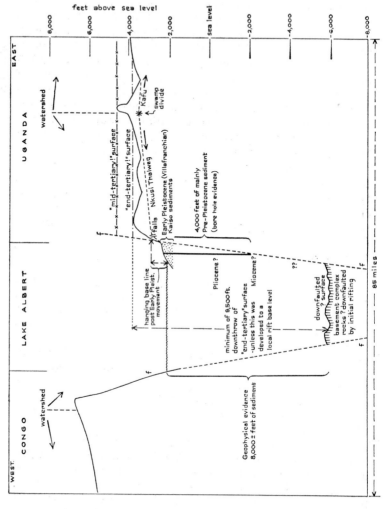

Fig. 6. Diagrammatic cross-section of the Albertine Rift Valley, western Uganda

Willis's total influenced Bullard's interpretation of his gravity results, and also probably coloured the views of other workers until the true situation was established with the publication of the results of the Geological Survey in 1956. The age of the initial rift-faulting is still rather uncertain, but is probably pre-Miocene at least and may well be older still. It would certainly appear much earlier than Plio-Pleistocene. Hence inferences about the age of the adjacent erosion-surface need revision in the light of more detailed field observations (Fig. 6).

Dating of the establishment of local base-levels in the western rift to some time before the Plio-Pleistocene is particularly important in view of the control which faulting exercised in Uganda, both on the initiation of local erosion-cycles and on preventing the extension into Uganda of cyclic erosion originating at the coast.

### Late Pleistocene Deformation associated with the rise to the rift shoulders

During the Earlier Pleistocene the Kagera River was one of the major rivers which drained westwards from central Uganda into the Western Rift Valley. With the major post-Kaiso (post-Villafranchian) fault movement which rejuvenated the rivers and caused a relative lowering of the rift valley floor, there seems to have been associated a rise of the shoulders of the rift, uplifting the area east of the rift valley. The tilting, although possibly intermittent, ultimately ponded-up lakes, or greatly increased the area of existing lakes in the headwaters of the major rivers. These lakes were the forerunners of Lakes Kyoga and Victoria.

As the uplift continued well into the later Pleistocene, the initial lakes extended much farther to the west than those of today. They may for some time have continued to discharge to the west, until up-tilting on that side forced the waters to retreat eastwards, stranding their former shorelines and deposits. Overflow took place through other outlets, as uplift to the west exceeded the rate of downcutting by rivers.

An arm of Lake Victoria, occupying the Kagera Valley during the Middle Pleistocene, extended as a long finger-like embayment some 70 miles west of the present shoreline into the Nsongezi area (Fig. 3). To the west of the extremity of this embayment, the river passes through a narrow gorge cut in pre-Cambrian Karagwe-Ankolean quartzites, which uplift converted into an excellent natural dam behind which a lake was impounded. The tilting, which initiated and was eventually to end the lacustrine phase at Nsongezi, also resulted in the reversal of the Kagera River, causing it to flow in its present direction eastwards to Lake Victoria across the former lake deposits. These remain underlying extensive flats on either side of the river, and about 100 ft above it.

In 1930, cuts for a new road from Kagera Port to Kikagati exposed, in the lake deposits near Nsongezi, a rich artifact horizon, of which Wayland (1934, etc.), Solomon (1939), and Bishop (in press) describe the stratigraphical relations, while O'Brien (1939) and Lowe (1952) describe the typology. The lower deposits of the series are not well exposed, but extensive trial excavation by Wayland provides a number of good sections through typical lacustrine or estuarine sands and clays. The artifact level, which is probably best referred to as the M–N horizon, includes abundant Acheulean material with some tools of Sangoan type. The artifacts which are usually slightly rolled, are mixed on the M–N horizon with sub-angular boulders and blocks of grey quartzite—the raw materials of manufacture. The horizon marks a temporary fall in the lake-level during which rocks and debris used by man accumulated as lag material on or near the almost flat top of the old lake deposits.

The fall in lake-level was probably of climatic origin. It was of short duration and small amplitude, for the deposits under the M–N horizon are little weathered and indicate but slight erosion of the unconsolidated lake beds at the relevant period. When the lake-level rose again, it effectively sealed the artifact horizon and subjected the tools to no more than slight rolling. Lenses of beach-like gravel and sand sometimes overlie the stone tools, but normal lacustrine or estuarine conditions were soon re-established after the submergence.

Subsequent to the formation of the M–N horizon, tilting continuing throughout the Middle into the Later Pleistocene gradually converted the Nsongezi area into a swamp. The top of the lacustrine sequence consists of variable, slightly gritty, grey swamp-clays. These are well seen in a series of erosion gullies which, near Nsongezi, expose up to 20 ft of the deposits. Sections in the grey clay show horizons irregularly reddened or with ferruginous mottling or dark humic layers resembling palaeosols. Abundant artifacts, derived from temporary landsurfaces within the swamp clays, can be collected in the erosion gullies. The assemblage is middle Sangoan (Lowe 1952, O'Brien 1939), and includes beautifully made tranchets, lances and points in grey quartzite and white vein quartz, all of which date from a much later period than the implements of the M–N horizon.

The upper assemblages must be assigned to the later part of Pleistocene, by which time the head of the lake embayment at Nsongezi had become a shallow swamp. This, at least during dry periods, allowed man to hunt and possibly to live on the flats. But with the periodic return of moist conditions, valley bottoms were abandoned, and artifacts left to become buried and preserved under 6 to 12 ft of swamp clay.

Near the Kalambo Falls at the southern end of Lake Tanganyika, Clark (1962) has excavated a series of artifact horizons, where a radiocarbon date of 57,300 ± 300 B.P. fixes an Acheulean horizon, and a series of dates in the range 40,000–43,000 B.P. applies to overlying Sangoan industries. In the absence of more accurate dating, these indications might place the Acheulo-Sangoan assemblage of the M–N horizon in the bracket 50,000 B.P. or thereabouts.

Within the last 25,000 years, uptilt to the west finally caused the swamp fringes at the head of the valley to dry out completely; by that time, the lake waters had also gone. The Kagera River cut below the flat top of the lake beds, so that these now form terrace-like platforms, approximately parallel to the thalweg of the river but 100 ft above it. At Nsongezi the negative break of slope on the strand-line, at the junction of the former lake deposits and their old cliff line, is now 400 ft above Lake Victoria. The break appears to pass eastwards (= down-valley) into a strandline of Lake Victoria at about 100 ft A.L. [Above Lake], implying a relative westerly uptilt of about 300 ft in the 70 miles between the lake-shore and Nsongezi.

Uptilt of this extent has taken place during not more than the latter half of the Later Pleistocene; it is a visible expression of the continued tectonic movements associated with the rift valley, which commenced at the beginning of the Middle Pleistocene. The swamps and lakes typical of central Uganda are then features of extremely late Pleistocene origin.

*Conclusion*

In East Africa, as in other parts of the world, it seems essential to recall from time to time Charles Lapworth's assertion that geomorphology is the child both of geology and of geography, and that the separation of either parent from the offspring would be to the detriment of the whole family. In particular, the stratigraphical aspects of the subject call for further detailed studies before the full geomorphological potential of the East African landscape can be analysed. If a stratigraphical approach can be coupled with the application of recently-developed geographical techniques of morphological mapping, an accurately dated sequence of landsurfaces should emerge.

## References

Baker, B. H., 1963. 'Geology of the Baragoi Area.' Report No. 53, Geological Survey of Kenya, Nairobi.

Binge, F. W., 1961. 'Geology of the Kericho Area.' Report. No. 50, Geological Survey of Kenya, Nairobi.

Bishop, W. W., 1958. 'Miocene mammalia from the Napak Volcanics, Karamoja, Uganda.' *Nature*, 182, 1480–2.

Bishop, W. W., 1962. 'The mammalian fauna and geomorphological relations of the Napak Volcanics, Karamoja.' *Rec. Geol. Surv. Uganda*, 1957-8, 1–18.

Bishop, W. W., 1963. *The Later Tertiary and Pleistocene in Eastern Equatorial Africa*. Viking Fund Publications in Anthropology.

Bishop, W. W., in press. 'Pleistocene Stratigraphy in Uganda.' Memoir No. 10, Geol. Surv. Uganda.

Bishop, W. W., and Whyte, F., 1962. 'Tertiary mammalian faunas and sediments in Karamoja and Kavirondo, East Africa.' *Nature*, Vol. 196, No. 4861, 1283–7.

Brown, J. M., 1956. in Harris *et al.*, 'Oil in Uganda.' Memoir No. IX, Geol. Surv. of Uganda, Entebbe.

Caswell, P. V., 1956. 'Geology of the Kilifi–Mazeras Area.' Report No. 34, Geol. Surv. of Kenya, Nairobi.

Challinor, J., 1961. *A Dictionary of Geology*. Univ. of Wales Press, Cardiff.

Clark, J. D., 1962. 'Carbon 14 Chronology in Africa South of the Sahara,' pp. 303-13—*4th Pan. Af. Cong. Prehistory*.

Cooke, H. B. S., 1958. 'Observations relating to Quaternary environments in East and Southern Africa.' *Bull. Geol. Soc. S. Africa*. (Annexure) 1–73.

Dixey, F., 1945. 'The relation of the main peneplain of Central Africa to sediments of Lower Miocene Age.' *Quart. Journ. Geol. Soc. London*, 101, Pts 3 and 4, 243–53.

Dixey, F., 1948. 'Geology of Northern Kenya.' Report No. 15, Geol. Surv. Kenya.

Dixey, F., 1956. 'Erosion surfaces in Africa; some considerations of age and origin.' *Trans. Geol. Soc. S. Africa*, 59, 1–16.

Eames, F. E., and others, 1962. *Fundamentals of Mid-Tertiary Stratigraphical Correlation*. Cambridge Univ. Press.

Eames, F. E., and Kent, P. E., 1955. 'Miocene beds of the East African Coast.' *Geol. Mag.*, 92, 344.

Evernden, J. F., 1959. 'First results of research on the dating of Tertiary and Pleistocene rocks by the potassium/argon Method.' *Proc. Geol. Soc. London*, No. 1565, 17–19.

Evernden, J. F., and Curtis, G. H., 1962. 'Age of basalt underlying Bed I, Olduvai.' *Nature*, 194, 611–12.

Fleuty, M. J., in press. 'Explanation of the geology of Sheet 27 (Moroto).' Report, Geol. Surv. Uganda.

Harris, N., and others, 1956. 'Oil in Uganda.' Memoir No. IX, Geol. Surv. of Uganda, Entebbe.

Hartman, J. A., 1955. 'Origin of heavy minerals in Jamaican bauxite.' *Econ. Geol.*, 50, 738–47.

Hopwood, A. T., and Lepersonne, J., 1953. 'Présence de Formation d'age Miocene inférieur dans le fosse tectonique du lac Albert et de la basse Semliki.' *Ann. Soc. Geol. Belge*, 77, 83–113.

Kent, P. E., 1944. 'The Miocene of Kavirondo, Kenya.' *Quart. Journ. Geol. Soc.*, 100, 85–118.

King, B. C., 1949. 'The Napak Area of southern Karamoja, Uganda.' Memoir No. V, Geol. Surv. Uganda.

King, B. C., 1958. 'The geomorphology of Africa.' *Science Progress*, 15, 672–81; 16, 97–107.

King, L. C., 1948. 'A theory of Bornhardts.' *Geog. Journ.*, 112, 83–7.

King, L. C., 1949. 'On the ages of African land-surfaces.' *Quart. Journ. Geol. Soc.*, 104, 439–59.

King, L. C., 1951. *South African Scenery*. (2nd edn.) Oliver and Boyd, Edinburgh.

King, L. C., 1962. *Morphology of the Earth*. Oliver and Boyd, Edinburgh.

Leakey, L. S. B., 1962. 'A new Lower Pliocene Primate from Kenya.' *Ann. Mag. Nat. Hist.*, 4, No. 47, 689–94.

Lepersonne, J., 1956. 'Les aplanissements d'érosion du nord-est du Congo Belge et des regions voisines.' *Acad. Roy. Sci. Col.*, IV fasc., 7, 1–108.

Lowe, C. Van Riet., 1952. 'The Pleistocene geology and prehistory of Uganda: Pt. II, Prehistory.' Memoir No. VI, Geol. Surv. Uganda, Entebbe.

Macdonald, R., 1961. 'Explanation of the geology of Sheet 36. (Nabilatuk).' Report No. 5, Geol. Surv. Uganda.

McCall, G. J. H., 1958. 'Geology of the Gwasi Area.' Report No. 45, Geol. Surv. Kenya, Nairobi.

McConnell, R. B., 1955. 'The erosion surfaces of Uganda.' *Col. Geol. Min. Res.*, 5, 425–8.

McKinlay, A. C. M., 1956. 'The Karroo System.' in *Summary of the Geology of Tanganyika Part I*, p. 81 et seq. Geol. Surv. Tangan.

O'Brien, T. P., 1939. 'Prehistory of Uganda Protectorate.' *Camb. Univ. Press.*

Ollier, C. D., 1960. 'The Inselbergs of Uganda.' *Zeitschrift für Geomorphologie*, 4 (I), 43–52.

Pallister, J. W., 1954. 'Erosion levels and laterite in Buganda Province, Uganda.' *C.R. 19th Geol. Congr.*, 21, 193–9.

Pallister, J. W., 1956a. 'Slope development in Buganda.' *Geog. Journ.*, 122, 80–7.

Pallister, J. W., 1956b. 'Slope form and erosion surfaces in Uganda.' *Geol. Mag.*, 93, 465–72.

Pallister, J. W., 1959. 'The geology of Southern Mengo.' Geol. Surv. Uganda, Report I, 1–124.

Pallister, J. W., 1960. 'Erosion cycles and associated surfaces of Mengo District, Buganda.' *Overseas Geol. & Min. Res.*, 8, No. 1, 26–36.

Pulfrey, W., 1960. 'Shape of the Sub-Miocene erosion bevel in Kenya.' Bulletin No. 3, Geol. Surv. Kenya, Nairobi.

Ruhe, R. V., 1954. 'Erosion surfaces of Central African Interior High Plateaus.' *Publ. Inst. Nat. Agron. du Congo Belge.* No. 59, 1–40.

Ruxton, B. P., and Berry, L., 1959. 'The basal rock surface on weathered granitic rocks.' *Proc. Geol. Assoc.*, 70, 285–90.

Saggerson, E. P., 1952. 'Geology of the Kisumu District.' Report No. 21, Geol. Surv. Kenya, Nairobi.

Shackleton, R. M., 1945. 'Geology of the area between Nanyuki and Maralal.' Report No. 9, Geol. Surv. Kenya, Nairobi.

Shackleton, R. M., 1946. 'Geology of the Migori Gold Belt.' Report No. 10, Geol. Surv. of Kenya, Nairobi.

Shackleton, R. M., 1951. 'A contribution to the geology of the Kavirondo Rift Valley.' *Quart. Journ. Geol. Soc.*, 106, 345–92.

Solomon, J. D., 1939. in O'Brien 1939, q.v.

Thompson, A. O., 1956. 'Geology of the Malindi Area.' Report No. 36, Geol. Surv. Kenya, Nairobi.

Thornbury, W. D., 1954. *Principles of Geomorphology.* John Wiley & Sons, Inc., New York.

Trendall, A. F., 1959. 'The topography under the northern part of the Kadam Volcanics.' *Records Geol. Surv. Uganda.*, 1955–6, 1–8.

Trendall, A. F., 1961. 'Explanation of the geology of Sheet 45 (Kadam).' Report No. 6, Geol. Surv. Uganda.

Trendall, A. F., 1962. 'The formation of "apparent peneplains" by a process of combined laterization and surface wash.' *Zeit. für Geomorph.* 6 (2), 183–97.

Trendall, A. F., in press. 'Explanation of the geology of Sheet 35 (Napak).' Report, *Geol. Surv. Uganda.*

Wayland, E. J., 1921. Annual Report, Geol. Surv. Uganda, 1920, 10 ff.

Wayland, E. J., 1926. Annual Report, Geol. Surv. Uganda, 1925.

Wayland, E. J., 1933. 'The peneplains of East Africa.' *Geog. Journ.*, 82, 95.

Wayland, E. J., 1934. 'The peneplains of East Africa.' *Geog. Journ.*, 83, 79.

Whitworth, T., 1961. 'The geology of Mfwanganu Island, Western Kenya.' *Overseas Geol. & Min. Res.* 8, No. 2, 150–90. HMSO, London.

Williams, L. A. J., 1962. 'Geology of the Hadu-Fundi Isa Area, North of Malindi.' Report No. 52, Geol. Surv. Kenya, Nairobi.

Willis, B., 1936. *East African Plateaus and Rift Valleys.* Carnegie Inst., Washington.

# The Weathering of Limestones

## With Particular Reference to the Carboniferous Limestones of Northern England

## M. M. SWEETING

### Introduction

This essay touches upon many aspects of the weathering of limestones, but is particularly concerned with the weathering of the Carboniferous Limestone of northern England. It describes some recent observations and experiments connected with the origin of certain features of the Limestones. It attempts to interpret the role of solution, particularly in the light of modern chemical studies on limestones.

As is well known, the Carboniferous Limestone over a good proportion of its outcrop in the north of England gives rise to variously weathered bare rock surfaces. Recent work has contributed additional knowledge and ideas of their origin (Corbel 1957, Moisley 1953–4, Parry 1960). The main outcrops of the Carboniferous Limestone dealt with here are those in the Ingleborough district of northwest Yorkshire, and those in the dissected blocks surrounding the Lake District in northwest England. Though limestone beds occur at every height from sea-level to about 1700 ft, they do not form the highest land either in the Pennines or in northwest England. Extensive bare rock outcrops occur below 1000 ft, as at Hutton Roof Crag and at Farleton Fell, but the greatest expanses of bare rock are normally found above 1000 ft; in places, over a fifth of the total surface area consists of bare limestone (Fig. 1).

In northwest Yorkshire the total maximum thickness of the Carboniferous Limestone proper (i.e. The Great Scar Limestone) is about 600 ft, excluding the limestones within the Yoredale Series; in northwest England, where the rocks were deposited in a different environment, greater thicknesses occur, for instance, over 1000 ft in Ravenstonedale (Garwood 1912, Garwood and Goodyear 1924). The structure of these limestones is relatively simple. In northwest Yorkshire they have gentle dips varying from $\frac{1}{2}$ to 5 degrees, lying on a rigid foundation of older rocks and forming part of the Askrigg

Block (Marr 1921, Bott 1961). Surrounding the Lake District the limestones occur in a series of fault blocks with varying dips, from a few degrees to about 30 degrees, as at Hutton Roof Crag. In both regions, the effects of faulting are of great importance in the development of the landscape (Wager 1931). The lithology of the limestones is very variable in all the areas named and has been discussed in many contexts (Garwood 1912, Garwood and Goodyear 1924, Schwarzacher 1958). Variations are of fundamental importance in any consideration of weathering. Essentially the Carboniferous Limestones in northern England consist of two main types of beds: (a) more massive, usually purer limestone beds, in which the vertical joint planes are the dominant lines of weakness; and (b) thinner, usually less pure, beds in which the horizontal bedding-planes replace the joints as the dominant lines of weakness; these beds are frequently argillaceous or ferruginous bands. Though the thinner and more shaly beds tend to be more frequent towards the base, they occur at all levels in the limestone sequence. A measured section from the Great Scar Limestone on the northern slopes of the Ingleborough massif is shown in Fig. 2.

Where the Carboniferous Limestone is more or less horizontally bedded, as in the Pennine Dales, the relief is made up of the much-described alternation of cliffs (scars) and benches. Where the limestone dips, as in other parts of northwest England, sloping surfaces—often coincident with the bedding-planes—alternate with joint-faces forming the deep scars (Plate 21). The scars or cliffs excellently exemplify bare rock faces and screes are associated with them. Large portions of the platforms between the scars also consist of bare rock, forming the areas of the well-known limestone pavements (Kendall and Wroot 1924). Goodchild (1875) was the first to give an adequate explanation of the 'step-and-stair' relief. He recognized the stripping of less competent beds along the bedding-planes, and deduced that the relief was basically due to some form of glacial scour upon beds of varying resistance; and that 'the effect of ice erosion was to impart to the rock surfaces a flowing contour, and an association of scars and terraces which are quite different from what would naturally result from simple atmospheric erosion' (Goodchild 1890). This step-and-stair relief should be compared with the equally glaciated and scoured area of the Burren in County Clare, western Ireland. In the Burren, where the Carboniferous Limestone beds are of a distinctly uniform lithology with relatively few shale bands, glacial scour has produced less conspicuous scars and ledges, and has given a smooth and rounded relief, rather like 'boiler-plating' when compared with that of northern England. The Burren also possesses limestone pavements,

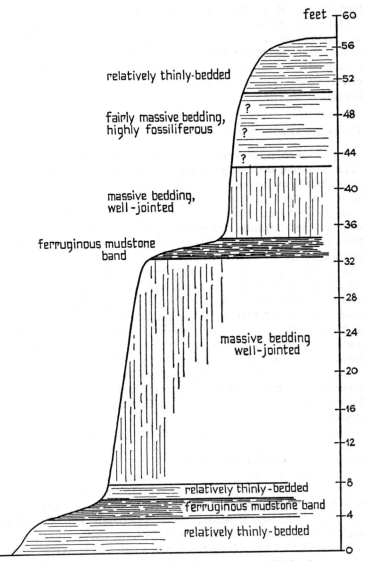

feet

relatively thinly-bedded

fairly massive bedding,
highly fossiliferous

massive bedding,
well-jointed

ferruginous mudstone
band

massive bedding
well-jointed

relatively thinly-bedded
ferruginous mudstone band
relatively thinly-bedded

Fig. 2. Measured Section at Salt Lake Quarry, Ribblehead.

but these occur in a slightly different context from those already mentioned (Praeger 1947, Sweeting 1955).

Differential erosion and scour by ice upon beds of distinctly varying strength have, then, been important factors in the development of the landforms of the limestones in northern England. Certain of these landforms will now be closely examined to ascertain the effects of present-day weathering and the extent to which the glacial relief is being modified.

### The Scars and the Screes

A generalized section to show the relief and the relative positions of the scars and the benches or ledges is given in Fig. 3. Vertical scars coincide with outcrops of relatively pure and massively-bedded limestone. The top and base of each scar is marked by the presence of strongly developed bedding-planes, and by the exposure of a band in which the horizontal bedding-planes become highly significant in the structure of the rock; frequently, argillaceous layers outcrop (Schwarzacher 1958). Where thinly-bedded limestone caps the top of a scar in which the joints are well-developed there occur overhanging ledges from beneath which the more jointed rock weathers out, as on Blue Scars near Arncliffe (Hughes 1901). Where the beds are thick and massive, scars form conspicuous vertical cliffs more than 15 metres high, but if the limestone includes numerous shaly partings, a greater number of smaller scars are formed: compare for instance the relatively few but fine high scars of Twisleton Dale with the more numerous lower ones in Kingsdale. The various lithological and fossil bands are occasionally important in scar formation; in the Ingleborough district the *Cyrtina Septosa* band usually forms a conspicuous scar, as at Sulber Scar.

The morphology of the scars depends upon the lithology of the limestone and upon the frequency of the jointing. Scars in the most massively-bedded limestones are made up of rectangular blocks 1–2 metres long, and have a rather columnar appearance, as in High Howeth near Chapel-le-Dale. Other scars in beds of medium thickness have a blocky appearance, like those at the southern end of Twisleton Scars near Ingleton. In the neighbourhood of fault lines, such as along the Craven and Dent Faults, the frequency of jointing is increased, with joints but a few inches apart. The scars then consist of thin vertical slabs, often resembling tombstones, as in Clapdale and in Chapel-le-Dale. If the rock is shattered along other lines of weakness in addition to those of the master joints, the scar-and-platform pattern may be replaced by less regular relief, as along the

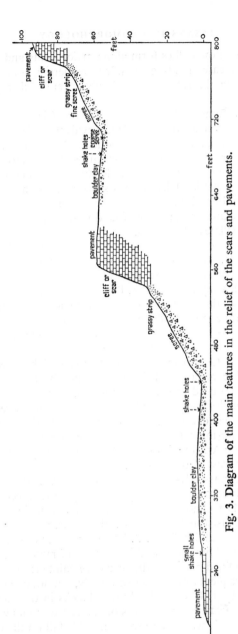

Fig. 3. Diagram of the main features in the relief of the scars and pavements.

G

Dent Fault. Shallow gullies form along major joints and small fault lines, where increased jointing has aided weathering, notably on Long Scars and along the small Sulber Fault, where Sulber Nick is so formed.

Certain scars, among them Kilnsey Crag and Clapdale Scars, show definite signs of glacial rounding. Other evidences of glacial smoothing occur, particularly where diffluent ice spilt over from one valley into another. Traces of glacial scour caused by the moving ice can still be seen on Smearsett Scar above Ribblesdale, and on the Norber Scars. Near Chapel-le-Dale, vertical slab-like scars have been truncated by glacial erosion, the limestone appearing to be scaling or exfoliating; isolated striae can be found in sheltered positions in the same locality (Plates 21 and 22).

The present rate of dislodgement of the blocks which form scars is very variable. Where the limestone is thinly-bedded or greatly jointed, as in the 'tombstone' type of scar, blocks are rapidly dislodged and fall away every winter. Roots of grass and trees, penetrating lines of weakness, assist frost-heaving and solution. Thinly-bedded limestone tends to flake off in thin slices along the 'bate' of the rock; observations made by Goodchild in 1890 suggested that the combined rate of flaking and solution in such limestones was about one inch (2 cm) in 300–500 years (Goodchild 1890). Some thinly-bedded scars have so disintegrated since the last glaciation that they are now reduced to small cliffs which, only a foot or so high, protrude through flat-weathered limestone slabs and scree. In areas of more thinly-bedded rock, scree belts or scree ridges separated by grassy strips are important features of the limestone landscape, as is well shown on Arnside Knott near Morecambe Bay and on Hawkeswick Clowder west of the Wharfe.

In the more massively-bedded scars, however, the rate of removal of individual blocks appears today to be very slow. A record has been kept since 1949 to find out what movements occur in a part of the scar behind Twisleton Dale House, about three miles northeast of Ingleton and about 1200 ft a.s.l. The scar under examination is in massively-bedded limestone and is from 10–15 metres high. In 1949, certain well-defined blocks in the scar were painted; these have been inspected at frequent intervals subsequently, but not one had become dislodged by 1961. It seems likely that blocks in the more massive scars only fall away during winters of severe frost; many fell during the winter of 1947, when there was a notable fall on the east side of Malham Cove. Other isolated rockfalls have been noted. In March 1958, after an intense frost, there was a rockfall from a scar above Crystal Beck (Littondale); the largest of the blocks dislodged on this occasion measured $9\frac{1}{2} \times 8\frac{1}{2} \times 3$ ft ($3 \times 2.5 \times 1.0$ metres), weighing $6\frac{1}{2}$ tons: it fell through a vertical distance of 60 ft (18 m). But falls such as this are very rare, and scarcely occur at all in mild winters such as those in 1959–60 and 1960–1 (Plate 21). It seems likely that although scars are affected by dislodgement by frost and by other mechanical action, removal of the limestone by solution is of much greater significance than rock fall, as will be seen below.

The rate of scree formation is much slower today than it must have been at the end of the glacial period and in parts of postglacial time. Though some screes are actively forming at the present day, many are now overgrown with turf and are completely inactive, particularly at lower levels; those at the foot of Kilnsey Crag in Wharfedale are now completely overgrown. At the foot of other scars, however, still-uncovered screes form fan-like expanses. Where the jointing is close and scree formation is particularly active, shallow U-shaped recessions of the scars occur, as above Ullet Gill in Twisleton Dale. Areas of less active scree formation become overgrown, strips of active scree alternating with vegetated scree, as below Moughton Scars, in Crummackdale. The extent of accumulation varies mainly with the height of the scar; screes of 30–40 ft (10–12 metres) are common, and in localities where the scars are particularly well-developed, screes of over 100 ft (30 metres) have formed, as in Gordale and at Whitbarrow Scar west of Kendal. On some of the bigger screes—those near Middle House and on Moughton—poorly-developed stone assortment can be seen; rudimentary stone striping also occurs at Moughton on scars at over 1000 ft. At the present time frost action is only likely on areas above about 1600 ft, and much of the poorly-developed patterned ground on the limestone screes probably dates from climatic phases more severe than the present.

The composition of the scree varies with the type of scar. Scree formed below massively-bedded rock consists of large blocks, but consists of thin flaky fragments below thinly-bedded limestone. The bigger blocks tend to roll to the base, while the finer material remains in the upper part (Plate 21). Between the base of the scar and the top of the scree there is frequently a narrow belt of vegetation (usually *Sesleria cerulaea*), its outlines following closely the surface outlines of the scar. This vegetation is probably nourished by water seeping out from the shaly bands at the lower limits of the scars, as is well shown on Sulber Scar.

It is difficult to get an accurate idea of the rate of movement of the scree material. Individual limestone blocks are often cemented together by thin tufa deposits which, particularly towards the foot of the scree, fix fragments and arrest their downward movement. In 1949, blocks in a well-developed scree on Twisleton Scar were marked

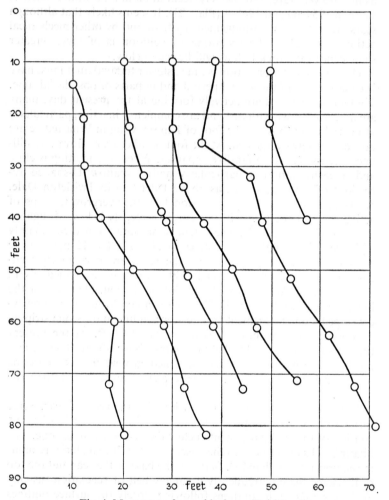

Fig. 4. Movement of scree-blocks on Twisleton Scar.

out in 10 ft intervals, and have subsequently been examined at intervals. The diagram (Fig. 4) shows the movements of individual blocks. As would be expected, maximum movement has occurred in the upper and middle parts; less movement has occurred in the blocks at the base. Movement in the upper part is predominantly vertically downward, but is rather diagonally outward in the lower part, accounting for the fan-like form of the scree.

Two pits were dug into two different screes about 30 ft (10 metres) high, at 6–10 ft (2–3 metres) vertically above the scree foot. Limestone in place was reached in both pits at a depth of 3–4 ft (about 1 metre) from the scree surface, probably indicating an apron of solid rock beneath the scree. In these sections, scree material was coarsest near the surface. These observations lend support to the ideas of Wood on the development of the free face and the constant slope— ideas which came from work in this type of country (Wood 1942).

## The Limestone Pavements

The steep scars and screes alternate with horizontal or sloping platforms (Fig. 3). Such platforms correspond quite often with bedding-planes of the rock. Parts of the platforms consist of bare rock outcrops, forming the well-known limestone pavements. As will be seen from Fig. 3, the inner edges of the platforms tend to be covered with thin deposits of boulder clay, while the pavements occur towards their outer edges. This distribution is largely due to glacial scour on the outer edges of the platforms and of glacial deposition along the feet of scars. The present distribution of the limestone pavements, however, is not entirely natural, for one or two firms have for many years been exploiting surface layers of the limestone in many parts of northern England to produce weather-worn rockery stones for south-country gardens. When the surface rock has been removed in this way, vegetation is frequently able to cover the pavements entirely, with the result that large areas of bare rock have disappeared. Farmers have encouraged the exploitation, which helps to clear the rocky pasture for cattle. The significance of the practice will be dealt with later.

The pavements consist essentially of straight-sided or furrowed blocks of limestone called *clints*. Each clint has its own dip or slope, which may or may not be the same as the local bedding or the regional dip of the limestone; the clint surface may be flat or furrowed, according to the lithology of the limestone. Deep clefts or widened joints called *grikes* separate the clints. A surveyed area of pavement is shown in Fig. 5; an aerial view is given in Plate 20.

Limestone pavements show an almost infinite morphological variety. Although they may be broadly classified into two main types, no two outcrops of pavement are exactly alike, and all are extremely difficult both to map and to classify. The rapidity of variation is shown in Fig. 5. Many of the hypotheses put forward to classify and to explain their origin have been dependent upon knowledge of only

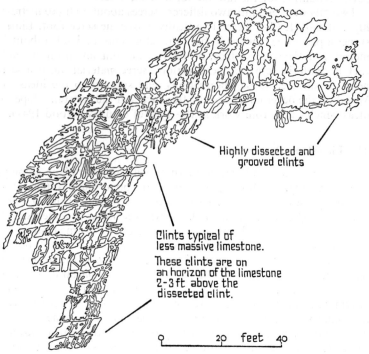

Highly dissected and
grooved clints

Clints typical of
less massive limestone.
These clints are on
an horizon of the limestone
2-3 ft above the
dissected clint.

0          20    feet    40

Fig. 5. Survey of limestone pavement in Chapel-le-Dales.

a few locations. The following factors are mainly responsible for the variations in the morphology of the limestone pavements and for their origin:

the structure and tectonics of the areas concerned, particularly the jointing;
the lithology of the limestones;
the severity of glacial scour during the period of the Newer Drift;
past and present chemical and biological processes, including the grazing of animals; these are also dependent upon climate and altitude.

*Jointing*

Both in the Ingleborough district and in the other areas of north-west England, the Carboniferous Limestone is characterized by strongly-marked faulting and jointing. Were it not for this jointing and faulting there would be no pavements. The variations in frequency, direction, and nature of the faults and joints cause fundamental variations in the morphology of the pavements. The generally rectangular or parallelogram-like plan of the clints is accounted for by the occurrence of two sets of master joints. A typical clint block is about 6 ft by 4 ft (1–2 metres). Grikes are widened joints in the form of ruts, usually about 6–24 in (15–60 cms) wide at the surface, narrowing towards the base. They are somewhat variable in depth, from about 2 ft (0·5 m) to about 12 ft (3 m) or even 15 ft (4·5 m). They correspond to the Alpine features known as *Kluft Karren* (Eckert 1896). The deepest grikes occur where several joints intersect, and where the walls sometimes are rounded into well-like hollows about 15 ft (4·5 m) deep; such hollows resemble the *Karrenröhren* or *lapiés wells* of the Alps (Eckert 1896). The deepest grikes occasionally develop into shallow caves leading under the limestone pavements.

Near fault lines, the jointing increases in frequency and the mesh of the clints becomes finer. In the neighbourhood of the North Craven Fault, near Clapdale, there are stretches of pavement where the greatly increased frequency of the joints has left narrow, almost knife-like clints of less than a foot wide, separated by grikes about 3 ft (1 metre) deep and 1 ft (30 cms) wide. Where two sets of joints are closely spaced, teeth-like residual clints remain. Where the joints become wide apart, the clints enlarge; on Scar Close, near Chapel-le-Dale, uninterrupted and unbroken clint surfaces of over 200 sq yd (170 sq metres) occur. Similar variations in the size of the clints according to the nature of the jointing can be seen in the limestone pavements of the Burren in County Clare.

As would be expected where the directions of the jointing change, the grike directions change also (Wager 1931). Most of the joints are straight and vertical, but other types are found in some massively-bedded limestones. Around Ingleborough, curvilinear and cross-jointing occur (Borrins Moor Rocks, near Alum Pot); at Hutton Roof Crag, west of Kirkby Lonsdale, in addition to the major jointing, there are many cross-joints which form a diagonal pattern (Plate 23). Enlargement of contrasting types of joints has influenced the morphology of the pavements.

*Lithology*

Lithological variations are probably the most important cause of contrast between one pavement and another. Accordingly, pavements are conveniently classified into those of the *thinly-bedded type* and those of the *massively-bedded type*. As a general rule, the thinly-bedded sections of the limestone tend to be strongly affected by mechanical weathering, particularly by frost action, and weakly by solutional weathering; the reverse is true of the more massive sections. Both types of pavement occur in both the Ingleborough district and in northwest England, variations in the lithology of the beds being extremely rapid; in the Ingleborough area, the massive type tend to occur in the western parts of the area, the thinner-bedded type being more common in the east.

In thinly-bedded limestones, the grikes tend to be shallow (usually less than 3 ft (1 m) deep), narrow (1–2 ft (0·5 m) wide), and frequently overgrown with vegetation. The clint surface is flat, not indented by troughs or hollows. The sides are straight, the shape of the clint being determined entirely by the directions and the spacing of the jointing systems. Such clints weather mostly along planes of bedding. The bed forming the surface of the clint is loosened, and in time flakes or peels off; it falls into the grike, exposing a new surface of rock. The off-scaling rock has contrasted upper and lower surfaces; the upper, the former clint surface, is usually smooth and convex, while the lower is rough, less evenly weathered, and usually faintly concave in outline. Thin-edged flakes of this description resemble the *karrenstein* of the Alps (Eckert 1896). The loosened flakes accumulate on the clint surfaces and in the grikes. If the accumulation is rapid, the whole pavement area becomes covered with loosened flags or chippings and takes the name of *shillow* or *shillet*. Shillow-covered pavement occurs on Moughton between Crummack Dale and Ribblesdale, and on Helsington Burrows, near Kendal.

In the massively-bedded sections of the limestones, solution takes place along vertical lines of jointing. The limestone pavements are cut by deep grikes, frequently over 6 ft (2 metres) and occasionally up to 15 ft (4·5 metres) deep. The beds usually consist of hard-blue impermeable limestone and are fairly resistant to frost weathering. The clint surface may be flat and relatively undissected, or cut up and dissected by runnels or grooves, depending upon the type of limestone.

Occasionally, the limestone is little affected by mechanical or chemical weathering or by jointing. The clints are then very flat and undissected by solution furrows and may exceed 100 sq yd (80 sq metres) in area. Pavements of this kind have been closely examined both in the Burren and in northern England. Their occurrence is primarily due to lithology, but strong glacial erosion has probably assisted their formation. The beds forming undissected pavements have been locally mapped on a 6 inch/mile scale both in the Ingleborough area and in the Burren; mapping shows a correlation between the beds and the location of the distinctive pavement form.

Moreover, a preliminary examination of the limestone in thin section suggests that it contains an unusually high percentage of silica, particularly in the form of sand grains in the shell of the foraminifer,

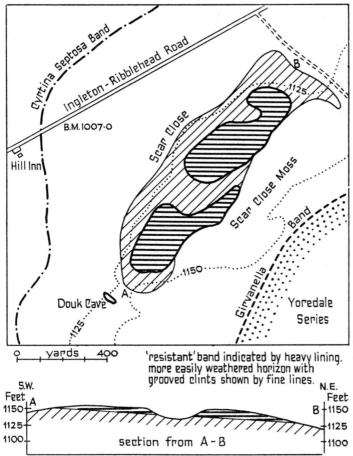

Fig. 6. Part of area of ungrooved pavement in northwest Yorkshire.

*Saccamina*, (probably *fusuliniformis carteri*), which appears to be more abundant in these beds than is usual (Fig. 6). Further work supports this conclusion.

The surface of the massively-bedded clints is, however, usually undulating and dissected by solution of the rock. The main solution-features are either hollows or solution depressions, or well-defined furrows or grooves, or water-cut runnels (Plate 24).

Solution depressions, varying in size from a few millimetres to about 60 cm in diameter, are often aligned in series in the directions of jointing (Plates 24 and 25). Shallow and pan-like, with steep rims and flat bases, they are normally less than 10 cm deep, but can exceed 50 cm. The limestone at their sides and base is usually cockled and fretted by the solution of the water in the pan, contrasting with the surface of the clint, smoothed as it is by the action of algae and lichens. Such solution hollows are like the *kamenitzas* of the Dinaric and Austrian Alps (Bögli 1960). If they remain damp for any length of time, moss and algal spores collect in them, a peaty soil accumulates, and they tend to become colonized by higher vegetation such as *Sesleria caerulaea* and other grasses. They become enlarged both by solution from the water, and by the action of the vegetation which smooths their walls.

Furrows or grooves are the most important form of dissection on the massively-bedded type of clint (Plate 24); they are very characteristic of large stretches of pavement in all parts of northern England and also in the Burren. Furrows begin on the up-dip slope of the clint with little or no collecting ground; they cross the clint in the line of the steepest slope and lead into the grike bounding it on the down-dip side. They may occur singly, or integrated into systems (Fig. 7). Although they form pseudo-dendritic networks and 'run together as the valleys do' (Phillips 1853), furrows have undulating long-profiles and do not resemble channels formed by running water, although they could have been formed by stagnant water. The furrows are rounded and smoothed like the upper surface of the clint, but meet it at a fairly sharp angle. They vary in size, but are typically about 20–30 cm wide and about 30–50 cm deep; their transverse profile is U-shaped, though the walls are sometimes slightly undercut by increased solution at the base. They are usually widest and deepest a short distance above the points where they enter grikes, so that wedge-like or triangular facets of the clint surface are left between them (Fig. 7). The length of the furrows usually but not always varies according to the angle of inclination of the individual clint. Where the clint surface is more or less horizontal or only slightly inclined, furrows tend to range up to 100 cm in length; where the dip of the clint surface is greater than 4 or 5 degrees, furrows of several metres may occur: at Hutton Roof Crag, limestone surfaces dip at from 30–50 degrees and furrows attain lengths as great as 10 metres (Plate 23). Short and long furrows alike are in part similar to the *Rundkarren* described by Bögli (1960), though occasionally they resemble *Rinnen-Karren*.

There is a third type of solution feature which dissects massively-

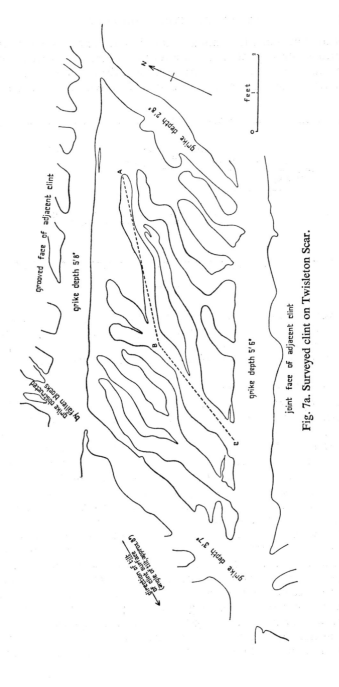

Fig. 7a. Surveyed clint on Twisleton Scar.

bedded clints only. It comprises runnels which have probably been formed by flowing water. They are at least 50–100 cm wide and 50 cm deep and may be as much as 10–15 m long. Examples of these occur at Borrins Moor Rocks near Alum Pot. Such runnels cut diagonally

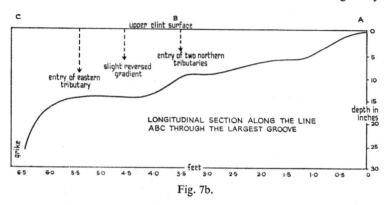

Fig. 7b.

across the clints and are entirely independent of the local outline of the clints. They are also associated with boulder clay, as at Great Runscar, Ribblehead, where they cut a limestone surface inclined at about 70 degrees and are approximately four metres long.

*Effects of glacial erosion*

As we have seen, the original scar-and-ledge relief of northern England is believed to be due essentially to some form of glacial scour. The limestone pavements show many examples of glacial abrasion. On the slopes of Ingleborough, Penyghent, and Whernside, the most striking areas of pavement appear to occur where intensive scour affected the most massively-bedded limestones. In contrast, areas of massive bedding situated in less favourable areas for maximum scour have less well-developed pavements (Fig. 1). In northwest England, the fine pavements on Farleton Fell are similarly the result of the situation of the hill in relation to the advancing ice. In addition, therefore, to the flat planed surfaces caused by glacial grinding, stripped surfaces and glacially scoured ledges occur. The stripped surfaces shown on Borrins Moor Rocks would seem due to glacial erosion. Rounded and scoured ledges with effects of 'boiler-plating' or pseudo-exfoliating resembling the relief of Clare, is typical of some of the homogeneous and massively-bedded sections of the limestone on the slopes of Ingleborough; it is exemplified by the photo of the clints on Scar Close. Such relief could be due to glacial pressure upon the hard sections of the limestones. The more thingly-bedded parts of the limestone are much more likely to have become disintegrated and broken up. The large runnels already described are frequently associated with those pavements which show the most strongly marked glacial effects; while many of these runnels have been caused by the action of peaty waters from the boulder clays, it is tempting to suggest that some at least were formed by glacial meltwater. Glacial meltwater and to some extent snow may also have been responsible for the enlarging and deepening of joints to form grikes. Such meltwater would wash away the residual material formed in a previous non-glacial environment.

It is therefore tempting to believe that glacial scour was responsible for the originally relatively planed surface of the limestone and hence for the original clint surfaces. This view is supported by the survival of occasional striae beneath erratic blocks perched upon the limestone pavements, as at Norber and Newbiggin Crags. The pavements preserved beneath the erratics are usually less dissected than where there are no erratics. The main argument against the contention that the pavements are of glacial origin is the probable extent of post-glacial weathering, the evidence for which will be discussed later.

There is some circumstantial evidence in favour of the suggestion of a glacial origin of clints. It has often been noted that while scars and pavements are characteristic of the limestone in northern England, the Carboniferous Limestone in Derbyshire and in the Mendips does not show any such development; both these areas were ice-free during the period of the Newer Drift (King 1960). In Derbyshire, the many quarries have enabled stripped limestone surfaces to be examined: clint-like surfaces are rare. As a general rule the weathered limestone surface in Derbyshire is quite different from that in northern England.[1] The same is true of the Mendips. Consideration of some of the localities in western Europe where limestone pavements occur also suggests a correlation with recent glacial erosion. Clint-and-grike associations, additional to those named, occur in North Wales, in the highest parts of the Grands Causses of France, in north Norway, in many of the high-level 'déserts' of the French and Swiss Alps, and in a few places on the summits of the Velebit Mountains in Dalmatia (Corbel 1957, de Martonne 1925, Roglič 1931). Completely different weathering-forms, without enlarged joints of the grike type, occur in limestone areas of Mediterranean and Central Europe, where glaciation is known not to have taken place (Cvijic 1924).

[1] See also Pigott, C. D. *The Structure of Limestone Surfaces in Derbyshire*, in 'Denudation in Limestone Regions: a Symposium'. *Geog. Journ.*, Vol. 131, 1965, p 41.

*Chemical and Biological Processes acting upon the Pavements*

The effects of present-day climate are important in any study, since exposure to southwesterly gales affects the rapidity with which the pavements can become colonized by vegetation and overgrown. In general, clints formed at low altitudes have become overgrown and only those at levels above about 1000 ft remain bare. Near the sea in northwest England, however, exposure is great and clints and grikes occur as low as 300–400 ft, as at Warton Crag. Pavements tend to become rather more overgrown to the east; an easterly thickening of cover can be observed in the Ingleborough district.

Within the grikes occurs a shade-loving flora (Proctor 1960). On the clint surfaces, epilithic lichens colonize the bare limestone and eventually cover it entirely, giving it a smooth surface. The hyphae penetrate into the limestone itself (Jones 1957). The lichen cover causes the surface of the rock to remain rather damper than uncovered rock. Endolithic lichens also occur, excavating cavities in the rock and causing rough, careous weathering, so that the limestone becomes pitted with minute holes (Jones, *op. cit.*).

Various evidence suggests that the vegetation of the limestone pavements has varied in postglacial time. Firstly, the peat deposits which occur on many hills of northern England contain tree remains up to about 1700 ft (Raistrick and Blackburn 1932–3). Secondly, within the last 80 years, much juniper scrub has disappeared from areas in the Ingleborough district and in the Morecambe Bay area (Cheetham 1947). Thirdly, the effects of grazing are known to be particularly damaging upon young vegetation, especially trees; it is useful to compare the vegetation on those parts of Warton Crag which have been kept as a nature reserve with that on the nearby Farleton Fell where the grazing has been unrestricted. Fourthly, there is the evidence of ancient enclosures (Raistrick 1946). Fifthly, it has already been noted that if the surface layers of the clints are removed, the pavements tend to diminish in area; this suggests that the pavements are relict landforms and are not being produced under present climatic conditions.

It is, however, difficult to say whether the pavements are increasing or decreasing in extent at the present time: the evidence is somewhat conflicting. It is quite possible that in one place the pavements are tending to become colonized by vegetation, whereas in another they are emerging from their vegetal cover. Thus, Jones (*op. cit.* 1957) holds that the pavements are 'essentially . . . emergent features of the landscape . . . sculptured by solution while lying beneath the drift and vegetation'. However, in many parts of northern England, especially where the limestones are rather thinly-bedded, a pattern of clints and grikes can be shown to exist beneath a turf cover—indicating that the pavements have become overgrown with vegetation, as on the southern slopes of Whernside, on the Great Scar Limestone, and also on the Main Limestone (Yoredale Limestone) on Cam Fell.

With this question in mind, the author has watched closely for the past 13 years a sample of pavement, about 100 sq yd (80 sq m) in area, on Twisleton Scars near Ingleton. This pavement is part of that shown in the survey in Fig. 5. It lies at about 1150 ft above sea-level. Towards the inner edge of the observed pavement (i.e. the side nearest the scar), the grikes are wide and shallow; during the period of observation, the grass has here advanced very slightly (2–5 cm) upon the edge of the clint surface. Towards the middle of the pavement where the grikes are deeper but narrower, the exposed area of clint surface has remained unchanged, but vegetation within the grikes has increased noticeably and the soil is now in some places 10 cm higher than it was when the recordings were first started. Thus in this area of pavement, the grikes show a definite shallowing and filling (Plate 24).

As already noted, furrows which indent the clints resemble the rundkarren of the Alps, which some workers believe have been formed under a soil or vegetational (forest) cover (Bögli, op. cit. 1960). The furrows are certainly different from the sharp *rillenkarren* and *rinnenkarren*, described originally as karren or lapiés by Heim (1878) and in more recent years by Bögli. It is believed that rillenkarren and rinnenkarren are formed by the very rapid chemical dissolving by water or snow as it falls upon and runs down the rock (Bögli, op. cit. 1960). The smooth furrows on the clint surfaces in northern England appear however to have been formed by a much slower solutional process than that responsible for the sharper rillenkarren. Two possibilities have been suggested: firstly, that the furrows were formed under snow, and secondly that they originated under a soil or peat cover like the Alpine rundkarren (cf. Bauer 1962).

Corbel (1957) and Parry (1960) both thought that the furrows may have been formed by solution associated with the long-lying snow of periglacial climate: as is well known, snow contains a high percentage of $CO_2$ (Williams 1949). In some localities, as at the top of Malham Cove, it is possible that extensive solution by snow has taken place; here the furrows are relatively small and regular and dependent upon the relief of each clint. In the Vercors, similar furrowed surfaces on steeply-inclined rock occur in actual association with snow banks, and the surfaces are not unlike those at Hutton Roof Crag. However, where large furrows cross the clints obliquely, it is difficult to think of melting snow as the chief means of their formation. Furthermore, many areas of the pavements are accompanied by stripped and channelled beds, suggesting that snowmelt was not a sufficiently active agent in their formation; running water either from a glacier or from peaty vegetation on boulder clay seems to be more likely.

Jones (*op. cit.* 1957) has recently examined the furrows with the view that they have been developed beneath a soil cover. There is some evidence for this contention. As can be seen from the Fig. 1, the limestone pavements form discontinuous strips and crescent-like expanses along the outer edges of platforms. Normally the pavements extend to the outer edge of the 'tread', overlooking the scar below; they are also interrupted by scattered patches of thin boulder clay. At the inner edge of the tread, or platform, nearest the foot of the scar, drift deposits form irregular but more-or-less continuous strips. Many excavations into these boulder clay deposits have been made in order to examine the nature of the limestone surface below. From the observations both of Jones and of the present author, the limestone below the boulder clay is mostly highly furrowed and dissected, the rock being reduced to rib- or bolster-like masses, separated by grikes and deep furrows. The grikes and furrows are choked with boulders, clay, and sand, derived from the drift. In an area cleared of drift on Scales Moor, hollows over 80 cm in diameter were found to occur in the limestone, and to contain relatively large erratic boulders 50–60 cm in diameter. The highly-dissected nature of the limestone surface under drift can also be seen at the quarry at Ribblehead Station, where the cover is being removed, and where glacial striae have been found. This may be due to a less complete form of glacial scour.

On the whole, some evidence from this type of excavation suggests that the limestones tend to be rather more dissected when buried beneath thin deposits of boulder clay than they are when uncovered. Detailed examination of pavements and of drift also shows that sometimes the pavements are much more dissected near to the drift deposits than they are farther from them—a fact at variance with the finding of Hughes (*op. cit.* 1901). Furthermore, a comparison of these smooth and furrowed limestones of northern England with those in other parts of the world where their development beneath a soil and forest cover is more obvious suggests a certain similarity. Thus the furrows on the Gordon limestone (Ordovician) in Tasmania and also on the Ordovian limestones of Takaka in South Island, New Zealand, should be compared with those in northern England.

Smaller-scale solutional features include sharp and narrow longitudinal runnels (1–2 cm wide and 1–2 cm deep), caused by solution from relatively acid waters (pH 4·5–5·0) which trickles off peat; the runnels are crinkled and cockled with transverse ribs, on account of the intermittent flow of the water. Such small-scale forms differ from the smoothed furrows; they more nearly resemble rillenkarren, and in some ways resemble the solutional features formed by direct action of sudden heavy rainbeat in semi-arid areas. Pitting or honey-combing of the rock, which is of great importance in some tropical limestone areas, is not significant in northern England (Sweeting 1956), nor is there any of the giant fluting which characterizes the weathering of many tropical limestone areas (Scrivenor 1933) (Plate 22).

## The Rate of Weathering of the Limestones

It is well known that erratic blocks occur scattered on limestone pavements of northern England. These erratics consist of pre-Carboniferous rocks, of Yoredale and Millstone Grits, and also of blocks of Carboniferous Limestone.

The limestone erratics can usually be distinguished by their cockly or crinkled weathering, caused by the direct atmospheric action of rainwater and distinguishing them from smoothed rocks detached from the limestone pavements. The Norber boulders, near Austwick, standing upon pedestals of limestone 30–50 cms above the surrounding pavements, have many times been described and photographed (e.g. Kendall and Wroot 1924); Hughes (1886) recorded similarly perched blocks in other localities in the north of England. It is always assumed that erratic-bearing pedestals indicate the amount of lowering that the limestone surface has undergone since the erratics were lodged; thus the lowering of the whole surface by solution must be considered as indicated by the pedestals on which some of the Norber Boulders rest (King *op. cit.* 1960). So far, however, no quantitative work has been done to test this assumption (Plates 22 and 26).

The problem of the absolute rates of erosion and solution of limestones has been given much attention since 1954 (Lehmann and others 1954). Its development has been helped by the improvement of chemical techniques, particularly in the estimations of those small quantities which are involved in determinations of the amounts of dissolved calcium in limestone waters. The application of chemical analyses to the denudational problems of limestone is still very new; much controversy surrounds the relative rates of chemical erosion in different environments (Corbel 1959).

The total amount of calcium carbonate in solution in the waters of limestone areas is dependent, apart from the presence of water, chiefly upon the temperature and upon the pressure of $CO_2$ present. In northern England, limestone is dissolved chiefly by the direct action of the rainwater and snow, and by the action of $CO_2$ and humic acids in association with a cover of soil and vegetation. In the writer's opinion, the second process is the more effective.

Rainfall in northwest England is high—about 1000 mm on the lower ground and in the lee of hills, over 2000 mm on the higher ground. The number of days on which rain falls is generally over 200, the number of days on which snow lies at 1000 ft and over is about 50. Some analyses of falling rain and snow are given in Table I.

TABLE I

| | pH | Ca ppm | Mg ppm | Temp., °F. |
|---|---|---|---|---|
| *Rainwater*<br>Several samples | 4·0–7·1<br>(nearly always<br>less than 7·0) | 6·0–7·0 | 0 | 55–60 |
| *Snow*<br>Freshly falling | 6·6<br>4·0<br>5·0 | 6·0 | 0 | 36 |
| 24 hrs after falling | 4·6 | 6·0 | 0 | 33·5 |

In northern England, the relatively low pH of falling rain and falling snow alike is due partly to the proximity of the industrial regions of the West Riding and of Lancashire: pH of rainwater is distinctly lower when the wind is from the east or southeast than when it is from the northwest, and the efficiency of rain and snow in the dissolution of limestone is correspondingly increased. However, the best examples of the direct effects of rainwater are seen in scars and in isolated erratic blocks which lie in the path of the south or southwest winds; the relevant limestone faces frequently bear fretted, cockled surfaces caused by the dissolving action of small trickles of water running down their sides. Fretting of this type is less evident on the north- or east-facing sides; in any event it is usually no more than 1 cm wide and 1 cm deep (Plate 22).

It is known that snow, and waters near 0°C, are able to dissolve more $CO_2$ than can warmer waters; it would be expected that direct solutional action would be greater in a cool climate like that of northern England than in warmer climates, yet rillenkarren and

solutional runnels are not well developed in Britain. The lack of
solutional runnels on the British limestones may in part be due to the
low intensity of the rainfall, but must also be due partly to rapidly-
growing vegetation which obliterates surface forms.

Rainwater and snowmelt collect in the hollows of limestone pavements. Analysis of the water in clint pools shows that the water
rapidly takes up calcium carbonate until the solution becomes
saturated or even supersaturated, according to the curves devised by
Trombe (1952). Certain observations are here listed in Table II, and
are plotted on Trombe's curves in Fig. 8. It can be shown that the
pools take up more calcium carbonate, the longer they remain. The
pH of the surface layers of water is approximately 6·5–7·0, while that
of water at the base of the pool in contact with the limestone is
higher, often 7·6–7·9. This circumstance relates to the type of slow
solution referred to by Bögli (*op. cit.* 1960), which that author regards as producing a kind of landform different from that produced
by more rapid solution.

TABLE II

|  | Temp. °F. | pH | Ca ppm | Mg ppm | Ca + Mg ppm |
|---|---|---|---|---|---|
| *Clint Pools* |  |  |  |  |  |
| Twisleton Scars | 51·5 | 8·75 | 75 | 3 | 78 |
| (3 hrs after rain) |  |  |  |  |  |
| Nether Hesleden | 37 | 7·55 | 116 | 8 | 124 |
| (24 hrs after snow) |  |  |  |  |  |
| Scar Close | 54 | 7·8 | 202 | 4 | 206 |
| (9 hrs after rain) |  |  |  |  |  |
| Hutton Roof Crag | 50 | 8·3 | 278 | 8 | 286 |
| (12 hrs after rain) |  |  |  |  |  |
| *River (dry bed) Pools* |  |  |  |  |  |
| Pool (Skirfare river) | 57·5 | 7·45 | 312 | 30 | 342 |
| (after dry summer) |  |  |  |  |  |
| Pool (Hesleden Beck) | 59 | 7·9 | 126 | 19 | 145 |
| Crystal Beck | 51·5 | 8·35 | 126 | trace | 126 |

The pools and hollows become the foci for the accumulation of
lichens and moss spores. The accumulation of these tends to increase
the $CO_2$ content of the water and the hollow deepens. In the hollows,
peaty deposits accumulate, which with small animals (worms, etc.)
further increase the acidity of the environment, giving it a pH of
about 5·0–6·5 in actual contact with the limestone. An analysis of
some of the greyish peaty and residual accumulation in the clint
hollows is given in Table III.

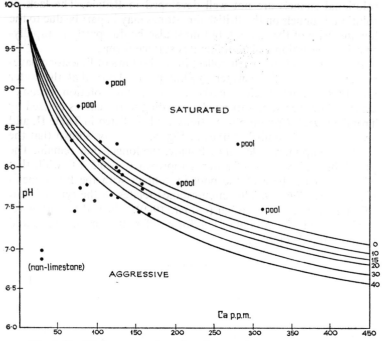

Fig. 8. Equilibrium curves for selected waters in north-west England.

TABLE III

*Analysis of dark grey powder (residual soil) occurring in the furrows and hollows of the limestone pavements*

| *Matter insoluble in HCl, %* | | *Matter soluble in HCl, %* | |
|---|---|---|---|
| Carbon | 2·37 | Ferric, aluminium and titanium oxides | 4·19 |
| Hydrogen and combined water | 5·84 | Calcium carbonate | 62·27 |
| Mineral residue on incineration | 24·55 | Magnesium carbonate | 1·74 |

(Analysis made for the writer by Dr G. W. Himus, Imperial College)

By far the most potent agent of solution of the limestones is the acid water, already referred to, which drains from peat. Peat accumulates on the shales and sands of the Yoredales and on the boulder clays derived from these rocks. Boulder clay occurs in patches on the limestones and hence in association with the pavements. Waters draining from this drift can be shown at the present time to be most efficacious solvents of the rock.

In 1947, an area of about 2 sq metres of glaciated limestone pavement, near Long Kin East Cave, was stripped of its sandy and shaly drift. The rock thus exposed was a clearly striated pavement of blue *Girvanella* limestone, the locality being the one described by Tiddeman (in Dakyns, Tiddeman and others 1890). Much water from the peaty moor has drained on to this pavement and a close watch has been kept on the striae. By 1954, only a few striae were left; by 1960 all had been dissolved away, and the limestone surface lowered in places by as much as 3–5 cms. In a second field trial, peaty vegetation covering a few square metres of the limestone on Scales Moor was removed. Runnels of peaty water were allowed to drain on to the freshly-cleared rock surface. After thirteen years, many runnels from 7–15 cms deep have been cut into the limestone. Both these examples show solution under rather favourable conditions.

These results are thought to bear on the occurrence of perched blocks. Perched blocks of limestone, similar in placing to the grit boulders on Norber, are very common. Some of the best localities are those on Harry Hallam's Moss and on Scar Close on the northwest side of the Ingleborough massif. Here there seems to be no doubt that the clint surfaces have been lowered by about 50 cms since their formation. Closely associated with the pavements in these two areas are small drift mounds, from which many small peaty streamlets, particularly after heavy rain, drain directly on to the limestone. The pavements are dissected by wide shallow runnels, 25–50 cms deep and often up to 2 metres wide. The floors of these runnels are wavy and undulating, occasionally indicating flow of water; their sides are smooth and frequently undercut, suggesting solution in the base. Residual masses of the dissected pavements are often left standing mushroom-like above the stripped surfaces. Abandoned by streams, the runnels become filled in by mosses and grasses. Solution is then continued below the vegetation cover where the runnels can be shown to be deeper. Runnels formed in this way by the solutional action of peaty waters are referred to by Bögli (*op. cit.* 1960) as *höhlenkarren* (Plate 26).

It is clear that a great deal of the limestone pavement has been stripped and lowered since its original formation. Both on Harry Hallam's Moss and on Scar Close, perched blocks occur on pedestals up to 50 cm high. Many of them may be true erratics, i.e. blocks brought by ice over a short distance like those at Norber; but many are probably what Corbel (1957) has called *pseudo-erratics*, i.e. residuals left by stripping of the beds by solution in the way described

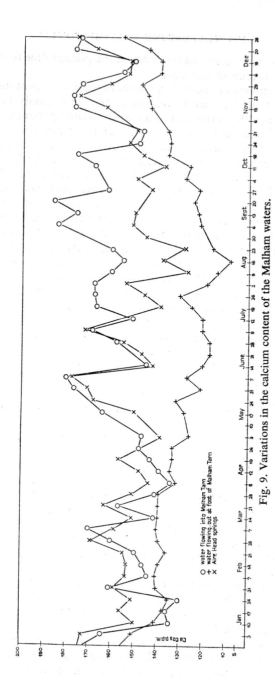

Fig. 9. Variations in the calcium content of the Malham waters.

O  water flowing into Malham Tarn
+  water flowing out at foot of Malham Tarn
X  Aire Head springs

above (Plate 26). At Norber, conditions for solution under peaty drainage are less favourable than those at the trial sites, and many erratics are raised above the surrounding limestone on the downslope side only. On the upslope side they are at the same level as the limestone, a fact which suggests soil-creep as a contributory agent in the development of the pedestals.

From a study of perched limestone blocks in the Müren Mountains

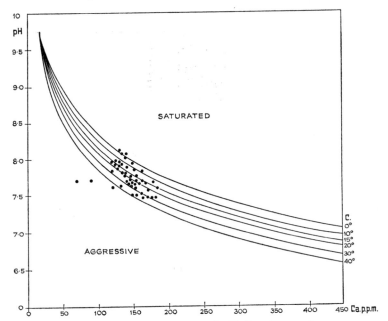

Fig. 10. Equilibrium curves for the Malham Tarn waters.

in the Alps, Bögli (1961) estimates that the amount of corrosive degradation of the limestone in that area amounts to 1·51 cm per year. Additional quantitative data is now becoming available for northern England, particularly on the amounts of calcium carbonate dissolved by streams. Analyses of spring waters associated with the Malham Tarn System have now been made. Those for 1961–2 are shown in the graph in Fig. 9. In this figure the simple variations in the calcium content of the waters of three localities are given. It is hoped that a detailed study of these analyses will be made later, but a few preliminary comments are possible. The calcium content of these waters shows variations which are related to amounts of rainfall; it rises after dry periods and falls after heavy rain. Plotting of the observations on Trombe's curves (Fig. 10) shows almost all of them to lie on, or very near to, the equilibrium curves; hence these waters are saturated for the temperatures concerned. This situation is probably true of the other main limestone springs in northern England. Analyses from other waters and springs are also plotted in Fig. 8, where waters from non-limestone environments in northern England are shown for comparison.

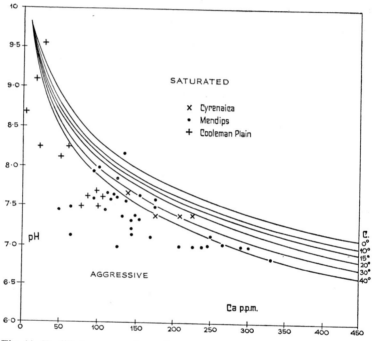

Fig. 11. Equilibrium curves for springs and waters in Cyrenaica, Mendips, and Cooleman Plain.

Analyses from springs and waters in the Mendips,[1] Cyrenaica[1] (Libya), and from the Cooleman Plain area of southeast Australia[1] are shown in Fig. 11. Those from the Mendips record, in general, slight undersaturation. The waters from the Cooleman Plain—a high-level snowy area in the Australian Alps—are also undersaturated. These graphs should be compared with those produced by the writer and

[1] Mendips: analysed by D. C. Ford. Cyrenaica: analysed by I. Douglas. Cooleman Plain: analysed by J. N. Jennings.

J. N. Jennings for three other Australian areas (Sweeting and Gerstenhauer 1960).

Averages of the analyses in northern England give some preliminary figures on the absolute amount of calcium carbonate dissolved. The average calcium content of waters flowing off the non-calcareous rocks before they reach the limestones is about the order 30–36 ppm. Analyses of limestone springs, i.e. those recording calcium picked up by surface solution and by solution underground, give an order of 140 ppm. Analyses of water from surface streams confined to the limestones run lower, averaging 80–90 ppm. Systematic sampling of some streams indicates that at the surface, calcium is picked up at the rate of about 20 ppm/800 metres, until saturation is reached. The average increase in calcium within the Ingleborough-Malham limestone areas is: for streams at the surface, of the order of 40–50 ppm; for surface and underground streams together, of the order of 90–100 ppm. The rate of underground solution is about the same as, or slightly greater than, the rate of solution at the surface. This fact may help to explain, for northwest Yorkshire at least, the relative abundance of caves, in terms of total area of the limestone.

Corbel (1959) has devised a formula to calculate the number of millimetres of limestone per 1000 years removed by unaided solution only in a limestone region. Applied to the figures obtained for northern England, Corbel's formula[1] gives the following result for northwest Yorkshire, at the present rates of solution of the limestones and with the present rainfall: solution of the rock is equivalent to a lowering of the surface by:

> 0·04  mm per year by solution at the surface
> 0·043 mm per year by solution underground
> _____
> = approx. 0·083 mm per year total lowering

The rate of the lowering of the surface of the limestone deduced in this way is approximately 41 mm in 1000 years.

This result can be referred to the development of pavements and to the location of perched erratic blocks. The erratics may be regarded as dating from the late-glacial period in northern England, approx. 12,000 years ago. Assuming the rate of dissolution of the limestone at the surface to have remained much the same as it is now (which

---

[1] *Corbel's formula*

$$\text{Erosion (x) in m}^3/\text{a year/km}^2 = \frac{4 \text{ ET}}{100}$$

Where E = height of water in decimetres
       T = amount of $CaCO_3$ in mg per litre

is by no means likely, however), the amount of lowering of the surface of the limestone would be 12 × 41 mm, about 49 cm. This result is of the same order as the height of the pedestals which support perched boulders. In this connection, Goodchild's observations (1890) on the weathering of limestones are of interest. He used the rates of weathering on local monuments, tombstones, and so on, estimating the rate of the weathering of the limestones in northern England at about one inch in 500 years. On this basis, the weathering of the limestone since the last glacial would be about 2 ft, a figure similar to that already given. Goodchild put 1 inch in 500 years his lowest estimate, and thought 1 inch in 300 years might be nearer the truth, but his findings remain in good accordance with those obtained from the Corbel formula.

Locally, the rate of weathering and solution of the limestone is undoubtedly greater than these general totals require; so much has been indicated by the formation in the past thirteen years of the runnels on Scales Moor, where the conditions are favourable to rapid solution. High rates of solution occur in association with streams draining directly on to the limestones from peat-covered boulder clays and shales. Where such streams are large, gorges about 6 metres deep and 1·5 metres wide are common; they could be very largely of solutional origin. The gorge formed by the stream flowing into Long Kin East Cave on the southeast slopes of Ingleborough is a good example. There are, however, variations in the rates of solution, since basin-like depressions (locally called Dolly Tubs) alternate within the gorges with steeply-inclined falls. Solution of the rock is locally increased in the depressions, but it is decreased over the falls, where under dry conditions tufa may form. Variations in the rate of solution are confirmed by an examination of the pH of the stream waters. In the pools, $CO_2$ is absorbed from the atmosphere and the pH is low, at 5·8–6·0; solution of the rock takes place. In the waterfalls, the pH is higher, at 6·6–7·6, suggesting that some $CO_2$ is lost and that solution of the rock is lessened.[1]

Similar lines of argument can be applied to the features of underground solution. Where drumlins and boulder clays lie directly upon the limestone, streams draining off these deposits enter the rock along joints and bedding-planes, and solution along these lines of weakness produces caves, which are elongated vertically or horizontally according to whether they form along joints or along bedding-planes. They have been formed largely by solution, and are probably of postglacial age. They are usually about 1 metre across in one direction, and

[1] Observations of certain stalagmites and stalactites in northwest Yorkshire caves show that deposition of $CaCO_3$ is very active at the present time.

about 2 metres in the other, penetrating some metres into the limestone. A solution-rate of the order already described, 0·04 to 0·05 mm/year, would if concentrated along a defined line of weakness suffice in the postglacial time available to produce caves of this size. Many examples of such caves can be found, one of the best being at Blishmire, on the slopes of Penyghent; others have been recorded in Ireland and in Norway (Ollier and Tratman 1956, Renwick 1962).

The only other area in Great Britain for which comparable data on solution are available is the Mendips (Ingle-Smith and Mead 1962). From analyses made by D. C. Ford and by D. I. Smith, the figures for the calcium content of the Mendip waters are as follows:

*Waters above the Sinks*

| Temp °F | ph | Ca ppm | Mg ppm | Total Hardness |
|---|---|---|---|---|
| 68 | 7·6 | 100 | 8 | 108 |

*Analyses of surface streams flowing on the limestones*

| | | | | |
|---|---|---|---|---|
| 50·5 | 7·6 | 146 | 30 | 176 |

*Risings* (the limestone springs)

| | | | | |
|---|---|---|---|---|
| 50·0 | 7·2 | 250 | 3 | 253 |

At the surface, streams pick up calcium at about 24 ppm in about 400 metres, i.e. at about twice the rate of streams in northern England. Underground streams in the Mendips pick up 100–150 ppm, compared with about 80–90 ppm in northern England. On these figures, there should be relatively more limestone being dissolved in the Mendips than in the north, and the rate of the general lowering of the surface should be about 0·10 mm $CaCO_3$ per year per km². From these first and rather approximate figures, it would seem that although the Ca content of the waters in the Mendips is generally higher than in northern England, solution by underground waters is slightly less, relative to solution by surface streams. This might be one factor in explaining the greater abundance of caves per unit area of the limestone in the Ingleborough district than in the Mendips. Mead and Smith (*op. cit.* 1962) give more detailed figures for the Mendips, explaining the large amounts of calcium in the waters as being due to a soil rich in $CO_2$, associated with an extensive grass cover. If rates of solution of limestone are greatly influenced by the nature of the vegetation cover, as is probable, then the lower amounts of calcium in the waters of the limestone districts of northern England are partly explained by the existence there of the large areas of bare rock surfaces.[1]

[1] See Smith, D. I. and Nicholson, F. H., 1964. 'A Study of Limestone Solution in North-West Clare, Eire.' *Proc. Spelaeological Soc. Bristol*, Vol. 10, pp. 119–38.

This essay has attempted to indicate some of the new chemical methods that can be used in studies of limestone areas, and to indicate the possibilities of such methods. It has further shown that in northern England the dissolution of limestones is comparatively rapid. Today, perhaps even more than in former periods, solution is of fundamental importance in the formation of the landforms of the Carboniferous Limestones.

## Acknowledgement

Acknowledgement is due to Mr C. F. W. R. Gullick for reading the manuscript of this essay.

## References

Bauer, F., 1962. 'Karstformen in den Österreichischen Kalkhochalpen.' *Actes du Deuxième Congr. Internat. de Spéléologie*, 1958, vol. 1, 299–329.

Bögli, A., 1960. 'Kalklösung und Karrenbilding.' *Zeit. Geomorph. Supplementband*, 2. *Internationale Beitrage zur Karstmorphologie*, 4–21.

Bögli, A., 1961. 'Karrentische, ein Beiträge zur Karstmorphologie.' *Zeit. für Geomorph*. Band 5, Heft 3, 185–93.

Bott, M. H. P., 1961. 'Geological interpretation of Magnetic Anomalies over the Askrigg Block.' *Quart. Journ. Geol. Soc.*, 117, 481–95.

Cheetham, C. A., 1947. 'Moughton Scar.' *The Naturalist*, 59.

Corbel, J., 1957. 'Les Karsts du Nord-ouest de L'Europe.' *Inst. Etudes Rhodaniennes Mem. et Doc.*, 12. Lyon.

Corbel, J., 1959. 'Erosion en terrain calcaire.' *Annales de Géog.*, 68, 97–120.

Cvijic, J., 1924. 'On the evolution of Lapies.' *Geog. Review*, 14, 26–49.

Dakyns, J. R., Tidderman, R. H., and others, 1890. 'The geology of the country around Ingleborough.' *Mem. Geol. Surv.*

Eckert, M., 1896. *Das Karrenproblem, die Geschichte seiner Lösung. Zeit. für Naturviss.*, 58, 321–423.

Garwood, E. J., 1912. 'The Lower Carboniferous Succession in N.W. of England.' *Quart. Journ. Geol. Soc.*, 68, 419–586.

Garwood, E. J., and Goodyear, E., 1924. 'The Lower Carboniferous Succession in the Settle District and along the line of the Craven Faults.' *Quart. Journ. Geol. Soc.*, 80, 184–270.

Goodchild, J. G., 1875. 'The glacial phenomena of the Eden Valley and the western part of the Yorkshire Dale District.' *Quart. Journ. Geol. Soc.*, 31, 55–99.

Goodchild, J. G., 1890. 'On the weathering of limestones.' *Geol. Mag.*, p. 413.

Heim, A., 1878. 'Uber die Karrenfelder.' *Jb. d. Schw. Alpenclubs*, 13, 421.

Hughes, T. McK., 1886. 'On some perched blocks and associated phenomena.' *Quart. Journ. Geol. Soc.*, 13(4), 527.

Hughes, T. McK., 1901. 'Ingleborough: Part 1.' *Proc. Yorks. Geol. Soc.*, 14.

Ingle Smith, D., and Mead, D. G., 1962. 'The solution of Limestone; with special reference to Mendip.' *Proc. Univ. Bristol Speleological Soc. 1961–2*, 9(3), 188–211.

Jones, R. J., 1957. 'The nature and origin of clints and grikes, with special reference to the Ingleborough District.' Unpublished thesis, London University.

Kendall, P. F., and Wroot, H. E., 1924. *The Geology of Yorkshire.*

King, C. A. M., 1960. 'The Yorkshire Dales.' *British Landscape through Maps*, No. 2. The Geographical Association.

Lehmann, H., and others, 1954. in 'Das Karstphänomen in den Verschiedwen Klimazonen'. *Erdkunde*, p. 112

Marr, J. E., 1921. 'On the rigidity of N.W. Yorkshire.' *The Naturalist*, 63–72.

de Martonne, E., 1925. *Traité de Géographie Physique.* Vol. 2, Chap. 6. Paris.

Moisley, H. A., 1953/54. 'Some karstic features in the Malham District.' *Annual Report of the Council for the Promotion of Field Studies*, p. 38.

Ollier, C. D., and Tratman, E. K., 1956. 'The geomorphology of the caves of N.W. Clare, Ireland.' *Proc. Univ. Bristol Speleological Soc.*, 7(3), 138–57.

Parry, J., 1960. 'The limestone pavements of north-western England.' *The Canadian Geographer*, No. 16, 14–21.

Phillips, J., 1853. *Rivers, Mountains and Sea-Coast of Yorkshire*, p. 13.

Praeger, R. L., 1947. *The Way That I Went*, p. 237. Methuen, London.

Proctor, M. C. F., 1960. 'Mosses and liverworts of the Malham District.' *Field Studies*, 1, (2), 67.

Raistrick, A., 1946. *Pennine Walls.* Dalesman Publishing Co.

Raistrick, A., and Blackburn, K. B., 1932–3. 'The late Glacial and Post Glacial Periods in the North Pennines (West Yorkshire and Durham).' *Trans. Northern Nats. Union*, pt. 1., 16–36, pt. 2, 79–103.

Renwick, K., 1962. 'The age of caves by solution.' *Cave Science*, 4, (32), 338–50.

Roglič, J., 1931. 'Glacijalni tragovi na Biokovu/Les formes glaciaires sur le Biokovo.' *Posebna Izdanja Geog. Dr.* Vol. 10.

Schwarzacher, W., 1958. 'Stratification of the Great Scar Limestone in the Settle district of Yorkshire.' *Liverpool and Manchester Geol. Journal*, 2, (1), 124.

Scrivenor, T. B., 1921. 'Physical geography of the southern part of the Malay Peninsula.' *Geog. Review*, 2, 251.

Sweeting, M. M., 1955. 'The landforms of N.W. County Clare, Ireland.' *Trans. Inst. Brit. Geog. Publication No. 21*, 33–49.

Sweeting, M. M., 1956. 'Hydrogeological observations on the white limestone areas in Jamaica.' *Geol. Survey Dept., Jamaica, B.W.I. Bulletin No. 2.*

Sweeting, M. M., and Gerstenhauer, A., 1960. 'Zur Frage den absoluten Geschwindigkeit der Kalkkorrosion in verschieden Klimaten.' *Zeit für Geomorph. Supplementband 2. Internationale Beiträge zur Karstmorphologie*, 66–73.

Trombe, F., 1952. *Traite de Spéléologie*. Payot, Paris.

Wager, L. R., 1931. 'Jointing in the Great Scar Limestone of Craven and its relation to the tectonics of the area.' *Quart. Journ. Geol. Soc.*, 87, 392–424.

Williams, J. E., 1949. 'Chemical weathering at low temperatures,' *Geog. Review*, 39, 129–35.

Wood, A., 1942. 'The development of hillside slopes.' *Proc. Geol. Assoc.*, 53, 128–38.

# The Concept of Grade

## G. H. DURY

By its very persistence, debate suggests that the concept of grade offers persistent difficulties. Certain difficulties, indeed, become evident in each critique. But those which are deliberately examined, and for which resolution is attempted, often seem to be those of definition, even when they command treatment at length. It is perhaps for historical reasons that some conceptual difficulties secure no great attention, but discussions of grade could probably be reduced in bulk, and at the same time increased in value, if they began by questioning the validity of the concept itself. The very fact that debate is so prolonged suggests that certain matters are habitually, or at least frequently, overlooked, so that obdurate problems continue to withstand forceful attempts at rational solution of the whole matter. On general grounds, it seems possible that one of the untreated or little-regarded questions is that of validity.

Only if the concept of grade can be proved valid does it seem useful to go on to further questions, namely, whether or not the condition of grade as required by the concept is verifiable, and, if it is verifiable, whether or not it has been verified. Approached in this way, numbers of the difficulties which are usually encountered in the context of grade come to appear not so much theoretical, technical, or even conceptual, as linguistic. This is especially so, because the concept of grade has been introduced into the thought and literature of geomorphology by verbal means. On this account, the present essay will rely on verbal as opposed to numerical argument in seeking to review the declared bases of the concept, and will signalize linguistic rather than mathematical errors of description and definition.

The dual origin of the concept must be admitted at once. On the one side the idea of grade relates to the work of civil engineers concerned with stabilizing channels both natural and artificial, and with expressing their findings and their derived principles in terms of formulae. On the other side comes the work of geologists and physical geographers, most of whom until quite recently have dealt exclusively with the channels of natural streams and almost entirely in words.

The civil engineers have priority, their noteworthy contributions to the theory of channels dating back to the seventeenth century. But the influence of W. M. Davis ensures that many geomorphologists encounter the concept of grade first, and perhaps alone, in the context of natural erosion. This is not to imply that Davis was unaware of engineering literature—on the contrary, he appended references to this literature to his principal statements about grade. Nevertheless, geomorphologists tend to think of grade in relation to natural streams, especially since the postulate of a graded condition is entangled with postulates relating to channel-habit and to the general development of terrain in fluvial conditions.

When, at the end of the nineteenth century, Davis elaborated his ideas on grade, some at least of the writings of civil engineers were familiar to workers in Europe who, under the names of various forms of study, were engaged with problems of fluvial morphology. Since one of the chief aims of hydrologic practice was to produce and to maintain the so-called slope of equilibrium, it is in no way surprising that the Davisian idea, with its emphasis on balance, was readily adopted into European writing about natural rivers. It seemed to establish by theoretical means precisely that principle which many years of empirical work demanded. Several of Davis's contemporaries in North America were arriving on their own account at ideas closely similar to, or even identical with, those which Davis recorded. Indeed, Davis claimed neither to originate the concept of grade, nor even to be the first to give it a name. Gilbert in 1876 and McGee in 1891 had used the term *grade*, or some cognate form, before Davis adopted it in 1894; Gannett followed in 1896, and Johnson in 1901. Certain other writers were using the term *base-level* in the sense which *graded profile* was later to convey. However, Davis appears mainly responsible for introducing the word *grade* into widely-read geomorphic literature, at the very time when the concept for which the word could stand was developing among original workers. And Davis seems mainly, and perhaps wholly, responsible for that deductive elaboration of the concept which has promoted so voluminous and so recurrent a discussion.

Now although the name and the idea of grade appear and reappear at many points in the Davisian opus, the most accessible and the most widely current of the relevant early works are two: *The Geographical Cycle*, first published in the Geographical Journal of 1899, and *Base-level, Grade, and Peneplain*, which appeared in 1902 in the Journal of Geology. Each of these professed specifically to examine the concept of grade for its own sake—by contrast, for example, with incorporating it in the description of some particular terrain. Each

1. ISLANDMORE AND DUNSY ISLAND, STRANGFORD LOUGH, CO. DOWN. This is an example of the archipelago of drowned drumlins in Strangford Lough, Northern Ireland. The ice moved from upper left to lower right in the area shown on the photograph, to produce the characteristic stream-lining of the little hills of boulder clay. Fossil, raised cliff lines are indicated by the strong shadows in the right foreground and centre, and by fainter but unmistakable breaks of slope in the distance. These cliffs are the shorelines of the eustatic *Littorina* marine transgression (dating approximately from Zone VIc–VIIa, 5000–6000 B.P.). Some of the more distant drumlins show traces of complete truncation during the earlier Late-Glacial *Yoldia* transgression, but no cliff lines can be seen. (*Photograph by Aerofilms Ltd.*)

2. PORTHLEVEN, CORNWALL. The Porthleven erratic rests in a hollow some 5–7 ft deep which it has worn for itself in the wave-cut rock platform. This rock platform is awash at high spring tides, but is an example of an exhumed platform. The caves and wave-cut notches which can be seen in the photographs are fossil features, as is the cliff and the greater part of the platform. In the caves and notches beach deposits are seen to be firmly cemented to the smooth, polished rock faces, and it is these deposits which are being re-excavated at the present. Thick head deposits cap the rock cliffs and formerly extended seawards to bury the cliff, the former beach notches and platform during the Pleistocene.

3. GIANT'S CAUSEWAY CLIFFS, NORTH CO. ANTRIM. These cliffs are formed of lava (basalts) tiers, which when weathered take on a stepped outline. This kind of selective etching produces a cliff profile which resembles a series of fossil, raised, wave-cut rock platforms. In the foreground a well-developed fresh wave-cut platform can be seen, which is probably a recent feature of this coastline. Above this lowermost platform stacks rise almost vertically to what may be another platform some 30–50 ft above high-water mark. There are, however, many difficulties in attempting to distinguish marine

4. SAUNTON, NEAR BARNSTAPLE, NORTH DEVON. The horizontally bedded sand and shingle of the raised beach is seen to rest upon a well-planed wave-cut rock platform, which is here within the reach of spring tides and storm waves. Above the raised beach proper fossil sand dunes show inclined bedding; head forms the capping to the cliff, resting unconformably upon the blown sand.

5. PENCIL ROCK, NEAR BAGGY POINT, NORTH DEVON. The height of the rock platform in the foreground is 45 ft O.D., which is about 25–30 ft above high-water mark. On the platform rest a series of deposits, the lowest being a shell-bearing shingle beach (5–6 ft thick) which contains large quantities of angular and sub-angular blocks—the beach seems to have incorporated a head deposit. Horizontally bedded layers of shelly sand with some pebbles reach a maximum thickness of some 20 ft and form part of the raised beach resting on the rock platform.

6. GODREVY, NEAR ST IVES, CORNWALL. At the base of the section a foot or so of raised bea shingle rests upon a wave-cut rock platform (16–20 ft above high-water mark). Three feet sand forms the next horizon, above which 5–6 ft of massive angular head is seen. This low (main) head is severely cryoturbated into festoons. At the top of the section a thin layer modern blown sand rests upon a foot or two of an upper (younger) head or solifluction ear

7. ROVANIEMI AIRPORT, LAPLAND, FINLAND. The summit of this hill is capped by a thin cover till which does not extend below the marine limit. In the foreground wave-action has remov the till, exposing the bare rock. The expansion of winter ice that formed on the frozen surfa of the sea has concentrated a line or zone of large boulders at the marine limit, some of whi can be seen.

orthward-sloping crest-
and smooth upper slopes
he east end of the Lara-
pinta Ridges.

l Pass, typical of smaller
through the Heavitree
e, showing smooth up-
er slopes and gorge.

Ellery Creek gap through
Heavitree Range, with
Alice Valley etch plain in
middle distance and the
hly accordant rounded
nits of the Chewings
ge behind. The foothills
Bitter Springs Limestone
e foreground are planed
t the high terrace level.

11. Ridges of Areyonga sandstone being etched out from beneath the high terrace.

12. Junction of the weathered high terrace and the bevelled Heavitree Range with its hillslope bench.

13. The first stage in scarp recession. A new cycle working back into the Shebshi Mountains, Northern Nigeria, by retrogressive erosion of streams and gullies. The summit surface is still largely undisturbed. (*U.S. Air Force photograph.*)

15. The final stage in scarp recession. Residual inselbergs on the north side of the Shebshi Mountains. The drainage of the new cycle is becoming integrated away from the pedimented scarps. Small fragments of the upper surface are still apparent on a few residuals. (*U.S. Air Force photograph.*)

The second stage in scarp recession. Dissection he Alantika Mountains, Northern Nigeria, by ward extension of the streams of the new cycle. upper surface remains as little more than a ummit plane. (*U.S. Air Force photograph.*)

16. Kopje standing above dome-shaped residual of bornhardt form, Zaria–Kaduna road, Northern Nigeria.

17. Marginal depression between bevel of lower dome (*right*) and free face of upper dome (*left*). Kafena Hill, near Zaria, Northern Nigeria.

18. View from the Uganda Museum showing typical landscape elements in Kampala district, Buganda. The flat-topped mesas of the Buganda Surface are separated by steep slopes from the pediments which combine to form the Kasubi Surface. Below the Kasubi Surface a series of valleys are incised and the upper slopes of one valley can be seen between the 'Museum' flat in the foreground and the buildings upon the Kasubi pediment in the middle distance. The scale may be judged with the aid of the 500-ft high television mast on Kololo Hill.

19. The lower landscape elements of the Kampala district of Buganda. View towards the Uganda Museum which is built upon the Kasubi Surface, showing the slope down into the Kitante Valley in the bottom of which erosion has reached the Basal Surface of Weathering and exposed a Valley Bottom Tor of fresh gneiss.

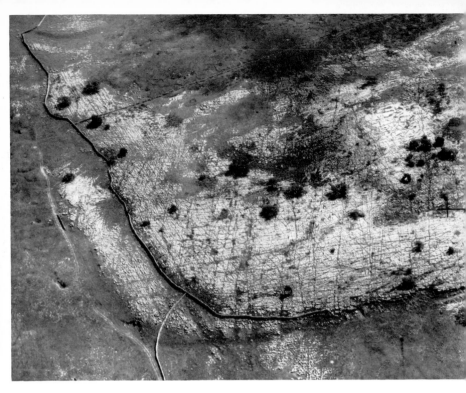

20. Limestone pavement, Scar Close, Ingleborough. (*Aerial photograph by J. K. St Joseph. Crown Copyright Reserved.*)

21. Twisleton Scars and Screes: measured scree in the foreground.

22. (*Right*) Isolated erratic block showing characteristic 'crinkled' or 'cockled' weathering: Kingsdale

23. (*Below*) Limestone pavement with both Rillen and Rund Karren; on Carboniferous Limestones dipping at approx. 25°; Hutton Roof Crag, Westmorland.

24. Limestone pavement: Twisleton Scars.

25. Limestone pavements weathered by so[lu]tion depressions: western slopes of Ing[le]borough.

26. Blocks left perched by solution of the limestones: Scar Close, Ingleborough.

was included in *Geographical Essays* in 1909. It is likely that these are Davis's two most influential statements about grade: they provide the starting-point of the discussion which here follows.

When all possible allowance is made for the great cogency of a new name in its application to a developing concept, and for the association of the idea of grade with the exhilarating scheme of sequential evolution of landscape, the portions of *The Geographical Cycle* and of *Base-level, Grade, and Peneplain* which actually say anything about grade do not, in total, bulk large. Aside from brief comments on changes in stream-velocity with advance of the erosion-cycle, and from a tenuous treatment of hillside slopes, the relevant passages are the following:

1. *The Grade of Valley Floors.* Load is small at the beginning and rapidly increases in quantity and coarseness during youth . . . it continues to increase in quantity, but probably not in coarseness, during early maturity . . . but after full maturity, load continually decreases in quantity and coarseness of texture (1899).

2. [On] a young consequent river . . . valley deepening will go on most rapidly at some point, probably nearer head than mouth. [Below] this point the river will find its slope and velocity decreasing and its load increasing, that is, its ability to do work becoming less, while the work that it has to do is becoming greater. The original excess of ability over work will thus . . . be corrected, and when an equality of these two quantities is brought about, the river is *graded* . . . When the graded condition is reached, alteration of slope can take place only as volume and slope change their relation (1899).

3. It is evidently desirable to employ the term 'grade' for the balanced condition of a mature or old river . . . the balance between erosion and deposition . . . is brought about by the changes in the capacity of a river to do work, and in the quantity of work that a river has to do. The changes continue until the two quantities . . . reach equality, and then the river may be said to be graded (1902).

4. 'Grade', meaning a condition or balance, must not be confused with the same word with another meaning, namely, the slope . . . of the river when the graded condition is reached; for 'grade', meaning slope, varies in place and time, while 'grade', meaning balance, always implies an equality of two quantities . . . [it] is an essential balance between corrasion and deposition (1902).

5. . . . 'slope of equilibrium' may be taken as a descriptive phrase, essentially synonymous with 'graded slope' . . . a river grades its course by a process of cutting and filling, until an equable slope is

H

developed along which the transportation of its load is the most effectively accomplished (1902).

6. . . . the maintenance of grade, during the very slow changes in volume and load that accompany the course of the cycle, involves an appropriate change of slope as well . . . in virtue of the continual, although slow, variations of stream volume and load through the normal cycle, the balanced condition of any stream can be maintained only by an equally continuous, although small, change of river slope, whereby capacity to do work, and work to be done, shall always be kept equal (1902).

These extracts are even less bulky than they at first appear, for they include some repetition. However, they also touch on many considerations in addition to grade in the Davisian sense. Here is one signal difficulty in criticizing Davis's writing—reaffirmation on the one hand, and multiple reference (cross-reference, side-reference) on the other.

Reaffirmation is obvious enough, when the various passages are juxtaposed as they are above. The idea of a graded condition as balance between erosion (or corrasion) and deposition occurs in 6, but is previously implied in 5, is mentioned in 4 and 3, and occurs initially in 2 on which all the rest depend. The phrase *equality of two quantities*, or a near variant, is found in 4 and 3, but again originates in 2. The notion of a long-continued change in slope, subsequent to the first establishment of grade, and related to changes in volume, load, or both, constitutes the whole of 6, but forms in actuality an extension of 2 and is partly implicit in 1. There is no need for the present purpose to trace similar reaffirmation of these ideas further, e.g. into writings of Davis which are concerned primarily with regional geomorphology, or to provide parallel instances of reaffirmatory treatment, such as occur in his quite early works, of which a number are scattered and somewhat obscurely published. But the practice of reaffirmation is so important that it deserves to be emphasized. It requires that Davis's ideas should be traced back to their original stated form, or, as here, to their earliest influential stated form, in order that they may be tested from the beginning.

The overlap between one and another of the citations given above justifies a summary re-statement of the ideas involved, as follows:

(*a*) Grade is the balanced condition of a mature or old river: the balance is that between capacity to do work, and quantity of work to be done. It is expressed by an equivalence of erosion and deposition.

(b) The slope of the graded river is the slope [profile] of equilibrium: this slope permits the most effective transport of load.

(c) Once the graded condition is attained, slope can be altered only by changes in the volume/load relationship: such change, operating slowly, is expectable in the normal cycle.

(d) Load increases in quantity and coarseness during youth, in quantity but probably not in coarseness during maturity, and after full maturity decreases both in quantity and in coarseness.

(e) Grade is first established in downstream reaches, where valley-deepening reduces downstream gradient, until eventually the excess capacity of the river to do work is wholly offset.

Although this summary and the preceding quotations are meant fairly to represent Davis's views, it would be unjust to consider them wholly out of context. Thus, the central extracts 1 and 2 come from the essay on the Geographical Cycle, where Davis is concerned not so much with hydrologic principle as with the sequential development of landforms. His reference to decrease in downstream gradient on the lower river, as an accompaniment of valley-deepening, cross-refers to the standard form of the long-profile as a concave-upward curve (parabolic, logarithmic, exponential, or other). The idea of balance between work done and work to do is therefore inseparable from his ideas on valley-cutting and of the shaping of the long-profile, making it difficult to confine examination of his writings to single principles at a given time.

In addition to what has already been quoted, reference to amount of load is explicit in:

7. . . . if the maximum of load is not reached until after the first attainment of the graded condition by the trunk rivers, then the valley floors will be aggraded (1899).

while reference to calibre is explicit with respect to valley-sides in:

8. Just as rivers slowly degrade their courses after the maximum load is past, so graded waste sheets adopt gentler and gentler slopes . . . when the graded slopes are first developed they are steep, and the waste that covers them is coarse and of moderate thickness . . . in a more advanced stage of the cycle graded slopes are moderate, and the waste . . . is of finer texture and greater thickness than before . . . in old age, when all the slopes are very gentle . . . the waste sheet . . . assumes a great thickness [and] is reduced to extremely fine texture (1899).

9. [On] outcrops of weaker rocks [on] freshly cut valley sides . . .

graded waste sheets are locally developed. [In] advanced old age [the] surface soil, greatly refined in surface texture by long exposure to the weather in its deliberate journey slowly creeps and washes to the streams (1902).

Once again, re-statement or reaffirmation occurs. But the immediate points are two: that it is scarcely possible to examine Davis's views on the significance of load in streams without reference to his accompanying views on hillside slopes, and that in extracts 8 and 9, as in some of the earlier quotations, he poses more problems than he answers. In one sense, the complexity of the total array of ideas results from Davis's richness of thought; in another sense, however, it signalizes a remarkable lack of caution. Many of his statements appear open to verification. It is a grave weakness of the deductive method, as Davis sought to apply it, that verification can seem unnecessary to him.

Consider for instance the central notion of balance. Having postulated that a balance will be achieved, Davis proceeds to describe how it is first achieved and how thereafter maintained. In this, he seems to fall into linguistic error. Instead of attempting to explain the attainment and maintenance of balance, he ought surely to have asked whether or not such a balance is achieved at all—that is, he should so have framed his initial question as to call for a useful answer. When the question is put as Davis put it—whether explicitly or implicitly—the type of answer possible has already been determined.

Portions of the early literature of civil engineering, from which the notion of balance seems to derive, are reviewed by Kesseli (1941) and Woodford (1951), who trace the idea of equilibrium between force and resistance from Guglielmini in 1697 (quoted by Baulig 1926), through Surell in 1841 and Dausse in 1857, to Gilbert in 1877. The view that streams adjust their slope until equilibrium is reached already appears in Guglielmini, as does the scheme of a concave-upward long-profile. Surell claimed to recognize in a mountain torrent three reaches—an eroding reach above, a depositing reach below, and an intermediate reach which, being in a state of balance, neither erodes nor deposits. Gilbert concluded that, in certain conditions of loading, the entire energy of the stream is consumed in the work of transport—i.e. that when power and load are balanced, corrasion ceases: a fully loaded stream is poised between corrasion and deposition.

It seems clear enough that Davis accepted as they stood the views expressed by Surell and Gilbert. Capacity to do work, as Davis used the phrase, cannot mean anything but capacity to transport and to

cut down. Work to be done cannot relate to anything other than
transport of delivered load to be effected, and resistance of the bed
and banks to be overcome. On the general principle that action and
reaction are equal, the notion of equilibrium between capacity and
work can, in some manner, be defended. The acceleration due to
gravity is countered by the internal friction of the flowing water and
by friction against the bed and banks of the channel—but only in
part: if it were wholly offset, the water would have nil velocity.
Similarly, Gilbert's idea of nil corrasion by a fully loaded stream is
justly challenged by Kesseli, who observes that, so long as the load
remains in motion, the bed must undergo corrasion. It follows, as
Kesseli also points out, that since underloaded and fully loaded
streams alike erode, and since overloaded streams deposit, a neutral
condition of balance is impossible.

Already, then, the idea of a graded stream as one in a state of
balance between erosion and deposition is seriously weakened. To
some extent, the difficulties, confusion, or error which are becoming
apparent seem to result from the difference between the practical
aims of engineers and the long-term interpretative purposes of geomorphologists: engineers would probably be satisfied if they could
succeed in stabilizing channels for a single lifetime, whereas the condition of grade, in the Davisian system, is supposed to persist for
many hundreds of thousands and possibly for millions of years. By
implication, Davis took note of the contrast between the short and
the long terms in dealing with the maintenance of grade after its first
attainment, although, as will now be shown, he involved himself in
this context in a kind of reversed argument.

Assuming for the moment that the concept of grade as Davis presented it is valid, then Davis was entirely correct in declining the
proposition that the establishment of grade causes downcutting to
cease. For if a trunk river becomes graded by landscape maturity, it
is entirely possible for the vertical distance between source and
mouth to be still the same then as in the preceding stage of landscape
youth. The general reduction of the landscape which the Davisian
scheme requires, between the first onset of landscape maturity and
the ultimate peneplanation, means a lowering of summits and a
marked net reduction in stream-gradients. Considerable erosion and
transport must therefore be admitted, subsequent to the first attainment of grade.

Davis's views on slope/velocity relationships, in the context of
planation, are given in:

10. . . . in old age even the headwaters must have a gentle declivity

and a moderate velocity . . . an old river must be free from rapid movement even near its head (1899).
11. In the old age of the region the . . . river will flow with sluggish current on a nearly level bed (1902).
12. In late old age even the headwater streams are weak and sluggish (1902).

As stated in the foregoing extracts 2 and 6, Davis relied on slow changes in volume and load to permit equally slow changes in slope; and extract 1 refers to a postulated reduction, from maturity onwards, both in amount and in calibre of load. Rivers on a peneplain should, according to Davis, be characterized by low gradients, low velocities, small loads consisting of fine-grained material, and volumes differing in some necessary but unspecified fashion from the volumes of maturity. However, while these various tenets seem to follow directly from the original proposition of balance, they emphatically do not follow if that proposition is declined, and do not all necessarily follow even if it be accepted. Davis appears to have reasoned as follows:

(f) Rivers can become graded (balanced) well before a landscape is peneplained—that is, while they still have much downcutting to perform.
(g) Since grade involves an equilibrium among slope, load, and velocity, since downcutting involves progressive reduction of slope, and since reduced slope means reduced velocity, *therefore*
(h) reduction of slope and velocity must be accompanied by changes in load.

Accordingly, Davis proceeds to specify the types of change in load. By so doing, he places himself in a false position, and exemplifies one of the main weaknesses of his deductive method. To repeat: his initial question should have been, Is a balance between erosion and deposition ever achieved? In the long-term context of the erosion-cycle, the answer to this question must be negative. Once the question has been so put and answered, it becomes unnecessary to postulate changes in load, velocity, and volume as compensations for reductions in slope.

As has been pointed out, some of Davis's postulates are open to testing. But it simply has not yet been verified that rivers on peneplains have lower velocities than their mature predecessors. Nor has it been demonstrated that changes in amount of load [sc., amount delivered through a given cross-section in unit time] and calibre of load [? average, median, modal, other] take place with progress of the cycle. Although Davis himself rebutted the scheme wherein the upper reaches of a river are supposed to be youthful, the middle reaches mature, and the lower reaches senile, he does not seem to have escaped its implications altogether. Calibre of bed-load poses certain problems, which cannot be examined in full without reference to secular changes in volume such as fall mainly outside the scope of the present essay. What is immediately relevant, and what seems to have been overlooked by Davis, is that calibre of material in the stream bed is controlled initially by the joint-lattices of outcrops from which the bed-material comes (cf. Hack 1957). In associating coarse load with youthful development and with steep downstream gradients, Davis seems to have ignored the fact that many headwater courses are cut in mountains where the load supplied to streams is inevitably coarse, whereas material delivered to many downstream reaches from the valley-floor or from nearby valley-sides is commonly fine- or medium-grained. In any event, his neglect to specify any scale for the measurement of calibre leaves his statements under this head no more than partially meaningful, while it is difficult to place any firm construction whatever on the expression 'an equable slope . . . along which the transportation of . . . load is the most effectively accomplished' (1902, and extract 5 above).

Another practical consideration, which seems to have attracted little notice hitherto, is that headwaters can differ signally from middle and lower reaches in their relationship of channel to valley. On the principle (which will recur below) that slope and channel-characteristics are determined by discharge at bankfull and near-bankfull stage, the shifting of very coarse debris at times of high discharge can be taken as not very relevant to the notion of grade. However, it seems desirable here to distinguish between streams on flood-plains and streams in gorges, for channel/valley relationships are not identical for the two groups. Whereas velocity in the main channels of streams on floodplains appears not to rise inordinately above bankfull velocities, even at times of very high floods, gorges appear to act as if they were V-shaped notches, permitting at times of very high stages very high velocities indeed. In some gorges, the contrast between channel and valley does not exist. Direct readings of the velocities attained at very high stage are understandably lacking, but computations from amount and intensity of storm rain and from duration of discharge combine with observations of marked super-elevation at bends and of bulky deposition beyond the gorge mouths to indicate very great power to transport remarkably coarse material. It would clearly be unreasonable, however, to make a direct comparison between events in deep, narrow, and enclosed valleys with those in valleys with open floors. But such a comparison can easily be implied by qualitative observations of the visible differences between the bedload of headwaters and that of other reaches, and can perhaps enhance the impression that steep gradients are necessarily associated with coarse calibre of load.

Again, it has yet to be verified (or falsified) that graded hillside slopes when first developed are steep and covered with coarse waste, whereas in more advanced age they acquire progressively gentle slopes, and become progressively thickly covered with waste of increasing fineness (extracts 8, 9). In addition, the implications about speed of movement of waste—supposed to be greater on first establishment of grade than late in the cycle—still remain to be tested. This is not the place to discuss the proposition of downwasting, which is made to follow deductively from the idea of graded slopes covered in rock-waste; but the serious lack of information about this whole topic requires Davis's statements to be regarded, not as descriptions of what actually happens, but as expressions of personal views of what *may* be happening. Moreover, logical cases can be argued, beginning with the proposition of balance, for graded hillside slopes very different from those which Davis envisaged. Since a balance between erosion and deposition should permit transport of all material delivered from above, but no corrasion of the transporting slope, this slope could therefore conceivably be that of a scree, that of a hillside cut in rock but uniformly mantled with waste, or one cut in bare rock which experiences neither erosion nor deposition.

The last case has its fluvial analogy in Johnson's attempt (1932) to explain so-called rock-fans in arid regions. As is well known, Johnson regarded the features in question as associated with the middle reaches of streams which he supposed to erode in their upper reaches—i.e. within the mountain rims of desert basins—to deposit in the basin centres, and to be balanced between erosion and deposition in the piedmont areas. But Johnson's exposition has been overtaken by work on pediments, while the whole idea of a strict balance between power and load has been strongly challenged by Kesseli, who demonstrates that Surell's notion of balance in the mid-part of a mountain torrent applies, when closely examined, not to a reach but to a point. If he does not by this immediate means succeed in confuting the argument from aggradation (or from infilling), Kesseli does at least reveal the exceedingly slight nature of one of the bases on which rests the Davisian concept of grade. He also removes the justification for Johnson's views on rock-fans in arid regions, and forestalls the above suggestion that some graded hillside slopes could be cut in bare rock. It may be well to reiterate that this suggestion is introduced merely as a possible logical inference from Davis's propositions. The hypothetical hillside slopes in question are not identical with stripped benches and stripped hilltops. But stripped flat-lying surface also confute the propositions offered by Davis, for they require material to be moved across, and removed from, slopes of very low gradient, instead of accumulating thickly in accordance with the principle of grade. Furthermore, the idea that waste on gentle slopes is necessarily of fine texture has yet to be investigated.

Dealing with the balance between power of streams and stream-load, Kesseli declares this to be a postulate which remains unsupported by observations. He states that the attributes commonly associated with all graded rivers are incompatible with the postulate. Reasoning from the variability of discharge, he concludes that there is no time when graded conditions are attainable, either along the full length or along a large sector of the course, and recommends that a graded stream be taken as one without waterfalls or rapids. That is to say, he defines grade in terms of profile [whether or not obviously broken] instead of in terms of transporting power, load, velocity, or tendency to cut or to fill. To this extent his proposed redefinition is limited. It has the advantage of being workable, but offers little scope for the introduction of hydrologic principles. As will appear presently, these principles themselves in their usual forms are coming to be regarded as deficient for purposes of describing, defining, and interpreting the behaviour of rivers; but it is not surprising that Kesseli has been subjected to challenge on hydrologic grounds.

In opposition to Kesseli, Mackin (1948) undertakes to modify and extend the theory of grade originally set forth by Gilbert and Davis. He regards as indispensable the concept of equilibrium in streams as transporting agents. However, he rejects the strict view that a graded stream is one in which energy and work are balanced; the proposition that in a graded stream slope is adjusted to load; the idea of a graded stream as one loaded to capacity (because streams never carry capacity loads by Gilbert's definition); and the inference that a graded stream cannot abrade its bed because all its energy is used in transportation. Mackin redefines a graded stream as:

> ... one in which, over a period of years, slope is delicately adjusted to provide, with available discharge and with prevailing channel characteristics, just the velocity required for the transportation of load supplied from the drainage basin. The graded stream is a stream in equilibrium; its diagnostic characteristic is that any change in any of the controlling factors will cause a displacement

of the equilibrium in a direction that will tend to absorb the effects of the change.

Now although Mackin supplies extensive commentary on the implications of this redefinition, it does not seem greatly to advance the discussion of the concept of grade. Its references to channel-characteristics, to velocity, and to absorption of the effects of change are useful and constructive; but what it amounts to is a re-statement (explicitly made elsewhere in Mackin's paper) that a graded stream neither cuts nor fills. Once again, linguistic difficulties appear. In beginning with the view that the concept of equilibrium is indispensable, Mackin limits in advance the scope of his treatment—as will become clearer below when the concept of quasi-equilibrium is introduced. Using the notion of equilibrium as his point of departure, Mackin obliges himself to frame his redefinition of grade in a particular manner. It would surely have been better, not to begin with equilibrium and to aim at a definition of grade, but to ask (in this particular context) whether or not, over a term of years, any streams do fail either to cut or to fill their valleys; and, if they do so fail, why this should be.

Because Mackin uses the expression *over a term of years* to exclude seasonal and suchlike fluctuations, he is able to free his argument from the effects of short-term changes, for instance those involved in the rise and fall of a single peak of discharge. But because he means it also to exclude the exceedingly slow changes which accompany the progress of the erosion-cycle, he provides no help in understanding how grade, if definable and if ever achieved, could be maintained during the general reduction of the landscape. He does admittedly envisage a state of shifting equilibrium, wherein a graded stream responds to a change which tends to cause downcutting by lowering itself so slowly that approximate adjustment is maintained; but he clearly regards this approximate adjustment as differing from the graded condition in the strict sense. Because, however, the long-term activity of rivers is a leading interest of geomorphology, and because this activity includes the progressive reduction of downstream slope, Mackin's deliberate restriction of his terms of reference seems to make his discussion in large part irrelevant to geomorphological problems. In making allowance for shifting equilibrium, Mackin does little more than Davis had previously done in calling for progressive but slow changes in the factors of control.

As his text shows, Mackin regards transporting power as depending on velocity, and velocity as depending on slope. Velocity here presumably relates to mean velocity through the cross-section, while slope may be taken as the downstream slope of the floodplain, or of the water-surface at the bankfull stage. Complications arise where natural levees occur, for the definition of bankfull stage on naturally embanked rivers remains imprecise and unsatisfying. Additional complications are encountered where rivers are now cutting slightly into their floodplains, without however ceasing to inundate them, and without as yet having developed new floodplains at levels slightly below those of existing valley-bottoms. Such matters as these, however, concern techniques of observation rather than the concept of equilibrium.

Mackin observes that energy can be dissipated as heat developed by viscous shear within the stream, by external friction loss along the wetted perimeter, by internal friction loss among turbulent threads of current, and in transporting load. He quotes Rubey (1952) to the effect that frictional energy loss is 96 per cent or more in some streams, and notes that slight changes in channel characteristics (roughness, alignment, form) cause marked changes in transporting power. He correctly states that mere increase in discharge in the downstream direction requires—or permits—downstream decrease of slope, on account of the reduced friction which results from downstream changes in channel form. In all probability, downstream increase in size of channel, quite apart from changes in form, should be taken also as tending to reduce the average effect of friction on unit volume of water; the usual downstream decrease in calibre of load acts in the same sense, by decreasing channel roughness. Mackin's treatment of channel characteristics lead directly towards later work, in which these characteristics receive even greater prominence, and where the concave-upward form of long-profiles is dealt with in terms of the hydraulic properties of channels instead of in terms of balance between capacity and work. But the very high proportion of frictional energy loss which Mackin signalizes, and the powerful effects of changes in channel characteristics which he also records, ought, it would seem, to place the matter of balance between cutting and filling in a greatly reduced perspective, instead of in the foreground of the argument which it occupies with Mackin.

Although Mackin identified part at least of the complex of factors which require, or permit, downstream decrease of slope, he is still able to claim (p. 488) that velocity also decreases in the downstream direction. There seems no *a priori* reason why this should be so; and the tendency of recent work in observation and analysis seems to be to demonstrate a constant velocity along the length of the stream, when this velocity is measured at the bankfull stage. Analysis of bankfull velocities is handicapped by the dredging and embanking of river-channels, and also by the customary practice of taking records at bridges, where cross-sections are mainly artificial and where velocity-values can be greatly disturbed at all but low stages of flow. Mean-time, however, if the available records do not justify a definitive statement about constant velocity along the length of the stream at the bankfull stage, they equally do not justify claims that velocity decreases in the downstream direction. Mean velocity, indeed, has been shown to *increase* in the downstream direction (Leopold 1953) —a circumstance which suggests, on general grounds, that constant velocity is expectable at some stage between the stage of mean dis-charge and any stages of high overbank discharge which can be shown to correspond to downstream decreases in velocity. By intro-ducing channel-characteristics into his discussion of downstream change in slope, Mackin departs radically from the views expressed by Davis, e.g. in extract 2 above, and the form of his argument would be unaffected by any corrections which became necessary to his state-ments about velocity. But if constant velocity along the length at the bankfull stage can be conclusively demonstrated, even for no more than a sizable reach where gradient decreases significantly in the downstream direction, then another redefinition of grade becomes possible, in terms of velocity alone; the hypothesis seems at least worthy of investigation, that a graded stream (or graded reach) is one where the bankfull stage is associated with constant velocity through the cross-section.

Since velocity is affected not only by volume and by slope, but also by channel-characteristics, account must be taken even in preliminary investigation and reasoning of the form of the cross-section. A princi-pal distinction here is that between single channels on the one hand and braided channels on the other: single channels, constituting the more efficient group (cf. Leopold and Wolman 1957) require the slighter downstream slopes, volume for volume of water. Mackin (p. 487) holds that change from meandering to braiding may result from increase of load, but it is difficult to envisage the short-distance changes in load which would be required to explain the alternation on certain rivers of braided and meandering reaches. A more likely view of braiding is that it constitutes a response to highly erodible banks; and if this is so, then the discussion of slope/velocity relation-ships becomes still further detached from questions of material in transport.

In his concluding summary, Mackin states (p. 491) that each seg-ment of a graded stream has the slope that will provide the velocity required for transportation of all the load supplied to it from above. In one sense, this is no more than a re-statement of the postulate that a graded stream neither cuts nor fills; but in another sense it reveals the difficulties into which Mackin's line of argument leads. If this proposition relative to slope/velocity/transport is accepted, then no stream which fails to possess the velocity which permits it to transport all the supplied load is a graded stream, and streams which by this definition are ungraded cannot provide data for use in definition and analysis of the graded condition.

If Mackin's views on grade are to be useful in the study of natural rivers, then graded streams as he defines them could, perhaps, be expected to occur numerously in nature. Reasons will now be given, quite independent of the long-term tendency of streams to cut down, for considering that streams exhibiting a fine balance among velocity, load, slope, and transporting power are likely to be most uncommon at the present day. Many existing rivers of mid-latitudes have been reduced to a misfit condition by shifts in climate (Dury 1954, 1958, 1960, 1964, 1965). In consequence, the beds of many river-channels are separated from the underlying bedrock by fill, in which the bases of existing floodplains are cut. It may have been this fact which led Kesseli to regard floodplains as resulting from alluviation; even the moderate statement of Baulig (1926), that a graded river should flow on a continuous bed of alluvium, makes no allowance for the possible contact of the stream with bedrock at times of scour. But beyond all this, the alternating history of cut-and-fill which typifies very many valleys and very many streams during at least the last 12,000 years, and the demonstrable alternation of braiding-plus-filling with meandering-plus-cutting which occurred on certain rivers throughout the glacial Pleistocene (cf. Troll 1954) suggests that the concept of grade as a balance between infilling and excavation has very little relevance to the development of the actual streams which exist today. Whether it bears on pre-Pleistocene events remains to be established.

In calling for just that velocity which will permit transportation of load supplied, Mackin appears to assume that the supplied load will in fact be moved. The results of study of climatic shifts in relation to stream-channels greatly enlarge the scope of enquiry into precisely what does happen to very large rock-fragments which fall into stream-beds. In some valleys, part at least of what now constitutes coarse bed-material was fed into the valley-bottom in conditions unlike those of today—e.g. conditions of periglacial climate, of very high runoff in the short term, or of both together. It follows therefore that existing bed-material may by no means indicate the transporting power of present-day streams. Both in this connection, and in relation to present-day falls of large rocks, it seems necessary to concede that some detached fragments are capable of acting as bedrock in place.

To this extent, analyses of particle-size and block-size seem not to be sufficient in themselves: data on movement are also required.

This and similar considerations reinforce the view that empirical observations of actual streams are more likely to produce coherent and satisfying descriptions of fluvial behaviour than is reasoning based on first assumptions. Nevertheless, empirical work can still be expected to lead to the formulation and testing of hypotheses, and eventually to theoretical statements, as is usual in natural science. In quite recent years, a series of enquiries made by the U.S. Geological Survey, beginning empirically but taking on a progressively theoretical cast, has led to the emphasizing not of precise balance but of quasi-equilibrium or steady-state. References to equilibrium or to the state of grade do in fact occur in the relevant papers, but seem to be introduced rather for the sake of establishing some kind of connection with previous writing, than to provide end-points of discussion. Even when grade, or equilibrium, is specifically mentioned, the condition identified is that of approximate equilibrium and not of exact poise.

For instance, Leopold and Maddock (1953) describe the equilibrium-profile as differing from all other possible profiles in the relative rates of increase of velocity and depth in the downstream direction (p. 50), but go on to identify slope as the one factor which can be adjusted over a period of time by changes within the stream, and which makes the final adjustment for *quasi*-equilibrium (pp. 51–2). It is clear from the full context that the two authors do not regard the term *equilibrium-profile* as implying an exact equilibrium among the factors at work. They conclude (p. 51) that the average system of river-channels tends so to develop as to produce an *approximate* equilibrium between the channel on the one hand, and the water and sediment it must transport on the other. This approximate equilibrium, identified by a tendency towards a regular downstream increase of width and depth, is associated with an increase in discharge and decrease in slope in the same direction. It can be identified not only in lower and middle reaches, but also in headstreams which, because they are manifestly downcutting, cannot be called graded in the sense of being balanced or poised.

Leopold and Maddock place more stress on adjustments in cross-section, as opposed to those in slope, than do most previous writers on the subject. They regard slope as determined primarily by physiographic history. Their conclusion, that conditions of approximate equilibrium tend to be established in a given reach as soon as a more or less smooth long-profile has been established, recalls the limited and general definition of the graded condition offered by Kesseli, but

Leopold and Maddock use in their reasoning quantitative specifications of systematic variation in fluvial geometry and fluvial behaviour along the length of a stream. On their view, the elimination of falls and rapids would appear not so much diagnostic in itself, as the process whereby a continuous channel is established. Once such a channel exists, quantitative descriptions of the stream fail to provide criteria whereby so-called graded reaches can be distinguished from so-called ungraded reaches. The notion of the graded condition, as first established in the lower course and as extended progressively headwards, seems irrelevant to the facts of nature.

In relying on physiographic history as the ultimate determinant of slope, and in allowing for continued downcutting, Leopold and Maddock take account of actualities: flowing water acts, in the long run, to strip away the land. Although, however, slope is but one of the factors in hydraulic geometry, it can be considered the sole fully dependent factor, and thus different in kind from those other factors which contribute to channel characteristics. Load and discharge, which are characteristics of the drainage basin, constitute independent factors. Width, depth, velocity, bed roughness, and size of sediment-particles are semi-dependent factors. The shape of the cross-section (width/depth ratio) determines the distribution of velocity and of shear; for a given width and discharge, total load depends on the ratio of velocity to depth; and velocity/depth ratio is provided in part by adjustment of bed roughness, which is itself a function of grain-size and of suspended-sediment concentration. Changes in the velocity/depth ratio, such as are required for quasi-equilibrium with load, are brought about primarily by changes in bed roughness, in association with changes in the concentration of suspended sediment.

Merely to list the factors with which Leopold and Maddock deal is to re-emphasize the crudity of attempts to describe grade in terms of power to erode or to transport. The interrelationships of certain variables, and the change in these interrelationships along the length of a stream, are especially instructive. Thus, Leopold and Maddock explain differences in the concavity of long-profiles by differences in the relationship of velocity and depth to discharge; they show that, for a given stream, a downstream decrease in slope is *necessary*, in conditions of nearly constant roughness, to provide the required velocity/depth ratio. In this way, the observed concave-upward form of long-profiles becomes entirely detached from any postulated equivalence between power and work: it follows directly from the principles of fluvial mechanics. In any event, as has been pointed out, insistence on precise equilibrium, among whatever quantities, becomes no longer essential when quasi-equilibrium is alone at issue;

and with its abandonment go the linguistic difficulties which it entrains.

The possible complexity of the interrelationship among load, channel form, slope, and the processes of cutting and filling enjoin great caution on the use of former profiles as reconstructed from terraces. The technical difficulties of specifying profiles by empirical equations, and the serious doubts which apply to the extrapolation of profiles to past base-levels, have been well demonstrated by Miller (1939), without however preventing repeated subsequent exercises in extrapolation by other writers. In direct contrast to Mackin's claim (Mackin, *op. cit.* 1948) that terraces can be used to indicate or to restore the graded profiles of former times, studies of existing streams indicate that quasi-equilibrium can obtain where long-profiles are anything but regularly concave-upward. Wolman (1955) identifies quasi-equilibrium on most reaches of Brandywine Creek, Pennsylvania, despite the fact that the profiles of both main branches are interrupted by nickpoints; moreover, the nickpoints are *not* associated with increases in velocity (p. 48). Wolman, whose results accord completely with the conclusions of Leopold and Maddock, infers that adjustments on the Brandywine have been made both in section and in slope, and observes that no definition of grade should show preference for adjustments in slope as opposed to those in cross-section (pp. 45, 47).

These alternate possibilities of adjustment mean that many rivers need never achieve completely smooth long-profiles, and also that, if such profiles are ever developed, they need not be maintained. The onset of braiding in some reaches of a meandering stream, or of meandering in some reaches of a braided stream, can be expected to involve changes of slope sufficient to appear in a profile diagram. But nickpoints can also be generated by changes which do not involve alteration of channel-habit: wherever the qualities of bed and bank material, on a single non-braiding channel, cause the cross-section to become either less or more efficient than is usual on the particular stream, adjustments of slope are to be expected. Efficiency both greater and less than usual is entirely possible—e.g. outcropping bedrock may act to make a channel wide at the expense of depth, or deep at the expense of width. If there is such a thing as an average form of channel, it is less efficient than a semi-circular cross-section, because bank-material is normally too weak to sustain the semi-circular form and the form of the bed is affected by material in transit. For all these reasons, a considerable potential range of slope must be admitted for quasi-equilibrium in given conditions of load and discharge. It must also be conceded that nickpoints can be generated in mid-profile, independently of shifts of the controlling base-level.

Wolman takes local geology as the determinant of the initial size, slope, and resistance of material delivered to the channel (cf. Hack, *op. cit.* 1957), and considers geology to set limits to the operation of discharge and suspended load. Traction-load introduces still further complications, additional to those of climatic history which are briefly stated above. Leopold and Wolman (1956; cf. also Wolman and Eiler 1958) describe erosion, transport, and deposition on Connecticut streams as patchy and irregular during great floods, e.g. that of 1955, which succeeded in moving large boulders through reaches where gravel remained undisturbed. Quite obviously, calibre of load is not the only control of movement in given conditions of discharge. For all that, the hydraulic geometry of the Connecticut streams is generally similar to that of the Rio Grande system, where scour-and-fill is associated with the annual flood-flows produced by snowmelt (Leopold and Wolman, *op. cit.* 1956).

The middle reaches of the Rio Grande are subject to scour during high flows, but the channel fills almost to its pre-flood level as the flood recedes. Large suspension-loads, high velocities, and shallow depths are typical of the rising limb of the flood in the middle reaches. Farther downstream, however, suspension-load is greater on the falling than on the rising limb of the flood, being accompanied by high velocity, shallow depth, and increasing elevation of the bed. Deposition in the lower reaches occurs when velocities are greatest, near the time of peak discharge. Although the differences are not understood which separate rising and falling stage, and the contrasted modes of behaviour of the middle and the lower reaches, roughness seems likely to be an important factor. As Leopold and Wolman state, it is impossible to say which is cause and which is effect of increased roughness and decreased suspension-load. The uncertainty here signalized throws more doubt than ever on efforts to equate transporting-power with total load. The observed modes of relationship among depth, velocity, suspension-load, incidence of scour and fill, and rise or fall of stage show once again that the simple connections required by the concept of grade do not obtain in nature. They commend to the future an enquiry into the conditions which make long-term sedimentation possible, independently of tectonic influences and also of climatic shifts.

Leopold and Wolman (1957) take up some of the implications of the work of Einstein and Barbarossa (1951), drawing attention to the complexity of the way in which roughness is determined. They observe (pp. 71–2) that, if part only of the size-range of particles can be moved, then mean size of bed-material increases, and slope must increase in consequence. But when the configuration of the bed enters into the determination of roughness, then resistance is not necessarily governed by calibre of load. Where no change in roughness occurs at constant discharge, a large increase of load is *not* accompanied by an appreciable increase in slope. In certain quite probable circumstances, an increase in load is capable of leading to an *increase* in velocity. Both aggradation and degradation, therefore, may occur without increase in slope.

These and other discussions of roughness show that bed-load and suspension-load need to be considered separately, in relation not only to discharge, but also to width/depth ratio and to roughness. Davis's original contention that calibre of load decreases progressively with advance of the erosion-cycle ought, presumably, to suggest an accompanying decrease in roughness. Whether or not this latter decrease could serve to maintain velocity on the progressively-decreasing downstream gradients of a wasting landmass remains to be investigated; but, until it has been investigated, there seems no reason to accept out-of-hand the idea of a progressive decrease in velocity with advance of the cycle, and more than the idea of a progressive downstream decrease in velocity on a given stream at a given time.

Very little now remains of the concept of grade, as usually stated in relation to streams. Kesseli's doubts on the value and validity of the concept are strongly reinforced. The writings of Leopold, Maddock, and Wolman deal with streams not as exemplifying some particular condition, but as working systems. Furthermore, systematic workings can extend not merely into distant headwaters, but also on to the interfluves themselves, for some catchments are known to supply remarkably even increments of water per unit area, throughout a range of discharge which widely brackets the bankfull stage (cf. Dury 1959). Breaks of long-profile on the trunk streams do not exclude highly systematized discharge of wet-weather rills and of surface flow generally; nor do marked breaks of profile on the trunk inhibit a remarkably systematic downstream increase in amount and duration of bankfull discharge (Dury 1962; cf. also Green and Hoggatt 1960).

Wolman and Miller (1960) draw attention to the geomorphic significance of events of moderate magnitude but of frequent recurrence, such as bankfull discharge by rivers, at or near which Wolman and Miller regard the dimensions of meandering channels as shaped. They also show, by an analysis of records, that much of the total load carried by many rivers is transported by flows which occur on the average once or twice each year—that is, as can be shown by analysis, flows of about bankfull. Although Mackin's definition of the graded condition would exclude from the discussion as irrelevant the changes produced by near-bankfull flow, or the annual scour-and-fill on the Rio Grande, the fact remains that it is by events of these kinds that long-profiles, in addition to channels, are determined. Whether or not these events can be brought within the scope of linguistic postulates does not seem germane to the investigation of the behaviour of actual rivers, or even to theoretical analyses based on that investigation.

Leopold and Langbein (1962) further the discussion of downstream slope, and of stream-profiles, by introducing the concept of entropy into a theoretical analysis of landscape-evolution. They rely on the principle that, in a river system, the most probable condition exists when energy is as uniformly distributed as may be permitted by physical constraints. They derive theoretical long-profiles which are mathematically comparable to observed profiles, and conclude that the most probable profiles approach to the condition in which the downstream rate of production of entropy per unit mass is constant. In this, they go beyond the findings of Leopold and Maddock (*op. cit.* 1953), for they also state that hydraulic equations are insufficient to determine the velocity, depths, and slopes of rivers which are themselves the authors of their hydraulic geometries. Their solutions rely on the principle that the distribution of energy tends towards the most probable, as they illustrate by means of random-walk models.

One outcome of this analysis is that the most probable long-profile takes on an exponential form; departures from this form represent increasing degrees of improbability (p. A11). Variations in profile due to changes in rock type persist for periods of time which depend on the scale of the constraint. Theoretical considerations make it difficult to believe that long periods of time could elapse, in field conditions, before fluvial systems approach the condition of quasi-equilibrium. As Leopold and Langbein remark, their conclusions about the span of time needed to achieve a state of quasi-equilibrium accord with those reached, by other methods of reasoning, by Hack (1960). None of these three authors supports the Davisian concept that geomorphic youth is characterized by disequilibrium for an interval of any significant length. Once again, therefore, because the concept of grade necessarily involves the converse idea of an ungraded state, it is to be recognized as unserviceable both in the study of actual terrains and in the theoretical analysis of landform generally.

## References

Baulig, H., 1926. 'La notion de profil d'équilibre: histoire et critique.' *C.R. Congr. Internat. de Géog.* (1925), 3, 51–63.

Dausse, M. F. B., 1857. 'Note sur un principe important et nouveau d'hydraulique.' *C.R. Acad. Sci.* (Paris), 44, 757–66.

Davis, W. M., 1894. 'Physical geography as a university study.' *Journ. Geology*, 2, 66–100.

Davis, W. M., 1902. 'Base-level, grade, and peneplain.' *Journ. Geology*, 10, 77–111.

Davis, W. M., 1909. *Geographical Essays*. Ginn & Co., Boston, New York, Chicago and London.

Dury, G. H., 1954. 'Contribution to a general theory of meandering valleys. *Amer. Journ. Sci.*, 252, 193–224.

Dury, G. H., 1958. 'Tests of a general theory of misfit streams.' *Trans. Inst. Brit. Geog.*, 25, 105–18.

Dury, G. H., 1959. 'Analysis of regional flood frequency on the Nene and the Great Ouse.' *Geog. Journ.*, 125, 223–9.

Dury, G. H., 1960. 'Misfit streams: problems in interpretation, discharge, and distribution.' *Geog. Review*, 50 (2), 219–42.

Dury, G. H., 1962. 'Bankfull discharge: an example of its statistical relationships.' *Bull. Internat. Assoc. Sci. Hydrology*, vi année (3), 48–55.

Dury, G. H., 1964. 'Principles of underfit streams.' Professional Paper 452-A, U.S. Geol. Survey, Washington D.C., and 'Subsurface exploration and chronology of underfit streams.' Professional Paper 452-B, U.S. Geol. Survey, Washington D.C.

Dury, G. H., 1965. 'Theoretical implications of underfit streams.' Professional Paper 452-C, U.S. Geol. Survey, Washington D.C.

Einstein, H. A., and Barbarossa, N. L., 1952. 'River channel roughness.' *Trans. Amer. Soc. Civ. Engrs.*, 117, 1121–46.

Gannett, H., 1896. 'Physiographic types', in U.S. Geol. Survey, *Topog. Atlas U.S., Folio 1*, Washington D.C.

Gilbert, G. K., 1876. 'The Colorado Plateau Province as a field for geological study.' *Amer. Journ. Sci.*, 12, 16–24, 85–103.

Gilbert, G. K., 1877. 'Report on the Geology of the Henry Mountains.' U.S. Geog. & Geol. Survey, Washington D.C.

Green, A. Rice, and Hoggatt, Richard E., 1960. 'Floods in Indiana, Magnitude and Frequency.' U.S. Geol. Survey, in co-operation with the State of Indiana. Indianapolis, Indiana (open file).

Hack, John T., 1957. 'Studies of longitudinal stream profiles in Virginia and Maryland.' Professional Paper 294-B, U.S. Geol. Survey, Washington D.C.

Hack, John T., 1960. 'Interpretation of erosional topography in humid temperate regions.' *Amer. Journ. Sci.*, 258-A (Bradley Volume), 80–97.

Johnson, D., 1932. 'Rock fans of arid regions.' *Amer. Journ. Sci.*, 223, 389–416.

Johnson, W. D., 1901. 'The High Plains and their Utilization.' *U.S. Geol. Survey, Ann. Rept.*, 21, Washington D.C., 601–741.

Kesseli, John E., 1941. 'The concept of the graded river.' *Journ. Geology*, 49, 561–88.

Leopold, Luna B., 1953. 'Downstream change of velocity in rivers.' *Amer. Journ. Sci.*, 251, 606–24.

Leopold, Luna B., and Langbein, Walter B., 1962. 'The concept of entropy in landscape evolution.' Professional Paper 500-A, U.S. Geol. Survey, Washington D.C.

Leopold, Luna B., and Maddock, Thomas, 1953. 'The hydraulic geometry of stream channels and some physiographic implications.' Professional Paper 252, U.S. Geol. Survey, Washington D.C.

Leopold, Luna B., and Wolman, M. Gordon, 1956. 'Floods in relation to the river channel.' *Darcy Symposia, Assoc. Internat. d'Hydrol.*, publication 42, Dijon, 85–98.

Leopold, Luna B., and Wolman, M. Gordon, 1957. 'River channel patterns: braided, meandering, and straight.' Professional Paper 282-B, U.S. Geol. Survey, Washington D.C.

McGee, W. J., 1891. 'The Pleistocene History of Northeastern Iowa.' *U.S. Geol. Survey, Ann. Rept.* 11, Washington D.C., 189–577.

Mackin, J. Hoover, 1948. 'Concept of the graded river.' *Bull. Geol. Soc. Amer.*, 59, 463–512

Miller, A. A., 1939. 'Attainable standards of accuracy in the determination of preglacial sea levels by physiographic method.' *Journ. Geomorph.*, 2, 95–115.

Rubey, W. W., 1952. 'Geology and mineral resources of the Hardin and Brussels quadrangles (Illinois).' Professional Paper 218, U.S. Geol. Survey, Washington D.C.

Surell, A., 1841. *Étude sur les torrents des Hautes-Alpes.*

Troll, K., 1954. 'Über Alter und Bildung von Talmäändern.' *Erdkunde*, 8 (4), 287–302.

Wolman, M. Gordon, 1955. 'The natural channel of Brandywine Creek, Pennsylvania.' Professional Paper 271, U.S. Geol. Survey, Washington D.C.

Wolman, M. Gordon, and Eiler, Jack P., 1958. 'Reconnaissance study of erosion and deposition produced by the flood of August 1955 in Connecticut.' *Trans. Amer. Geophys. Union*, 39 (1), 1–14.

Wolman, M. Gordon, and Miller, John P., 1960. 'Magnitude and frequency of forces in geomorphic processes.' *Journ. Geology*, 68 (1), 54–74.

Woodford, A. O., 1951. 'Stream gradients and Monterey Sea Valley.' *Bull. Geol. Soc. Amer.*, 62, 799–852.

# Morphometry from Maps

## JOHN I. CLARKE

Morphometry may be defined as the measurement and mathematical analysis of the configuration of the earth's surface and of the shape and dimensions of its landforms. The main aspects examined are the area, altitude, volume, slope, profile and texture of the land as well as the varied characteristics of rivers and drainage basins. A wide variety of methods are employed, which can be classified in different ways (Dury 1952, Christian, Jennings and Twidale 1957) and lead to expression by graphs, maps or statistical indices.

The term *morphometry* is a comparative newcomer to geomorphological and cartographic texts in English, though not those in French or German. Some confusion may have arisen from the tendency to group certain morphometric methods under the heading 'slope analysis'. The explanation may be that morphometry is increasingly concerned with the measurement of slope, now recognized as the cardinal relief feature. Further confusion may be due to the use of the term in connection with the measurement of dimensions of pebbles.

Morphometry is not new, but its aims and methods have evolved (Birot 1955, Baulig 1957, 1959). Some of the methods now in current use were devised during the last century, although today they are often put to new purposes. Broadly speaking, measurements by nineteenth-century physiographers were largely for the sake of description, especially in relation to the comparative study of continents. It was hoped that area–height relationships would reveal significant structural levels. A number of calculations were made of average height, volume, average slope as well as the construction of hypsographic, clinographic and hypsoclinographic curves. Unfortunately, early morphometry suffered from inadequate and inaccurate small-scale maps.

During the present century, morphometry has been used primarily to facilitate description of specific relief features—erosion-surfaces, slopes, valleys—and that of the character of relief-as-a-whole. It has also been used as direct or indirect evidence for the genesis and evolution of certain landforms. The study of long-profiles of rivers provides one instance. In this second phase, morphometry had relied chiefly on the analysis of large-scale topographic maps.

Since World War II, morphometry has entered a third phase, in which it is concerned mainly with intensive analysis of small morphological units—notably drainage-basins. Its aims are to determine the nature of erosion, and the formation of slopes, in order to elucidate morphological laws. This phase of micro-morphometry requires precise field measurements, intensification of statistical analysis, study of erosion in homogeneous materials, and attempts to isolate the several effects of climate, geology, and vegetation. Micro-morphometry is of course closely associated with dynamic geomorphology, which is concerned with morphogenetic processes and morphogenetic environments. In short, morphometry has gone into the field.

No phase in the development of morphometry has been free from differences of opinion over the value of methods, whether general or particular. Exponents of morphometry have stressed above all the value of quantitative data and of objective measurement (De Martonne 1934, Jovanović 1940, Péguy 1942, 1947, 1948, De Smet 1951, 1954, and Strahler 1950, 1954, 1958). The initiator of much of the recent American work in micro-morphometry, Strahler has repeatedly emphasized the need to substitute quantitative statements for the qualitative statements of the Davisian school, and to replace geographical and descriptive analysis of landforms by statistical and dimensional analysis.

Critics of morphometry have stressed the difficulty of measuring the complexity and polymorphism of nature (Penck 1894); have considered that morphometry has no value in genetic explanation (Hettner 1921); or have made reservations about its utility and significance (Clarke and Orrell 1958, Baulig 1959).

Arguments against morphometric methods have included the following:

(a) that they reveal little in geomorphology that could not be discovered without their aid; in other words, that they are demonstrative rather than fundamental;

(b) that they are apt to give a false impression of objectivity, whereas the maps and/or field work upon which the data are based are inherently subjective and selective;

(c) that many morphometric methods rely on point or linear sampling, which may be hazardous when applied to areas of complex relief influenced by many sets of variables;

(d) that morphometry from maps is dependent upon contours, which are themselves merely regular linear samples of relief from which spatial diversity cannot be more than inferred: contours also vary in their significance;

(e) that cartographic subjectivity, or operator variance, is far from negligible, and that the mode of presentation of data may greatly influence subsequent interpretation;

(f) that great difficulty is experienced in the delineation on maps or in the field of breaks and inflexions of slope;

(g) that similar difficulty is encountered in the delimitation of areas possessing certain uniformity, e.g. of slope or ruggedness;

(h) that the time involved in morphometric analysis is excessive and not commensurate with the returns;

(i) that micro-morphometry of small areas in homogeneous materials will not necessarily assist in macro-morphology of large areas of complex materials;

(j) that measurement of the part played in the formation of relief by isolated factors at a moment or during a period of time may not be always valuable, as landforms are wholes which evolve in an irregular and discontinuous manner.

These objections may seem formidable. Indeed, morphometry from maps can admittedly attain but a low degree of accuracy, and a much higher degree is not always attainable by field methods. Moreover, most geomorphologists who have used morphometry agree that several different methods are advisable in the analysis of a single area or feature. In the study of erosion-platforms, for example, one might employ clinographic and altimetric frequency-curves, generalized contours, projected profiles, average slope maps, and hill-top envelope maps: the choice would depend upon the size of the area and on the character of relief. Height–range diagrams (Coleman 1954, Miller 1955) may also be constructed, but these are based on field analysis.

This paper will confine its attention to one aspect of morphometry from maps: the uses and merits of hypsometric, clinographic and altimetric frequency-curves. Although many of these curves are frequently employed, their relative merits are not always appreciated. Several of their originators have justifiably complained that their intentions have been misinterpreted by subsequent users.

## Hypsometry

Hypsometry is the measurement of the interrelationships of area and altitude. It has been used to depict steps on the earth's surface as a whole, or in countries, regions and drainage-basins. Data may be obtained (*a*) by measuring the areas between successive contours by polar planimeter, (*b*) by cutting along the contours and weighing the intervening strips, or (*c*) by mesh-sampling.

The third method is the least precise; on the other hand, sampling by groups of people can save time. It is important, however, to make numerous checks of sample data. One mesh-sampling technique, used by Wooldridge (1928) and described by Miller (1953), utilizes the lengths of intercepts along the equidistant parallel lines. The sums of the lengths of intercontour intercepts are considered proportional to intercontour areas. A test of this method, shown in Fig. 1, was carried out for the islands of Gozo and Guernsey. As seen in Fig. 2, Gozo is the more severe test of method, being the more dissected; an arbitrary

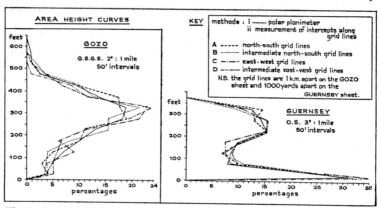

Fig. 1. Area-height curves of Gozo and Guernsey. Data calculated (i) by use of polar planimeter and (ii) by measuring intercepts along grid lines.

mesh is likely to miss several of its isolated mesas. Nevertheless, the results of four separate sets of grid lines are significantly alike.

De Smet (1954) has applied a second sampling technique to studies of the Ardennes, taking heights of the intersections of a superimposed grid to represent average height. Successively using squares of 250, 500, 1000 and 2000 metre side, De Smet found a close but diminishing degree of correlation with planimetric measurements. Geyl (1961a) found that this technique 'showed only a rather small frequency variation and only moderate agreement'. Obviously, it is not useful except in application to large areas.

A third sampling technique, suitable for determining the average height of a region, is to obtain the mean height of each grid square, either by finding the mean of the highest and lowest points (Miller 1953), or by adding the sum of the heights of the four corners to the

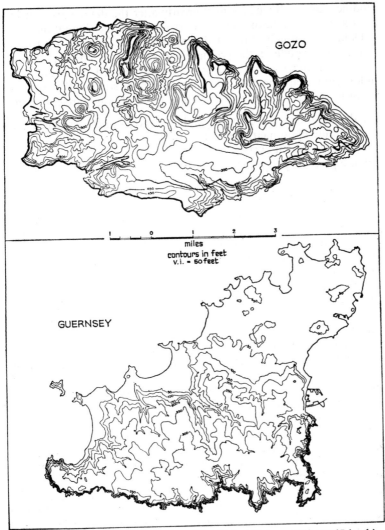

Fig. 2. Contour maps of Gozo (Maltese Islands) and Guernsey (Channel Islands). In several places contours have been omitted for clarity.

product of four times the height of the centre point and dividing by eight.

All hypsometric measurements are tedious, and much of their value depends upon satisfactory selection of the area analysed. Slight modifications of boundary may greatly alter the data. Variation in accuracy and significance of contours forms another limitation.

Data are normally presented graphically, as frequency-distributions, with altitude on the ordinate and area on the abscissa. Arithmetic, logarithmic or probability graphs may be used, the advantages of logarithmic and probability paper lying in the study of the normality of hypsometric distributions. Three types of graph are common:

(a) the hypsometric (or hypsographic) curve, sometimes called the absolute hypsometric curve;
(b) the area–height curve;
(c) the percentage hypsometric curve.

### (a) The Hypsometric Curve

This is an ogive, or cumulative-frequency curve, which represents the absolute or relative areas of land above or below each contour. Hypsometric analysis of the earth as a whole dates from the last two decades of the nineteenth century, to Lapparent (1883), Murray (1888), Tillo (1889) and Penck (1894). All of these produced hypsometric data of the earth's surface; important modifications were made later by Kossina (1933) and Orlicz (1931–5). The mean height of land and the mean depth of sea occur as two steps on the hypsometric curve of the earth's surface. These steps, called the continental platform and the deep-sea platform, are associated by Wegener and others with vertical differentiation in the earth's crust. The curve of the landsurface has also been likened to a synthetic profile of equilibrium, the result of general erosion over a long period of stability. Examination of the several curves for single continents, however, reveals signal contrasts (De Martonne 1934). Romieux (1923) advanced the idea of a *niveau d'equidéformation* or mean level of the lithosphere (c. −2450 metres), separating two equal areas corresponding to two equal volumes, one belonging to the upper crust and the other to the lower levels of the ocean, the two indicating a balance. Accepting this view, Soulier (1925) made a detailed analysis of theoretical hypsometric curves, and attempted to construct a so-called structural hypsometric curve showing the hypothetical structural relief which would exist if there were no erosion. He also examined possible modifications of the curve by erosion and deposition, elaborating an hypothesis of vertical distribution of relief and stressing the unequal balance of two homogeneous layers on either side of the *niveau primitif du sol*—a mathematically-determined level (c. −4500 metres) below which erosion and deposition would be negligible.

More recently, hypsometric curves have often been used in the analysis of the vertical distribution of land, for the area contained within the hypsometric curve and the axes is proportional to the volume of the relief considered. But the main problem in the hypsometric interpretation of large areas is to assess the relative influences of fluvial erosion, eustatic movements and structure (Birot 1955). De Martonne (1941c) examined some of these difficulties, in a comparison of the hypsometric curves of young fold mountains (French Alps and Pyrenees) and ancient massifs (Central Massif and Armorican Massif). Baulig (1957) however concluded: 'Very useful to the geophysicist who wants to know if a certain mountain massif is in isostatic equilibrium, the hypsographic curve teaches us hardly anything about its tectonic and morphological history.'

Many authors note that the hypsometric curve is by no means an average profile, for it does not record average slopes between contours. Average intercontour slope cannot be calculated from intercontour areas alone. Penck (1894) and later Uhorczak/Romer (1931) showed how the hypsometric curves of a cone, a concave cone, a hemisphere and a paraboloid differ from their average profiles. De Smet (1951, 1954) also demonstrated how a pyramid of basal area A and height $h$, has the same hypsometric curve as four pyramids each with a basal area of $\frac{A}{4}$ and height $h$, although the average slope of the smaller pyramids is twice that of the large pyramid (see Fig. 7). It is therefore dangerous to accept changes in slope on the hypsometric curve as indicating corresponding changes on the land. Hypsometric curves should then be avoided in the study of erosion-platforms, even when they seem to conform to preconceived ideas. They are of value only in depicting intercontour areas and in calculation of volume, average height, and degree of dissection.

Another problem in the interpretation of hypsometric curves is that they always seem extremely generalized. In Fig. 3, generalization is apparent in the curves for Gozo and Guernsey.

## (b) The Area–Height Curve

The area–height curve (or diagram) represents the absolute or relative areas of land between adjacent contours. Its character depends greatly on the selection of intervals for measurement, and on altitudinal grouping of data. Decisions about interval and grouping greatly influence the sinuosities of the frequency-distribution which is eventually plotted.

Because it uses hypsometric data, the area–height curve cannot be relied on to depict breaks of slope; peaks upon it should not be interpreted as indicating extensive flat surfaces. Peaks may be due, for example, to a variety of summits, slopes, and flats. On the other hand, a series of accordant summits of small total area, or a significant break of slope, may be completely concealed by the area–height curve. Interpretation should therefore be accompanied by very careful scrutiny of the topographic map.

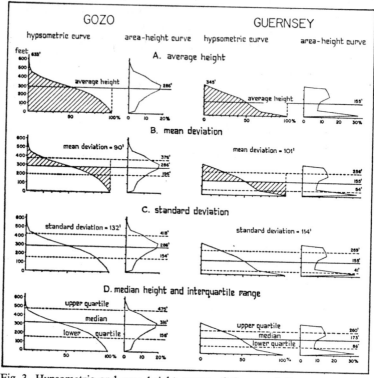

Fig. 3. Hypsometric and area–height curves of Gozo and Guernsey showing average height, mean and standard deviation, median height and interquartile range.

For the visual interpretation of area–height relationships, this curve must however generally be preferred to the hypsometric curve. The area–height curves in Fig. 3 show, for example, that Gozo has an unimodal distribution, whereas Guernsey has a bimodal distribution; Gozo has a Gaussian distribution because of its small extent of summits and valley-bottoms.

Lagrula (1950) states that the earth has not a Gaussian distribution, but two maxima—one at ocean depths and one near zero. Joksch (1955) goes further, producing a semi-logarithmic area–height graph, and showing it to be the sum of three elementary logarithmico-normal distributions with their medians at −4·5, 0·2 and 0·5 kilo-metres. These values might suggest that three major levels may have been created individually. The statistical method is hazardous, how-ever, and not improved by the use of uncertain data on ocean depths.

### (c) The Percentage Hypsometric Curve

The percentage hypsometric curve involves the two ratios of rela-tive height $\left(\dfrac{h}{H}\right)$ and relative area $\left(\dfrac{a}{A}\right)$. On the ordinate is plotted the ratio of the height ($h$) of any contour above base to the total height (H), while on the abscissa is plotted the ratio of the area ($a$) between any given contour and the lowest contour, to the total area (A). Strahler (1952) demonstrates the value of the percentage hypsometric curve in the study of the vertical distribution of volume in small drainage basins in homogeneous materials, showing that that value carries over to a comparison of erosional characteristics. Strahler gives the types of curve which correspond to the erosional stages of youth and maturity.

Total volume is obtained by calculating, mathematically or plani-metrically, the *hypsometric integral*—the proportionate area below the curve. Equally valuable is the inverse of the hypsometric integral, the volume removed by erosion, which may be termed the *erosion integral*. Figure 4 compares the percentage hypsometric curves of Gozo and Guernsey with absolute hypsometric curves of the two islands. Its most remarkable features are the similarity of the hypso-metric integrals, in spite of the contrasting percentage hypsometric curves. The curve for Gozo resembles that for a drainage basin in the equilibrium (mature) stage, while Guernsey's curve appears rather to correspond to the inequilibrium (youthful) stage.

### (d) Projected Area and Real Area

The discussion so far has been limited to intercontour areas as projected on maps. With angles of slope ignored, real intercontour areas have been left out of account. But real areas are easily obtain-able, by multiplying the projected intercontour areas by the secant of the mean angle of slope; this angle is determined by dividing the pro-jected intercontour area by the mean length of the two contours, and by reference to a table of tangents. Obviously, real areas need be calculated only when the mean slope is steep, or when they are to be

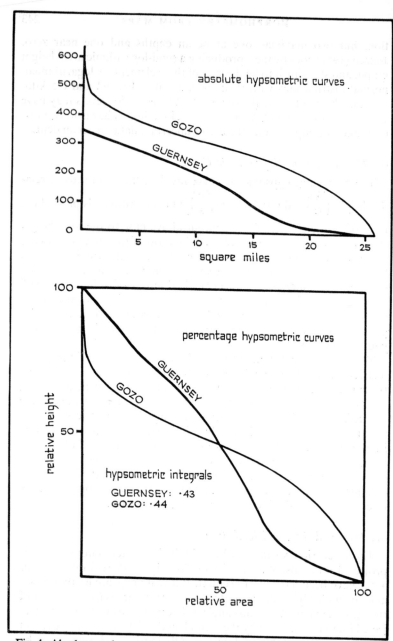

Fig. 4. Absolute and percentage hypsometric curves of Gozo and Guernsey.

compared with projected areas in studies of dissection. In general, differences are slight, as seen in Table I, which lists projected and real intercontour areas for Gozo and Guernsey. The real areas of Gozo and Guernsey are but 1·013 and 1·004 times their projected areas.

TABLE I

| | Gozo (area in sq miles) | | | Guernsey (area in sq miles) | | |
|---|---|---|---|---|---|---|
| | Projected Area | Real Area | Difference | Projected Area | Real Area | Difference |
| 0–50 | 0·97 | 1·01 | 0·04 | 7·86 | 7·87 | 0·01 |
| 50–100 | 1·25 | 1·29 | 0·04 | 1·96 | 1·99 | 0·03 |
| 100–150 | 1·56 | 1·61 | 0·05 | 2·07 | 2·09 | 0·02 |
| 150–200 | 2·34 | 2·38 | 0·04 | 2·38 | 2·40 | 0·02 |
| 200–250 | 3·30 | 3·34 | 0·04 | 3·69 | 3·70 | 0·01 |
| 250–300 | 4·67 | 4·71 | 0·04 | 3·48 | 3·49 | 0·01 |
| 300–350 | 4·88 | 4·91 | 0·03 | 3·02 | 3·02 | 0·00 |
| 350–400 | 3·48 | 3·51 | 0·03 | | | |
| 400–450 | 2·41 | 2·42 | 0·01 | | | |
| 450–500 | 0·66 | 0·67 | 0·01 | | | |
| 500–550 | 0·28 | 0·28 | 0·00 | | | |
| 550–600 | 0·02 | 0·02 | 0·00 | | | |
| 600+ | 0·03 | 0·03 | 0·00 | | | |
| | 25·85 | 26·18 | 0·33 | 24·46 | 24·56 | 0·10 |

The relationship of real area to projected area helps the study of dissection. It is the basis of the dissection-index proposed by Slaucitajs (1936) and termed *reliefentwicklung*:

$$\frac{\text{Real area} - \text{Projected area}}{\text{Projected area}} \, 100.$$

For example, the indices for Gozo and Guernsey are 1·276 and 0·409 respectively. De Smet (1951), however, finds this index incomplete without reference to volume: in the classical scheme of the erosion of an uplifted peneplain, volume should diminish constantly, whereas real area and average slope should pass by a maximum when the last remnants of the old peneplain disappear. Accordingly, De Smet proposes this more complex index of dissection:

$$\frac{\text{Real area} - \text{Projected area} \times \text{Average slope}}{\text{Volume}}.$$

I

This is the most satisfactory of several indices of dissection. However, these are all laborious to calculate, and their value becomes apparent only in the comparative analysis of diverse regions—a single scale of dissection has yet to be established.

### (e) Altitudinal Distribution

Altitudinal distribution can be expressed by a number of common indices, using hypsometric data. It is, for instance, a simple matter to determine *average height*:

$$\sum \frac{\text{Percentage intercontour areas} \times \text{mean intercontour heights}}{100}.$$

As the area contained within the hypsometric curve and its axes is proportional to the volume of relief, average height may be obtained by dividing this area by the maximum abscissa. On Fig. 3 it appears as the height of a rectangle with the same base and the same enveloped area as those of the hypsometric curve. Other methods involve the average height of superimposed grid squares or of a series of profiles (Demangeot 1944). The areas of the profiles are measured by planimeter, and are then divided by the total length of the horizontal axes. The main disadvantage of the index of average height is that different reliefs may have the same average height. Fournier (1960) shows that hypsometric curves of three drainage basins with different areas but similar height-range, or three curves of different area and different height range, may have identical average heights (Figs. 5A, 5B).

De Martonne (1941b) and other French geographers have made considerable use of average height in the study of the natural regions of France (Blanchard 1919). De Martonne also formulated an *indice d'articulation* (index of dissection) in which average height is expressed as a percentage of the maximum height. Unfortunately, this index has little value in the study of dissection, as it relates an average to a fortuitous maximum. A small absolute difference between two values in a lowland may give a higher index than a much larger difference in highland. Moreover, two areas of highly contrasted relief can have similar indices of 'articulation'.

Similar objections apply to De Martonne's (1941b) *coefficient de massivité* of a relief—the quotient of the division of the average height by the projected area. This quotient provides the value of the tangent of the angle of slope ($a$ in Fig. 5A). Fournier (1960), however, has attempted to remove the deficiencies of the *coefficient de massivité* and average height, by multiplying them together and producing the *coefficient orographique* which he finds of considerable value in characterizing the relief of drainage basins and in assessing their degree of erosion.

Another valuable use for average height is demonstrated by Dury (1951), who calculates the *mean available relief*, the difference between the average height of the actual surface on the one hand, and of the streamline surface on the other. The streamline surface is that which passes through the bottoms of main valleys, and is obtainable

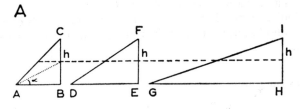

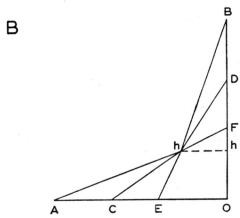

Fig. 5. In A all three hypsographic curves have the same average height. Similarly, in B curves AhB, ChD and EhF have the same average height (after Fournier 1960).

by drawing generalized contours. The streamline surface may be planimetered in the same way as the actual surface.

The *median height* merely divides the height-range into two equal halves; it is less affected by the highest peaks than is the average height. *Interquartile and interoctile ranges*, which are easy to determine, may be used for comparison of different reliefs. Péguy (1948) illustrates the utility of the *mean and standard deviations* of hypsometric data. Figure 3 herewith shows that mean deviation may be found graphically, by constructing a rectangle above the average height and equal in area to the sum of the two shaded areas on the hypsometric curve. The standard deviation is obtained graphically in a similar manner, but using on the vertical axis the squares of the deviations from the average height. Reference to the area–height curves of Gozo and Guernsey indicates that examination of altitudinal distribution is more meaningful for a unimodal distribution (Gozo) than for a bimodal distribution (Guernsey).

The indices named in this section do not assist the study of particular erosion-platforms; their only value lies in the comparison of regions.

## Clinographic Curves

There is still a tendency to infer changes in slope from hypsometric analysis, despite many warnings from authors of clinographic curves. Curves of the clinographic type have been applied, with varying success, to demonstrating average slope between contours. They include:

(a) the clinographic curve of Finsterwalder;
(b) the hypsoclinographic curve of Finsterwalder;
(c) the hypsographoid of Uhorczak/Romer;
(d) the clinographic curve of Hanson-Lowe;
(e) the mean slope curve of Strahler and the average profile of De Smet;
(f) the curve of average intercontour widths of De Smet;
(g) the slope–height curve of Moseley.

All the relevant methods are dependent upon contour lengths and/or intercontour areas, rather than on slope facets delimited by field analysis.

### (a) The clinographic curve of Finsterwalder (1890)

Contour lengths are measured by opisometer; a curve is then produced by joining the ends of horizontal lines, which are proportional to the lengths of the contours and are plotted at appropriate heights on the vertical axis. Unfortunately, this method cannot demonstrate average slope between contours. Although satisfactory for a regular geometric figure such as a cone, it is useless for a dissected landscape such as that of Gozo (Fig. 6A) where the mid-altitude contours are much longer than those above or below.

Average slope of the total area, however, may be obtained by dividing the area contained within the curve by the area of the region, and by consulting a table of tangents. Finsterwalder (1890) and Peucker (1890) both expressed the angle of average slope as

$$\frac{\text{contour interval} \times \text{total length of contours}}{\text{total area}}.$$

Tricart (1952), among others, commends this index, which is, however, less accurate than one to be described later. In any event, the index involves far more complication, in obtaining average slope for a whole region, than does the method devised by Wentworth (1930). Wentworth's method requires the calculation, along the lines of grid squares, of the number of contour crossings per mile. A second count, along a grid oblique to the first, provides additional data. The following formula is then applied to the mean of the two sets of readings:

$$\frac{\text{average number of contour crossings per mile} \times \text{contour interval}}{3361 \text{ [a constant]}}.$$

The Wentworth method, one of rapid sampling, provides a considerable measure of accuracy.

Péguy (1942, 1947) uses contour lengths and average slope in his *indice d'aération*:

$$I = \frac{D}{d.\tan \alpha}.$$ where D = length of longest contour

$$d = \frac{\text{sum of contour lengths}}{\text{number of contours}}$$

$$\tan \alpha = \text{tangent of average slope}.$$

But without inclusion of area and volume, this is not a really satisfactory index of dissection.

### (b) The Hypsoclinographic Curve of Finsterwalder

Suggested by Finsterwalder and described by Penck (1894), this curve incorporates hypsometric data and the length of contours alike. The horizontal axis is equal to the total area and is segmented cumulatively into intercontour areas. The vertical axis represents the sum of lengths of the contours multiplied by contour interval, again subdivided cumulatively, each segment being the length of one contour multiplied by the contour interval. The curve is obtained by joining the intersections, as in Fig. 6B. Because the lengths of the two axes represent the numerator and denominator of the Finsterwalder/Peucker formula, the angle of average slope is found by joining the extremities of the axes, as in Fig. 6B.

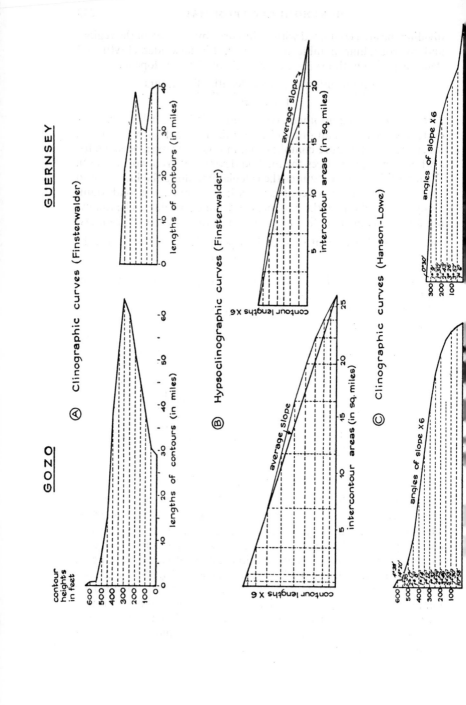

GUERNSEY

GOZO

Ⓐ Clinographic curves (Finsterwalder)

Ⓑ Hypsoclinographic curves (Finsterwalder)

Ⓒ Clinographic curves (Hanson-Lowe)

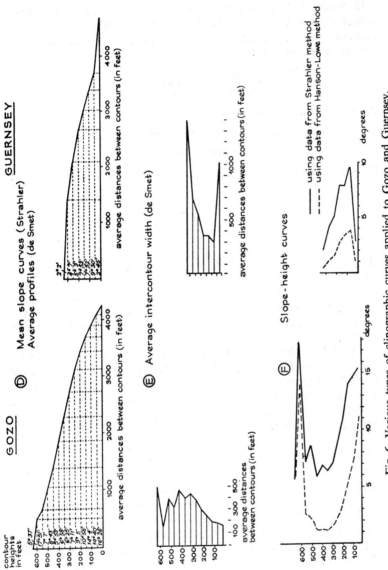

Fig. 6. Various types of clinographic curves applied to Gozo and Guernsey.

De Smet (1954) shows that the hypsoclinographic curve of Finster-walder does not show precisely the average slope of each inter-contour area. Intercontour angles of slope are not obtainable by the Finsterwalder formula:

$$\frac{\text{height} \times \text{length of lower contour}}{\text{intercontour area}} \qquad \left[\frac{h.L_1}{A_1}\right]$$

but by the following formula

$$\frac{\text{height} \times \text{mean length of two contours}}{\text{intercontour area}} \qquad \left[\frac{h.L_1 + L_2}{A_1}\right]$$

De Smet suggests that the vertical axis should be divided as follows:

$$h\left[\frac{L_1 + L_2}{2}\right] \quad , \quad h\left[\frac{L_1 + L_2}{2} + \frac{L_2 + L_3}{2}\right] \quad ,$$

$$h\left[\frac{L_1 + L_2}{2} + \frac{L_2 + L_3}{2} + \frac{L_3 + L_4}{2}\right] \quad \ldots$$

He also suggests that, as the slope of the area above the highest con-tour cannot be measured by Finsterwalder's formula, an approxima-tion could be found by dividing the length of the highest contour by two. But in no circumstances can the hypsoclinographic curve be regarded as an average profile, as the axes represent areas not lengths.

Péguy (1942) ingeniously incorporates both the hypsoclinographic and clinographic curves in a *clinographic diagram* with three axes. De Smet (1951) terms this a geometrical expression of the *indice d'aéra-tion*. As it contains many values, including those of average slope, contour lengths, real and projected areas, it is naturally exceedingly difficult to interpret.

## (c) *The Hypsographoid of Uhorczak/Romer* (1931)

Uhorczak, a pupil of Romer, wished to produce a graph which gave a more exact picture of average profile than the hypsographic curve. He envisages representation of relief by a series of concentric circles proportional in size to the areas above the contours. He con-structs hypsographoids with altitude on the central vertical axes, and with radii of circles arranged proportionally as horizontal lengths, the ends of these being joined. Uhorczak produces hypsographoids for continents, oceans and major drainage-basins, comparing them with hypsographic curves. By calculating the volume of a hypso-graphoid as $\pi r^2$ (area of base) multiplied by average height, and by representing it as a cone, Uhorczak then establishes average slope.

The hypsographoid, however, neither facilitates visual impression of area–height relationships, nor demonstrates a correct average profile, except for conical reliefs. The reasons for these disadvantages will be considered in the discussion of Hanson-Lowe's clinographic curve (1935), which is merely one half of the hypsographoid.

## (d) The Clinographic Curve of Hanson-Lowe (1935)

Hanson-Lowe devised his clinographic curve to demonstrate the average angle of slope of intercontour areas in the form of an average profile. He regards contours as a series of concentric circles, finding the radius of the area above a given contour by

$$\sqrt{\frac{\text{area above contour}}{\pi}}.$$

The average distance between two contours is therefore the radius of the lower contour minus the radius of the higher contour, and the slope of each intercontour area becomes

$$\tan \alpha = \frac{\text{contour interval (in feet)}.}{\text{intercontour distance (in feet)}}$$

These intercontour angles of slope are then drawn on a graph, beginning at the highest point and working down to the base. In most cases, all angles must be multiplied by a constant to enable the curve to be easily drawn, although re-scaling of vertical data can be effected merely by graphical means. The length of the horizontal axis is equal to the radius of the whole area.

Unfortunately, by ignoring the lengths of the contours, the clinographic curve of Hanson-Lowe maximizes intercontour widths and thus minimizes intercontour angles of slope. In Fig. 7, for example, the two conical reliefs A and B have identical intercontour areas and therefore identical clinographic curves, in spite of the fact that the real average intercontour slopes of B are much greater than those of A. Moreover, it has already been shown by De Smet that the large pyramid C and the four small pyramids D have identical hypsometric (and therefore clinographic) curves, although the angle of slope of the small pyramids is twice that of the large pyramid. In other words, the Hanson-Lowe method loses accuracy as dissection increases. Whilst it gives a reasonable representation for a simple plateau such as Jersey, which has been cut by streams but not elaborately dissected, its representation of a dissected relief, like Gozo, is utterly erroneous (see Table II).

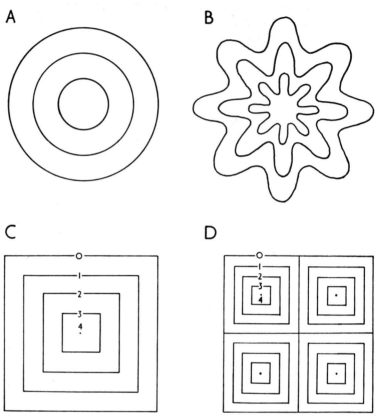

Fig. 7. The intercontour areas of the two cones A and B are equal. Similarly, the intercontour areas of pyramid C equal those of the 4 pyramids in D (after De Smet 1951).

(e) *The Mean Slope Curve of Strahler* (1952) *and Average Profile of De Smet* (1954)

Of much greater general utility than the above clinographic curves is the mean slope curve proposed by Strahler. Strahler finds the mean width of each intercontour area by dividing this area by the mean length of the two adjacent contours. The tangent of the angle of slope is the contour interval divided by the mean intercontour width. The mean slope of the highest intercontour area cannot be accurately obtained because there may be several distinct summits, but an approximation is possible when half the length of the highest contour is taken as denominator. For studies of small drainage basins,

Strahler suggests identical scales on the horizontal and vertical axes. He expresses the relationships of the hypsometric curve to the mean slope in the following equation

$$\frac{l}{L} \tan \theta = K \tan \alpha$$

where $\theta$ = slope of hypsometric curve
$\alpha$ = mean ground slope
$l$ = contour length at given relative height
L = length of longest contour in basin
K = a constant

Comparison of the Hanson-Lowe and Strahler methods for the islands of Gozo and Guernsey (Fig. 6C and D) reveals marked differences in results. Most emphatically, the Strahler method gives by far the more accurate representation. Table II shows that with the Hanson-Lowe method every intercontour width becomes longer and therefore every angle lower than with the Strahler method. Differences are not constant: slopes obtained by the Strahler method are from $1\frac{1}{4}$ to more than 5 times as steep as those obtained by the Hanson-Lowe method. Although more laborious than the latter, the Strahler method must be preferred. It is not infallible; in the example of the four pyramids, the mean slope curve for the lowest intercontour area is inaccurate (though much more accurate than the clinographic curve) because of common basal contours.

TABLE II

| | Gozo | | | | Guernsey | | | |
|---|---|---|---|---|---|---|---|---|
| | Intercontour distance (ft) | | Angle of slope | | Intercontour distance (ft) | | Angle of slope | |
| Method | Hanson-Lowe | Strahler | Hanson-Lowe | Strahler | Hanson-Lowe | Strahler | Hanson-Lowe | Strahler |
| 0–50 | 285 | 169 | 10°58′ | 16°26′ | 2598 | 1042 | 1°6′ | 2°45′ |
| 50–100 | 380 | 191 | 7°30′ | 14°40′ | 739 | 299 | 3°52′ | 9°30′ |
| 100–150 | 486 | 200 | 5°53′ | 14°4′ | 834 | 362 | 3°26′ | 7°52′ |
| 150–200 | 760 | 258 | 3°46′ | 10°58′ | 1051 | 362 | 2°43′ | 7°52′ |
| 200–250 | 1156 | 313 | 2°29′ | 9°5′ | 1911 | 565 | 1°30′ | 5°3′ |
| 250–300 | 1859 | 397 | 1°32′ | 7°11′ | 2476 | 693 | 1°9′ | 4°7′ |
| 300–350 | 2402 | 445 | 1°12′ | 6°25′ | 5122 | 1411 | 0°30′ | 2°2′ |
| 350–400 | 2323 | 409 | 1°14′ | 6°58′ | | | | |
| 400–450 | 2529 | 486 | 1°8′ | 5°53′ | | | | |
| 450–500 | 1251 | 326 | 2°17′ | 8°43′ | | | | |
| 500–550 | 1109 | 401 | 2°35′ | 7°7′ | | | | |
| 550–600 | 195 | 155 | 14°20′ | 17°51′ | | | | |
| 600 | 407 | 508 | 4°38′ | 5°37′ | | | | |

De Smet proposes a curve, similar to the mean slope curve, which he terms the average profile. He uses intercontour widths cumulatively on the horizontal axis, but suggests no means of calculating intercontour angles of slope: such calculations are however unnecessary for the construction of an average profile.

The average slope for a region or drainage basin can be easily calculated from mean slope data

$$\frac{(a_1 \times A_1) + (a_2 \times A_2) + (a_3 \times A_3) + \ldots (a_n \times A_n)}{A_1 + A_2 + A_2 \ldots A_n}$$

where $a$ = slope and $A$ = area of intercontour areas. This formula is more precise than the method advocated by Finsterwalder and Peucker.

### (f) The Curve of Average Intercontour Widths of De Smet (1954)

De Smet proposes that the average intercontour widths be presented as a simple non-cumulative frequency-distribution. As in the case of the area–height curve, this is a useful method of comparative analysis and emphasizes contrasts (Fig. 6E), and may in addition involve an increasedly meaningful presentation of data of angles of slope.

### (g) The Slope–Height Curve of Moseley (1961)

The slope–height curve merely demonstrates the mean slope for intercontour areas, using data obtained by the Hanson-Lowe or Strahler methods (Fig. 6F), or selected profiles or field measurements. Moseley uses this curve effectively in his studies of the erosion surfaces of Bowland Forest, after measuring with a graduated scale large numbers of slope angles at 1000-ft intervals along contours. As he states, uniform slopes appear as straight lines parallel to the vertical axis, while concave and convex slopes with uniform rates of change are straight lines sloping downwards to the right and left respectively. This form of graph is particularly valuable in comparison of area with area: the loss in visual impression of average profiles is compensated by the precise depiction of data.

### Altimetric Analysis

Methods of altimetric analysis are of two main types: those demonstrating the numerical frequency of certain levels, and those indicating areas or lengths of flats (summits, shoulders, benches) at various altitudes. The methods involve sampling with varying degrees of objectivity. Although methods differ, aims are constant: to demonstrate the existence of erosion surfaces or levels, and to correlate levels from area to area.

Disputes about the origins of erosion surfaces lie beyond this discussion. However, the theories of certain geomorphologists may well have inspired certain methods of altimetric analysis. Baulig (1935) has long advocated diastro-eustatism as principally responsible for erosion-platforms, considering that successive lowerings of sea-level caused successive widenings of valleys, with discrete episodes of widening represented today by flats and shoulders on valley-sides. In Britain, however, there is a marked tendency to attribute platforms to marine erosion (Balchin 1952), while in Australia (Geyl 1961a) and elsewhere it is often held that uplift and rejuvenation of ancient surfaces are possible. Obviously, regions of warping could present considerable problems of interpretation by altimetric analysis.

One of the main justifications of laborious quantitative techniques is their independence of subjective visual judgements in the field. Several authors stress that skylines can give a deceptive appearance of horizontality, because of the combined effects of perspective and distance.

A range of various altimetric techniques supplies histograms, showing at successive altitudes one of the following:

(a) frequency of spot heights, with or without summit-frequencies;
(b) frequency of the highest points in the squares of a superimposed grid;
(c) frequency of summit heights;
(d) area of summits;
(e) area of benches and summits;
(f) area of summits and lengths of shoulders and cols.

Frequencies, areas or lengths as totals or percentages are usually plotted on the horizontal axis, altitudinal groups on the vertical. Refinement is possible by subdividing the frequency columns, so as to illustrate the dimensions and lithology of flats (Geyl 1961a).

As in hypsometric analysis, interpretation of results varies with the altitudinal class intervals, which themselves are dependent upon the contour intervals of maps. Figure 8 shows how running sum class intervals merely smooth out some of the irregularities of simple class frequencies, just as large class intervals smooth out the irregularities of small class frequencies. In Fig. 8 the means of groups of three values are plotted at the level of the middle values. Groups of five values can also be used, although excessive smoothing is naturally undesirable.

Altimetric analysis has gone no further than frequency-distribution

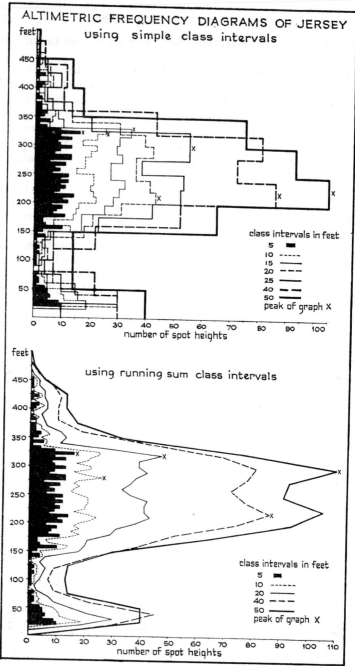

Fig. 8. Altimetric frequency diagrams of Jersey using simple and running sum class intervals. The effects of the grouping of data are clearly seen. Note the shifts in the peaks (X) of the graphs.

and the construction of histograms. Baulig (IGU 1948a) repeatedly emphasizes that the only way to interpret altimetric curves is to compare two or more curves for different parts of a region. In this sense, the geomorphological value of altimetric analysis depends upon subjective visual examination and interpretation of the inflexions of the frequency curves. Obviously, there is room for statistical correlation.

## (a) Frequency of Spot Heights

Baulig (1926, 1928a, 1928b) was first to examine the frequency of spot heights at successive altitudes, using 1 : 80,000 maps of Brittany where relief was depicted by hachures rather than by contours. Baulig assumes that spot heights are accurate, uniformly distributed, and sufficiently dense, but concludes nevertheless that summits are exaggerated. As he himself emphasizes in subsequent writing (IGU 1948a), his assumptions do not apply everywhere. Even on French maps, the distribution of spot heights follows no rigid rules. They are, for example, less frequent on slopes than on summits and in valleys. But Baulig feels that, as long as they are sufficiently numerous and do not systematically avoid certain areas and features, then the frequency-maxima should not be too obscure. On the other hand, the method is not very suitable for the analysis of British one-inch Ordnance Survey maps, as the density of spot heights varies greatly in area and with altitude. In one area all summit heights are marked; in another, spot heights are confined mainly to lowlands and to inhabited parts. Many spot heights have little morphometric significance, being frequently located along roads, as for example in Anglesey (Fig. 10). Flat surfaces tend to be poorly represented, but the introduction of summit levels which are not marked by spot heights can remedy this situation. Spot heights also tend to be sparse just above or below contours at some multiple of 100 ft, causing gaps in frequency if small class intervals (e.g. 10 ft) are used.

In general, surveyors by their choice of spot heights introduce a considerable element of subjectivity into the range of data, which do not provide random samples. De Smet (1954) argues against the use of spot heights that it is merely a modification of area–height analysis. Because slopes are not represented on the frequency-diagram of spot heights, this is therefore not really suitable for demonstrating planated surfaces. To these objections a word of warning may be added—in a small area, spot heights are rarely numerous enough to constitute a valid statistical sample, and only by comparison of several frequency curves of different areas can useful assessments be made.

## (b) The Grid Method

In an effort to counteract some of the deficiencies of spot heights, Baulig (1935, 1939) devised the use of a grid, in which the frequency-distribution of the highest points of grid squares is plotted. Although a quasi-random method of sampling, this is not entirely objective, for an initial decision must be taken about the size of the grid (Peeters 1944). Baulig believes that the region to be studied should be large enough to permit a large total of observations in order to reduce the effects of exceptional cases and to provide two or more comparative curves. Some 5000 squares (Maling 1955) are probably necessary to provide a good statistical sample. For a fairly small area, the mesh of the grid could be diminished in order to increase the number of observations, but this modification would inevitably lower the altitude of the frequency-maxima. In theory, the grid could be so reduced in size of mesh that the results would conform approximately to those of an area–height curve. The further question arises, as to whether the size of the grid should be influenced by texture of terrain. With an open grid, the highest points in individual squares are likely to be summits, but with a close grid, they are likely to occur on slopes, and may even lie on valley-bottoms. On the other hand, several planation-features in a single large square might have to be represented by a single value, or to be neglected altogether in favour of a highest point of no erosional significance. It follows, therefore, that a heavily-dissected terrain requires a close grid. Baulig asserts that the grid method works best on fairly weak relief. Figure 9 shows how variation in the size of grid used on four islands of widely-differing reliefs affects the curves of altimetric frequency. Jersey is a fairly easy test of method, being a gently-sloping plateau with deeply-incised streams but with broad interfluves; there is accordingly, a closer correlation between the types of curve for Jersey than between those for Arran, Anglesey and the Isle of Man. Comparison of area–height curves and altimetric frequency curves for Arran and Anglesey shows how the grid method emphasizes high points.

Another difficulty is that of determining the highest point on a contour map with few spot heights; since estimates are alone possible, detailed class intervals cannot be used. But perhaps the most severe criticism of this method is that its very objectivity is a disadvantage, leading as it does to the incorporation of much data of little geomorphological interest.

Baulig (IGU 1948a) believes that the pattern of highest points would define an upper enveloping surface which becomes closer to the real surface as the local relief becomes more gentle. He contends

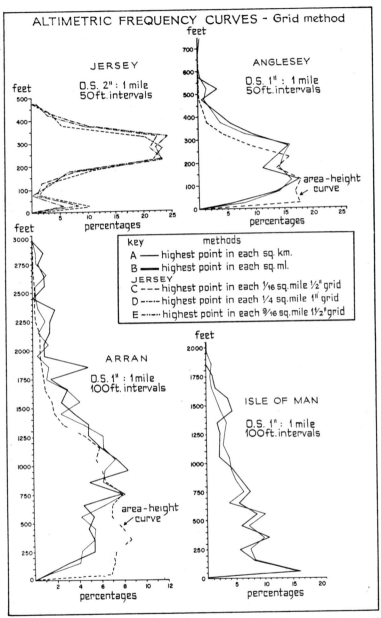

Fig. 9. Altimetric frequency curves of Jersey, Anglesey, Arran and the Isle of Man demonstrating how variation in grid size affects data. Area–height curves of Anglesey and Arran are included for comparison.

that if a region were affected by a single cycle of erosion at the mature stage, then all the forms would be concave, and thus the majority of the highest points would be near to base-level. A second cycle, also reaching maturity, would produce a lower segment to the curve, again with a maximum at base-level. The base-level of the upper segment, however, would have largely disappeared, so that the maximum frequency of highest points will be above the base-level. If this frequency were at the same level in entirely separate parts of a region, it would indicate an absence of appreciable deformation, and concordance of the two cycles. Baulig (IGU 1948b) insists that this method is valuable only when a concordant series of two or more cycles has operated, and that it is not valid in regions affected by widespread uplifts or characterized by horizontal structure. In a region of complex structure, non-cyclic elements will not produce clear maxima on curves for separate parts of the region. Baulig emphasizes that this statistical method is useful only in the landscapes of normal erosion, not being applicable, for example, to the terraces of Lake Bonneville. These displaced and faulted sub-lacustrine platforms were examined with the grid method by Fourmarier and Macar (IGU 1948a), who state—with some justification—that the upper remains of one cycle can easily be confounded with the lower remains of an earlier cycle, producing confusion of frequency-maxima. They question the logic of Baulig's reasoning, pointing out that, as cyclical elements are generally concave, high points tend to be slopes rather than flats. They think it preferable, therefore, to plot the lowest point in each square rather than the highest point. Here is the crux of the problem. Scrutiny of a map with a superimposed grid will soon reveal that in some squares it would be advantageous to select the highest point, in some the lowest, and in others an intermediate point. Arbitrary point-sampling is not effective in portraying the various heights of particular facets of relief. Moreover, it is not entirely satisfactory in the analysis of dissection; the two indices devised by Gassmann and Gutersohn (1947) termed *kotenstreuung* (dispersion of spot heights) and *relieffaktor* (coefficient of dispersion of spot heights) are limited in value to the comparison of similar reliefs (De Smet 1951).

### (c) Frequency of Summits

Several additional altimetric methods are concerned with summits, assuming that accordant summits may be remnants of erosion-platforms or peneplains. Although not all summits have such significance, it is not easy to select significant summits from maps alone. The boundary of a summit on a map is generally taken as the last closed contour. But, in this view, all summits are given a unitary value regardless of dimension, and undue weight is given to highest points at the expense of lower parts. Hollingworth (1938) counters the former criticism by stressing that calculation of summit-frequencies is suitable only for maturely-dissected plateaux, where dimensions of flats are held to be fairly constant; but this principle drastically limits the scope of the method. Miller (1939) points to the lower plateau of Pembrokeshire, which escaped recognition in Hollingworth's analysis because it is little dissected.

The summit-frequency method, first used by Thompson (1936) in a study of the Hudson Gorge, was later applied by Hollingworth to the Lake District and other mountain areas where errors due to thickness of drift are reduced to a minimum. Hollingworth notes the dangers of using marked summits alone, but, by recourse to manuscript maps, was able to include the exact heights of summits not normally published by the Ordnance Survey. There seems to be no case for using marked summits alone; they are not a random sample of all summits, but tend to be summits rising substantially above a closed contour.

Since the aggregate of summits in an area is often small, minor errors of calculation may falsify interpretation. Thompson remarks that the preponderance of summits at certain altitudes does not necessarily indicate peneplanation, but can result from rock-resistance and from distribution and stage of erosion. Some authors have therefore modified the summit-frequency method by counting only summits considered relevant in the study of platforms.

Figure 10 compares four separate frequency methods (all spot heights; all spot heights and unmarked summits; summit spot heights; summit spot heights and unmarked summits) for three islands—Anglesey, Arran and the Isle of Man. Similarities among the four sets of results vary according to the significance of spot heights, but, in general, the last two classes of data—those confined to summits—emphasize certain levels which are not always apparent in the first two classes. Comparison of Figs. 9 and 10 reveals the marked discrepancies between spot height counting and summit counting on the one hand, and the grid-analysis on the other. The respective curves are particularly divergent for Arran between 700 and 1400 ft.

O. T. Jones (1952) advances statistical analysis of summit levels by calculating mean elevation and standard deviation of summits for 100-sq-km blocks of Wales. He is able to show variations in degree of dissection of erosion-platforms. Unfortunately, he gives little clear indication about the method of selecting summits.

A useful modification in the graphical presentation of altimetric frequency data has been made by Moseley (1961), who constructs a

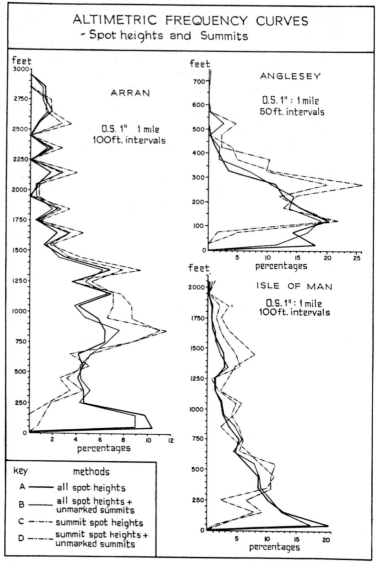

Fig. 10. Four different altimetric frequency curves of Arran, Anglesey and the Isle of Man using spot heights and summits.

step graph, in which the highest point of each flat is plotted as a short horizontal bar at the appropriate altitude.

### (d) Areas of Summits

The calculation by Thompson (1941) of areas of summits in the Appalachians overcomes one criticism of summit-frequencies, namely, that they are over-dependent upon degree of dissection. On the other hand, the area of each summit is calculated from the highest closed contour, which may not coincide with the true area of summit. Emphasis falls too heavily on altitude and too lightly on slope.

### (e) Areas of Benches and Summits

All the methods of altimetric analysis so far examined have been used with the specific aim of demonstrating erosion-platforms. While maintaining a fair measure of objectivity, all incorporate much data of little significance. With these objections in mind, Macar (1938, 1955) made detailed analyses of topographic maps on the large scale of 1:20,000, limiting attention to data of geomorphological value. He proposed the calculating of altimetric frequency of bench-units unités de replat), and used the method in a geomorphological study of the Ardennes. Macar's technique was subsequently applied by a number of Belgian researchers, notably Peeters (1944).

A bench was initially taken as an area of 16 hectares (40 acres or 1 sq cm on the 1:20,000 map) (Macar 1938), but later (Macar 1957) as a unit of 4 hectares (10 acres) in which amplitude does not exceed 5 metres—that is, where the slope is no more than 2·5 per cent (1°26'). The area of a large flat is expressed as a multiple of the chosen bench-unit. Macar's technique takes into account many small benches which would be overlooked in grid-analysis.

One of the merits of the bench-unit system is that it excludes steep slopes from its calculations. It is thus better designed for the study of benches than is hypsometry, for, with the latter, steep and gentle slopes alike can lie between successive contours. The limit of 2·5 per cent of slope, excluding many gentle slopes of 1 in 20 to 1 in 40, may however be too low. Furthermore, delimitation of slope-facets on contour maps is exceedingly difficult, unless the contour interval is small. Macar worked on the 1:20,000 scale with a 5-metre contour interval; it is doubtful whether his techniques could be used with much smaller scales and with larger contour intervals. He later explained (Macar 1957) that 'the method is not applicable everywhere, nor without care, but when the benches are fairly numerous and the erosion-levels are neither too steep nor too close together, it often provides very useful indications which have the advantage of being very little affected by the personal factor'.

The small size of the unit may lead to a large total of data, and to a complex frequency-distribution awkward to interpret. Macar states that benches tend to rise up-valley, to rise more rapidly in a tributary than in the main valley, and to rise with lateral distance from the valley on which they depend. In addition, he observes that many factors other than distance can modify either the slope of a partial erosion-platform, or the relative height of an isolated bench—for instance, the nature of the substratum, mass-movement, and erosion. Although the complications of interpretation undoubtedly increase with the size of the area examined, Macar's technique seems well suited to regional studies.

As De Smet (1954) notes, the curve of bench-units bears a fairly close resemblance to the hypsometric curve, with highest flats almost always represented poorly because of their small size. To free Macar's presentation from dependence on the hypsometric curve, De Smet produced an interesting curve showing for each hypsometric level the percentage of the area with a slope of 2·5 per cent or less. This new curve represents the relative rather than the absolute frequency of flats. In Fig. 11 are shown the absolute and the relative frequency of bench-units in the Ardennes (De Smet 1954). The relative frequency curve expresses the required relationships of slope, altitude

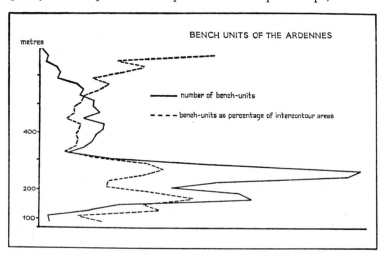

Fig. 11. Two ways of presenting bench-units as altimetric frequency curves; the number of bench-units (Macar, 1937-8), and bench-units as a percentage of intercontour areas (De Smet, 1954). Graphs from De Smet (1954).

and area, achieving considerable improvement over alternative forms. Unfortunately, it greatly increases the labour of calculation.

Baulig (1939; IGU 1948a) and Macar (IGU 1948a) express contrary views on the relative merits of their altimetric methods. In particular, Macar states that the use of units of area rather than of individual measurements overcomes Baulig's objection, that the bench-unit technique is substantially affected by rock-resistance. Baulig's fear that many so-called benches are merely lower parts of slopes, and that real horizontal non-structural benches which represent former valley-bottoms are rarely conserved, seems however justifiable.

## (ƒ) *The Shoulder, Summit and Col Method*

After much experimentation Geyl (1961a) arrived at the shoulder, summit and col method of morphometric analysis (S.S.C. method),

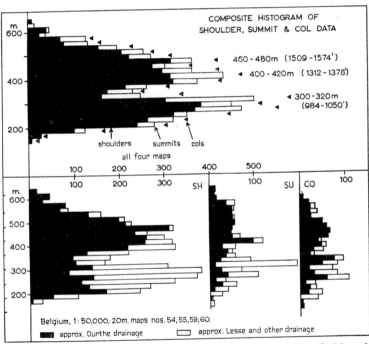

Fig. 12. Two ways of depicting shoulder, summit and col data and altimetric frequency-diagrams. The upper diagram is a composite histogram of the three lower graphs, which distinguish the Ourthe drainage basin from the Lesse and other drainage on four Belgian maps (after Geyl, 1961b).

in which calculations are made of the area of summits and the lengths of shoulders and cols. In an early version, cols were omitted. Graphs of the two or three frequencies are here presented side by side (Fig. 12).

Although Geyl was unaware of Macar's work before submitting his paper, the techniques of these two writers are similar in approach; both are based upon scrupulous analysis of topographic sheets. Using a system of points or units on 1:50,000 and 1:63,360 maps, Geyl allocates one point for each summit under 25 sq mm and another point for each further 25 sq mm or part thereof. The unit area of a summit is therefore approximately $6\frac{1}{4}$ hectares ($15\frac{1}{2}$ acres) on a 1:50,000 map and approximately $10\frac{1}{4}$ hectares ($25\frac{3}{4}$ acres) on a 1:63,360 map so that Geyl's unit is intermediate in size between the two units suggested by Macar. One point is also given for every 5 mm of shoulder or col. A shoulder is taken as any relatively flat area with an intercontour distance of at least 5 mm—representing about 820 ft on the 1:50,000 scale and 1050 ft on the 1:63,360 scale—provided that it is at least twice as great as the next lower intercontour distance. Cols are also considered significant because a great number of them are at the same altitudes as platforms, but Geyl points out that the frequency-maxima of shoulders and cols often occur at one contour below that of summits. Shoulders and cols exceeding 10 mm are considered as long, and may be distinguished graphically from others for the purpose of local studies; similarly, summits of more than 25 sq mm may be indicated separately.

Minor rules in the selection of summits, shoulders and cols complicate the method, without greatly reducing the personal factor in analysis. Although the need for separation of the three classes of feature is clear enough, the reason for correlating *areas* of summits with *lengths* of shoulders and cols is obscure. For consistency, it would seem preferable to use either areas or lengths throughout. Geyl admits that the use of lengths poses problems in the tabulation of shoulders in gently-undulating areas, but, like Macar, makes no claim of universal applicability, stating that it works best in areas of moderate relief. Perhaps the unit of 25 sq mm area could be extended with advantage to shoulders, measurement of which would be facilitated by the use of a sectional transparent plastic trace. Undoubtedly the difficulties in determining the areas of shoulders and cols are severe, but the use of length rather than area gives enhanced point values to narrow but fairly horizontal ridges devoid of flats. Moreover, the stipulation that the intercontour distance of a shoulder must be at least twice as long as the next lower intercontour distance must stress the height of the lower parts of shoulders (near the convex

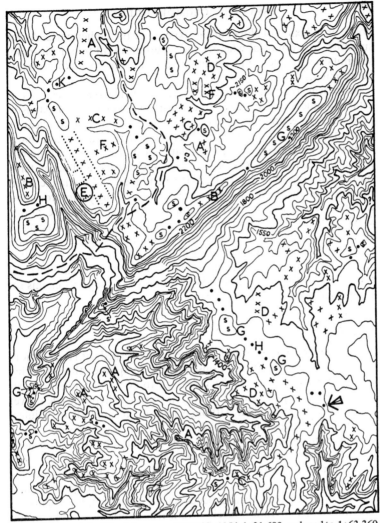

Fig. 13. Part of the Kinglake map, 7/829/C, 1954, 1:31,680, reduced to 1:63,360 (reproduced by permission of the Victoria State Lands and Survey Department), contours only. The points on the map regarded as significant for the S.S.C. method of morphometric analysis are shown thus: $x$ = 1 point for 5 mm of shoulder; $s$ = 1 point for 25 mm² of summit; • = 1 point for 5 mm of col. The points have been awarded as for the scale at which the map is here shown. The part of the map surrounded by a dashed line in the northwest corner of the map has been modified to enable examples, otherwise absent, to be shown. (Courtesy of *The Journal of Geology, The University of Chicago Press* and *W. F. Geyl.*) Source: W. F. Geyl, 'Morphometric Analysis and the World-Wide Occurrence of Stepped Erosion Surfaces,' *Journal of Geology*, 69, 1961, p. 397.

break or inflexion of slope) at the expense of the higher parts. As for summits, it is doubtful whether the inclusion of all minor pin-point summits is valuable; some minimum size of summit should probably be adopted.

Moreover, the value of data on cols is difficult to appreciate or to establish unless cols are taken as confirming the presence of extensive platforms. In examining the results of his technique, in application to many Australian, American, French, British and African maps, Geyl makes no reference to the col data. He makes interpretation rely primarily on the patterns of shoulder-frequencies, and secondarily on the data for summits. Indeed, the combined and complete interpretation of three separate graphs is not easy, suggesting for some instances an amalgamation of data in one comprehensive graph. Geyl (1961b) has experimented in combination, producing a composite graph (Fig. 12 herewith) of summit- shoulder- and col-frequencies of four Belgian maps at 1: 50,000. He has also plotted semi-logarithmically the frequencies of summits and shoulders of the Hunter Valley, New South Wales, in order to support claims for the presence of erosion-platforms.

## Conclusions

Nearly all the curves examined here are concerned with the relationships of area and altitude. Consequently, in spite of their differing usefulness, all forms have been applied to demonstrating the existence of erosion-platforms. For such a purpose, hypsometric curves cannot be recommended. Although relevant to analysis of volume, average height, and altitudinal distribution, they ignore slope. Some clinographic curves are mathematically unsound, but the mean slope curve (average profile) and the slope–height curve are extremely useful, especially in the study of small areas. Several altimetric frequency curves equal hypsometric and clinographic curves in objectivity, but lose accuracy through their dependence on point-sampling. Sparsely-distributed height-values rarely give a true synthesis of area–height relationships, or a good indication of erosion-platforms. The spot height/summit/grid methods seem best adapted to comparative analyses of large areas, where complexities of relief are not excessive, but may do no more than demonstrate the obvious. Though more subjective than the foregoing, the techniques of Macar and Geyl both involve careful examination of topographic maps and a real consideration of slope. They can provoke conclusions which would not readily follow from field studies. But an entirely satisfactory way of selecting relevant relief data from a map, and of interpreting it accurately in terms of evolution, may never be devised. Altimetric analysis is not suitable to all reliefs, and cannot be recommended as indispensable to regional geomorphology.

Fourmarier and Macar (IGU 1948) are concerned that interpretation of altimetric frequency curves should not be affected by pre-judgments, but Baulig retorts that in the observational science of geomorphology, experience is bound to influence interpretation. He states also that altimetric methods become useful only when cyclical analysis by other methods fails to provide conclusive results. This statement may provoke little disagreement; it remains true that in many instances satisfactory results have not been obtained otherwise than by altimetry.

## References

Balchin, W. G. V., 1952. 'The evidence for Late Tertiary eustatic changes of sea-level in Western Europe.' *Proc. IGU, 8th General Assembly, Washington*, 296–300.

Baulig, H., 1926. 'Sur une méthode altimétrique d'analyse morphologique appliquée à la Bretagne Péninsulaire.' *Bull. Assoc. Géog. Français*, 10, 7–9.

Baulig, H., 1928a. 'Les hauts niveaux d'erosion eustatique dans le Bassin de Paris.' *Ann. de Géog.*, 37, 289–305 and 385–406.

Baulig, H., 1928b. '*Le Plateau Central de la France et sa Bordure Méditerranéenne. Etude Morphologique.*' Armand Colin, Paris.

Baulig, H., 1935. 'The changing sea-level.' Publication No. 3 of the Inst. Brit. Geographers.

Baulig, H., 1939. 'Deux méthodes d'analyse morphologique appliquées à la haute Belgique.' *Bull. Soc. Belge Etudes Géog.*, 9, 165–84.

Baulig, H., 1956. *Vocabulaire Franco-Anglo-Allemand de Géomorphologie.* Paris.

Baulig, H., 1957. 'Les méthodes de la géomorphologie, d'après M. Pierre Birot.' *Ann. de Géog.*, 66, 97–124 and 211–36.

Baulig, H., 1959. 'Morphométrie.' *Ann. de Géog.*, 68, 385–408.

Birot, P., 1955. *Les Méthodes de la Morphologie.* P.U.F., Paris.

Blanchard, R., 1919. 'Altitudes moyennes des régions naturelles des Alpes Françaises.' *Trav. de L'Inst. de Géog. Alpine de L'Univ. de Grenoble*, 245–308.

Christian, C. S., Jennings, J. N., and Twidale, C. R., 1957. 'Geomorphology.' Chapter 5 in *Guide Book to Research Data for Arid Zone Development.* UNESCO, 51–65.

Clarke, J. I., and Orrell, K., 1958. 'An assessment of some morphometric methods.' Dept. of Geog. Durham Colleges in the Univ. of Durham, *Occasional Papers Series*, No. 2.

Coleman, A., 1954. 'The use of the height–range diagram in morphological analysis.' *Geog. Studies*, 1, 19–26.

Demangeot, J., 1944. 'Sur la détermination de l'altitude moyenne à partir de cartes topographiques en hachures.' *Comptes Rendus de L'Acad. des Sciences*, 218, 749–50.

Dury, G. H., 1951. 'Quantitative measurement of available relief and texture of dissection.' *Geol. Mag.*, 88, 339–43.

Dury, G. H., 1952. *Map Interpretation*, 167–79. Pitman, London.

Finsterwalder, S., 1890. 'Ueber den Mittleren Böschungswinkel und das wahre Areal einer Topographischen Fläche.' *Sitz.-Ber. k. bayer. Akad. d. Wissensch.*, 20, Heft. 1, 35.

Fournier, F., 1960. *Climat et Erosion*. P.U.F., Paris, 139–50.

Gassmann, F. and Gutersohn, H., 1947. 'Kotenstreuung und Relieffaktor.' *Geographica Helvetica*, 2, 122–39.

Geyl, W. F., 1961a. 'Morphometric analysis and the world-wide occurrence of stepped erosion surfaces.' *Journ. Geol.*, 69, 388–416.

Geyl, W. F., 1961b. 'Provisional thoughts on the mode of development of stepped erosion surfaces.' (cyclostyled). Paper read at Brisbane Congress of the Aust. and N.Z. Assoc. for the Advancement of Science, Section C (Geology) in conjunction with Section P (Geography).

Hanson-Lowe, J., 1935. 'The clinographic curve.' *Geol. Mag.*, 72, 180–4.

Hettner, A., 1921. *Die Oberflächenformen des Festlandes*, D. G. Teubner, Leipzig and Berlin.

Hollingworth, S. E., 1938. 'The recognition and correlation of high-level erosion surfaces in Britain: a statistical study.' *Quart. Journ. Geol. Soc. Lond.*, 94, 55–84.

International Geographic Union, Paris, 1948a. 'Problèmes des terrasses.' *Sixième Rapport de la Commission pour l'Etude des Terrasses Pliocènes et Pleistocènes*.

International Geographic Union, Paris, 1948b. 'Problèmes des terrasses. Eclaircissements et repliques', by Baulig, H.

Joksch, H. C. 1955. 'Statistiche Analyse der Hypsometrischen Kurve der Erde.' *Zeitschr. für Geophysik*, 21, 109–12.

Jones, O. T., 1952. 'The drainage systems of Wales and the adjacent regions.' *Quart. Journ. Geol. Soc. Lond.*, 107, 201–25.

Jovanovíc, P. S., 1940. *Les Profils Fluviatiles en Long, Leurs Formes et leur Génèse*. Armand Colin, Paris.

Kossina, E., 1931. 'Die Mittlere Höhe der Kontinente.' *ZG Erdkunde, Berlin*, 361–6.

Kossina, E., 1933. 'Die Erdoberfläche.' *Handbuch der Geophysik*, Bd. 2, 875.

Lagrula, J., 1950. 'Sur la courbe hypsographique.' *Comptes Rendus de l'Acad. des Sciences*, 230, 1413–15.

Lapparent, A. de, 1883. *Traité de Géologie*. Masson, Paris.

Macar, P., 1937–8. 'Contribution à l'étude géomorphologique de l'Ardenne.' *Ann. Soc. Géol. Belg.*, 61, 224–37.

Macar, P., 1946. *Principes de géomorphologie normale*. Vaillant-Carmanne, Liège.

Macar, P., 1955. 'Appalachian and Ardennes levels of erosion compared.' *Journ. Geol.*, 63, 253–67.

Macar, P., 1957–8. *Compte Rendu de la Session Extraordinaire de la Société Géologique de Belgique*, 81, 8–13.

Maling, D. H., 1955. 'The geomorphology of the Wear Valley.' Ph.D. thesis, Durham Colleges in the University of Durham.

Martonne, E. de, 1934. *Traité de Géographie Physique*. Armand Colin, Paris.

Martonne, E. de, 1940. 'Interprétation géographique de l'hypsométrie Française.' *Comptes Rendus de l'Acad. des Sciences*, 211, 378–80 and 426–8.

Martonne, E. de, 1941a. 'L'altitude moyenne de la France et de ses grandes régions naturelles.' *Bull. Ass. des Géogr. Français*, 134–5, 2–4.

Martonne, E. de, 1941b. 'Hypsométrie et morphologie.' *Ann. de Géog.*, 50, 241–54.

Martonne, E. de, 1941c. 'Morphométrie et morphologie comparées du Massif Central et du Massif Bohémien.' *Bull. Ass. des Géogr. Français*, 140–1, 113–14.

Miller, A. A., 1939. 'Attainable standards of accuracy in the determination of pre-glacial sea-levels by physiographic methods.' *Journ. Geomorph.*, 2, 95–115.

Miller, A. A., 1953. *The Skin of the Earth*. Methuen, London.

Miller, A. A., 1955. 'Notes on the use of the height–range diagram.' *Geog. Studies*, 2, 111–15.

Moseley, F., 1961. 'Erosion surfaces in the Forest of Bowland.' *Proc. Yorks. Geol. Soc.*, 33, 173–96.

Murray, J., 1888. 'On the height of the land and the depth of the ocean.' *Scott. Geog. Mag.*, 4, 1–41.

Orlicz, M., 1931–5. 'Krzywe hipsograficzne lądów.' *Przeglad Kartograficzny, Lwów*.

Peeters, L., 1944. 'De Waarde van Enkele Kartografische Methoden bij de Analyse van een Polycyclisch Relief.' *Natuurwetenschappelyk Tijdschr.*, 26, 25–35.

Péguy, Ch.-P., 1942. 'Principes de morphométrie Alpine.' *Rev. de Géog. Alpine*, 30, 453–86.

Péguy, Ch.-P., 1947. *Haute-Durance et Ubaye*. Arthaud, Paris.

Péguy, Ch.-P., 1948. 'Introduction à l'emploi des méthodes statistiques en géographie physique.' *Rev. de Géog. Alpine*, 36, 1–103.

Péguy, Ch.-P., 1956–7. *Elements de Statistique Appliquée aux Sciences Géographiques*. Cours Professé à la Faculté des Lettres de Rennes.

Penck, A., 1894. *Morphologie der Erdoberfläche*. Erster Teil, Stuttgart.

Peucker, K., 1890. 'Der Mittlere Neigungswinkel des Bodens.' *Mitteilg. d. Deutsch. u. Osterr. Alpenvereins*.

Romer, E., 1931. 'Une nouvelle représentation graphique de l'hypsométrie (L'Hypsographoïde, d'après Fr. Uhorczak).' *Comptes Rendus du Congrés Internat. de Géog., Paris*, 1, 328–40.

Romieux, A., 1923. 'Recherche géhypsographique des lois fondamentales de la déformation terrestre.' *Rev. de Génie Militaire*, 53.

Scheidegger, A. E., 1958. *Principles of Geodynamics*. Springer, Berlin.

Slaucitajs, L., 1936. 'Begriff der Reliefentwicklung und Berechnung des wahren Areals einer Topographischen Fläche.' *Peterm. Mitt.*, 82, 111–12.

Smet, R. de, 1951. 'Problèmes de morphométrie.' *Bull. Soc. Belge d'Etudes Géog.*, 20, 111–32.

Smet, R. de, 1954. 'Courbe hypsographique et profil moyen de l'Ardenne.' *Bull. Soc. Belge d'Etudes Géog.*, 23, 143–67.

Soulier, P., 1925. *Le Relief de la Terre.* Felix Alcharn, Paris.

Strahler, A. N., 1950. 'Davies' concept of slope development viewed in the light of recent quantitative investigations.' *Ann. Amer. Assoc. Géog.*, 40, 209–13.

Strahler, A. N., 1952. 'Hypsometric (area-altitude) analysis of erosional topography.' *Bull. Geol. Soc. Amer.*, 63, 1117–42.

Strahler, A. N., 1954. 'Statistical analysis in geomorphic research.' *Journ. Geol.*, 62, 1–25.

Strahler, A. N., 1958. 'Dimensional analysis applied to fluvially eroded landforms.' *Bull. Geol. Soc. Amer.*, 69, 279–300.

Thompson, H. D., 1936. 'Hudson Gorge in the Highlands.' *Bull. Geol. Soc. Amer.*, 47, 1831–48.

Thompson, H. D., 1941. 'Topographic analysis of the Monterey, Staunton and Harrisonburg Quadrangles.' *Journ. Geol.*, 49, 521–49.

Tillo, A. A., 1889. 'Srednaya Vysota sushi i srednaya glubina moria.' *Izvestya Geograficheskovo Obshchestva*, St Petersburg.

Tricart, J., and Muslin, J., 1951. 'L'étude statistique des versants.' *Rev. de Géomorph. Dynamique*, 2, 173–81.

Wentworth, C. K., 1930. 'A simplified method for determining the average slope of a land surface.' *Amer. Journ. Sci.*, 20, 184–94.

Wooldridge, S. W., 1928. 'The 200-foot platform in the London Basin.' *Proc. Geol. Assn.*, 39, 1–26.

# The Application of Statistical Methods to Geomorphology

## RICHARD J. CHORLEY

## 1. THE CLASSES OF GEOMORPHIC PHENOMENA SUSCEPTIBLE OF QUANTIFICATION AND MEASUREMENT

The application of rigorous statistical methods to geomorphology is little over a decade old (Strahler 1950), although Krumbein (1937 and 1939) began to pioneer the use of simple statistical techniques in geology during the 1930's. Fisher (1953, pp. 2–3) has also drawn attention to the essentially statistical basis on which Lyell paleontologically distinguished between time-rock units more than one hundred years ago. Even today, however, statistical methods face a considerable body of opposition among American geomorphologists (Miller 1959, p. 570) and virtually complete hostility from British students of landforms.[1] It is significant that this reaction is most marked among geographers, and it is a measure of the indifference of British geologists to geomorphic problems that geomorphology in this country encounters such resistance to the application of quantitative techniques in general, and to statistical methods in particular. Some of this resistance undoubtedly stems from what Reynolds (1956, p. 129) has termed the 'ideographic' nature of much geographical thought, which is preoccupied with the unique and is distrustful of, or backward in drawing, any broad statistical inferences from sample data (McCarty 1958). In addition, Strahler (1954a, p. 342) pointed to the tardiness of American geomorphologists 'in setting up standards of form measurement and securing numerical data', which he related to the fact that 'the explanatory descriptive system of Davis has not demanded it'. Even though past 'orthodox' work in geomorphology has occasionally utilized numerical data (commonly height values), what have been considered 'statistical studies' have merely involved the visual grouping of data and its placing in a sequence assumed to have

[1] This chapter was written in 1961; the position has improved significantly since that time.

historical significance (Hollingworth 1938, Davies 1958—see criticism by Thornton 1960). Another impediment to the application of statistical methods in geomorphology is that their use requires at least a rudimentary mastery of a branch of applied mathematics, which does not find favour with the older generation of scholars, or with those who are attracted by the intuitive or artistic aspects of natural science. It is common for such scholars to hold the erroneous belief that 'you can prove anything with statistics'; for them to dwell with satisfaction on the fact that, on Charles Darwin's death, his rulers were found to be of inexact length and his conversion tables incorrect; and for them to believe that the important, interesting and worthwhile aspects of natural phenomena are somehow bound up with departures from a predictable regularity (Thompson 1942, pp. 1028–9).

Duncan (1953, p. 5) has pointed out that: 'A body of organized knowledge worthy of the name of science may exist even when techniques of measurement have not been evolved; it is then a branch of natural history in the sense of the phrase introduced by Kelvin.' However, despite the fact that statistical techniques have been developed for the analysis of non-quantitative data; that, for example, botanists are profitably employing techniques of analysis based on the grouping of presence and absence information (Williams and Lambert, 1959 and 1960); and that some statistical methods involve the simple ranking of phenomena with reference to some attribute which may not be wholly quantitative (see 'ordinal scales' in next section), the use of statistical methods in geomorphology has been entirely geared to numerical data. This has given rise to some of the strongest objections from geomorphologists who believe that the quantification of much geomorphic data is either unnecessary or impossible (Wooldridge 1958, p. 32). Russell, however, made a plea for more objective, quantitative geomorphic data when he wrote that 'The geomorphologist may concern himself deeply with questions of structures, process, and time, but the geographer wants specific information along the lines of what, where, and how much' (1949, p. 4). The misgivings regarding the quantitative measurement and expression of geomorphic phenomena have not prevented, however, a recent dramatic increase in numerical data in geomorphology and in geology as a whole (Krumbein 1960a, 1960b) resulting from a quantification of earlier qualitative concepts (e.g. the hypsometric integral (Strahler 1952a)), from the development of new techniques (e.g. the measurement of soil resistive properties (Chorley 1959)), and from controlled experimentation on geomorphic processes (Gilbert 1914, Rubey 1938, Leopold and Wolman 1957). Table I (modified from Krumbein 1960a) illustrates the main branches of geomorphic

## TABLE I

*Examples of the main branches of geomorphic studies (modified from Krumbein, 1960a). The quantitative aspects are outlined with solid lines*

EXAMPLES OF GEOMORPHIC STUDIES

1. FIELD OBSERVATIONS

2. LABORATORY OBSERVATIONS

3. OFFICE OBSERVATIONS

4. THEORETICAL WORK
(e.g. the calculation of mathematical models.- Scheidegger, 1961).

A
numerical measurements
(e.g. stream discharge, valley-side slope angle, etc.)

B
qualitative observations

C
numerical measurements conducted on field samples.
(e.g. properties of soil samples)

D
measurements arising from controlled experiments
(e.g. rate of nickpoint recession - Brush and Wolman, 1960).

E
map analysis

F
extraction of the maximum amount of information from data collected by field, laboratory or map work.
(e.g. the "sorting out" of geological variables. Krumbein, 1959).

a. statements ultimately possible of numerical expression.
(e.g. relative becomes absolute age).

b. statements that may (and should?) remain qualitative.
(see Krumbein, 1960, p.364)

c. quantitative measurements
(e.g. leading to calculation of drainage density).

d. subjective analysis of attributes,
(e.g. delimitation of erosion surfaces).

studies, with those aspects depending on quantitative data specially outlined.

One of the problems facing attempts to extend the quantification of geomorphic phenomena is that the quantitative approach has been associated in the past with the so-called 'dynamic' geomorphology, which is commonly supposed to be in mutually exclusive opposition to the 'classical' approach. Strahler (1952b, p. 925) distinguished between the 'two quite different viewpoints' of 'dynamic (analytical)' and 'historical (regional)' geomorphology, and drew attention to Bucher's (1941) division of geological information as a whole into 'timeless' and 'timebound' knowledge. Although it has been recognized (Strahler 1952b, p. 925, Miller 1959, p. 570) that there is a certain overlap of the two fields of study, in that the dynamic geomorphologist has to allow for the historical elements (especially climatic ones) which often enter into the 'timeless' studies, and that a better knowledge of present conditions is necessary for an historical geomorphologist to interpret accurately past events, it is unfortunate that such a division should exist. Figure 1 represents an attempt to depict, as a three-dimensional diagram, the field of geomorphology in both its timeless and timebound aspects with special reference to the measurable aspects of the discipline. The timeless sphere of the dynamic geomorphologist is composed, firstly, of the plane YZ wherein operate the virtually instantaneous (and therefore timeless) relationships between force and strength which together control the form of the surface. Work in this plane is complicated because force and strength are not entirely independent factors; because 'force' in geomorphology is a highly variable quantity and can only be adequately represented by 'pulses' of different magnitude and frequency passing up the synchronous plane; because landforms themselves (particularly through the agency of relief and slope) influence the energy exerted upon them; and, finally, because form adjustment is liable to differing degrees of time-lag. This time element is represented on the figure by the third, or historical, dimension (plane XY). Both the magnitude and, to a lesser extent, the organizational aspects of form are capable of achieving a timeless or steady state (Von Bertalanffy 1950, Strahler 1950, p. 676), when form is adjusted to the ratio of force and resistance, after a greater or lesser time span depending on the magnitude of the ratio. This timeless, or equilibrium, condition is the second area of interest to the dynamic geomorphologist. Thus the hydraulic radius (R) of a stream is susceptible of almost instantaneous adjustment to a changing force field represented by the stream discharge, and notions regarding the 'history' of a hydraulic radius would seem to have little meaning. At the other end of the

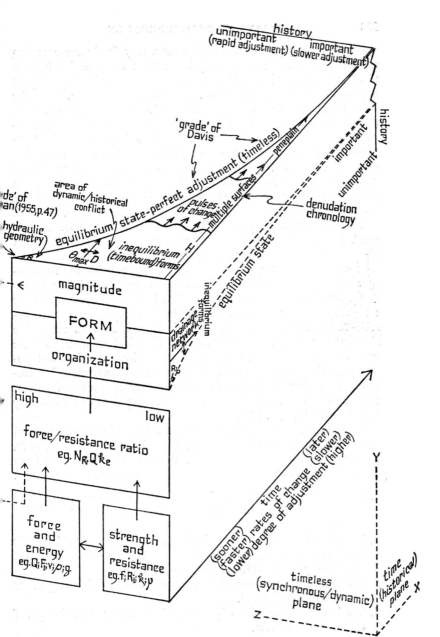

Fig. 1. The relationship between the 'timeless' and 'timebound' aspects of geomorphology.

scale, the form aspect of relief (H) adjusts very slowly to a changing energy balance and consequently is the form factor which is most timebound, susceptible of historical study and capable of bearing the imprints of successive pulses of force or strength change. Thus, the zones in the XY plane lying between the timeless, synchronous plane (YZ) and the timeless, equilibrium or steady state condition of complete form adjustment, represent those in which the historical approach has been practised in its cyclic, sequential and denudation chronology aspects. It is not difficult to understand why it is that much of the most productive work in dynamic geomorphology has been accomplished in the field of hydraulic geometry (Leopold and Maddock 1953, Wolman 1955, Leopold and Miller 1956, Wolman and Leopold 1957, Leopold and Wolman 1957, Hack 1957, Leopold *et al.* 1960, and Schumm 1960a) where the two timeless aspects of geomorphology converge; nor why the students of historical geomorphology have largely concerned themselves with the form sequences associated with those landforms susceptible of slow adjustment. At these two extremes there has been little opportunity for mutual contact or disagreement, but in the study of forms of intermediate rates of response to dynamic stimuli, such as valley-side slope angles ($\theta_{max}$), the dynamic and historical approaches have come into direct conflict. Moreover, the inability of the historical geomorphologists to identify themselves with the dynamic plane is exemplified by their minimizing of the importance of studies of process (Wooldridge 1958, p. 31), despite notable exceptions to the contrary (e.g. Leighly 1955, p. 318).

Many of the geomorphic parameters susceptible of measurement have been listed by Horton (1945), Leopold and Maddock (1953), Strahler (1958) and Melton (1958a). Measurements relating to force and energy (i.e. to 'process') are extremely difficult to make, in that:

1. Energy in geomorphology is made up of so many components which usually operate simultaneously and are difficult to disentangle.
2. The magnitude of geomorphic forces (Wolman and Miller 1960) is often so variable, even under the influence of the so-called 'uniform' processes (Krumbein, 1960b, p. 83).
3. The frequency of occurrence of processes of differing magnitude is also variable (Fig. 2).
4. The long-term variation of geomorphic forces involves changes of climate or base-level.

The first difficulty has sometimes been overcome by the recognition of an easily measurable parameter which synthesizes a number of energy factors, and the development of hydraulic geometry stems almost entirely from the ease with which discharge, or runoff intensity (Q), can be measured. The second difficulty is beginning to receive attention, particularly as studies of the desert areas of the earth characterized by highly variable processes are increasing. It has been suggested, for example, that extreme runoff conditions may exercise the most potent control over certain landscape form characteristics—e.g. drainage density (D). The third difficulty has been met

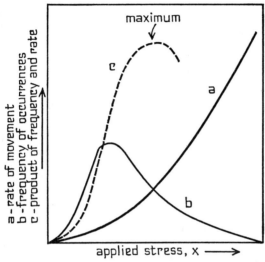

Fig. 2. The relations between rate of movement (transport), applied stress, and frequency (of occurrences) of stress application (from Wolman and Miller, 1960). The proposed combined frequency and rate curve (C) indicates that the greatest amount of erosional work is normally accomplished by medium-intensity stresses.

in the past by students of hydrology, and geomorphologists are beginning to concern themselves with questions of frequency (Wolman and Miller 1960) and recurrence-interval (Dury 1959) of geomorphic processes of differing intensity. The fourth difficulty itself varies in magnitude according to the assumed rate of adjustment of the forms upon which the forces act, increasing with the time-lag along with the importance of history (Fig. 1). Strahler (1958, p. 285) has identified certain force factors including runoff intensity (Q), rainfall intensity (i), eroding stress ($F_1$), flow velocity (v), depth of flow (d), unit weight of runoff (w), fluid density ($\rho$) and the acceleration of gravity (g).

The strength and resistance properties involved in geomorphic investigations are also difficult of recognition and measurement, and have received less quantitative attention than have geomorphic forces. Here, too, a number of difficulties arise:

1. The strength characteristics of the materials involve both the active vehicles of process (i.e. flowing water) and the landscape materials upon which action is taking place.

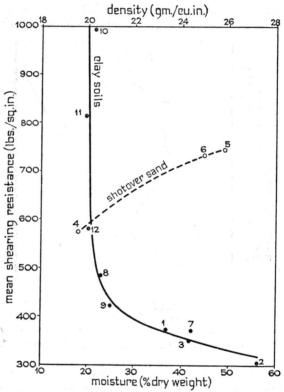

Fig. 3. The highly variable relationships between mean shearing resistance (to needle penetration) and the moisture content of clay soils near Oxford, and the density of Shotover Sand soils (from Chorley, 1959).

2. Strength characteristics are notably difficult to define (e.g. chemical strength, shear strength, tensile strength).
3. Geomorphic processes seldom operate on earth materials which have not suffered some secondary modification in their strength characteristics, chiefly through jointing and weathering.
4. The strength characteristics of comminuted material are highly variable (Fig. 3).

5. Strength characteristics are intimately bound up with the stress, or force, characteristics, making it difficult to define 'strength' independently of the force field to which it is referred.

Despite these difficulties, however, Strahler (1952b, p. 924) has pointed out that:

> The geomorphic processes that we observe are, after all, basically the various forms of shear, or failure, of materials which may be classified as fluid, plastic, or elastic substances, responding to stresses which are most commonly gravitational, but may also be molecular.
>
> Unless the fundamental nature of materials is understood, we are in a poor position to add anything worthwhile to what is already largely self-evident concerning the behavior of streams, landslides, glaciers, or wave-induced currents.

It is interesting and instructive to compare this comment with the following view:

> Dealing as we inevitably are with infinitely variable mixtures of solids, liquids and gases, it is manifest that the parameters in our imagined equations will not be constant, but themselves unmanageably variable (Wooldridge 1958, p. 32).

Strahler (1958, p. 285) has listed some of the geomorphic properties relating to strength and resistance—including infiltration capacity ($f$) (Horton 1945, Lewis 1943), resistivity of surface ($R_i$) (for geomorphic attempts to determine soil-shearing resistance, see Melton 1957, Chorley 1959), roughness ($k$) (for the Manning coefficient of roughness ($n$), see Woodford 1951, Langbein 1940, Boyer 1954) and viscosity ($\mu$).

The potentially most productive area of dynamic investigation, however, is undoubtedly that connected with the establishment of force/resistance ratios. Important as the absolute values of energy and strength are, it is ultimately the ratio between them which expresses the effectiveness of the force in producing changes in materials of given strength attributes. These ratios vary from the highly sophisticated, dimensionless ratios of universal application, to empirical, dimensional ratios which have been developed as the result of local studies relating to rigidly circumscribed bodies of information. The outstanding example of the first is the Reynolds' Number ($N_R$) (Reynolds 1883, Strahler 1958) which expresses the condition of fluid flow by equating the forces of inertia with those of viscosity. In geomorphology Strahler (1958) has developed a useful dimensionless ratio of this type, the Horton Number ($N_H$), by relating the runoff intensity (Q) and the erosion proportionality factor ($k_e$). Examples of the much less satisfactory dimensional ratios between force and resistance are provided by the climate/vegetation index and the index of erodibility of Chorley (1957, 1959). The value of the general approach to the problem of explaining the characteristics and rates of change of form in geomorphology by such ratios was expressed by Little (1940, p. 33) and Horton (1945), but were foreshadowed long before in the pioneer work of Gilbert (1877).

The form aspects of landscape obviously occupy a nodal position in geomorphic studies (Fig. 1) and the longest and most successful attempts have been made to quantify the geometrical qualities of landforms under a branch of the science more recently termed 'morphometry'. This interest in form is present by definition in geomorphology, but it is interesting that form *per se* has seldom been studied for its own sake. Form aspects, such as those represented by the longitudinal stream profile (Jones 1924), the hypsometric curve (Wooldridge 1928) and the clinographic curve (Hanson–Lowe 1935), have been quantitatively examined by historical geomorphologists in that they might give clues to the denudational history of those landforms. To the dynamic geomorphologist, however, aspects of landscape geometry seem to express the rapport between form and process, as Strahler (1950) demonstrated for maximum valley-side slopes ($\theta_{max}$) in the Verdugo Hills. Few workers have successfully embraced both the historical and dynamic aspects of landform development in any one study, and in this respect the paper by Schumm (1956) with its timeless and timebound overtones is of great interest. The most penetrating rationale of the value of studying form has been given in another connexion by Thompson (1942, pp. 1026–9). To the early morphometric studies, those primarily concerned with measures involving height determinations which were arranged in some assumed historical sequence, Horton (1945) added measurements relating to one of the most fundamental of all geomorphic units—the erosional drainage basin. This vastly increased the number and scope of possible form measurements in geomorphology and necessitated the utilization of statistical methods in the handling of this data, especially as many of the regionally significant aspects of morphometry could only emerge with the digestion of mass information provided by these methods. Strahler (1958, pp. 282–3) has listed many of these latter form aspects, which it is convenient to subdivide into the two groups, relating to organization and magnitude (Fig. 1);

1. *Organization*. This generally includes those properties relating to pattern or arrangement—e.g. joint or fabric patterns (Chayes,

1942a, 1942b, Pincus 1953); stream patterns; stream order ($u$); bifurcation ratios ($R_b$), etc. Figure 1 shows schematically that, like the magnitude aspects of form, organizational features are susceptible to different rates of adjustment, varying from the almost instantaneous adjustment of the bifurcation ratio (Leopold and Miller 1956, Carter and Chorley 1961, p. 122). to the greater time-lag of those associated with the maximum extension of an adjusted drainage network. The former is therefore useless as an historical indicator, the latter is more important.

2. *Magnitude.*
   a. Linear properties—e.g. stream length (L).
   b. Areal properties—e.g. drainage density (D).
   c. Relief properties—e.g. maximum valley-side slope ($\theta_{max}$); hypsometric integral (Strahler, 1952a); relief (H).

As has already been pointed out, the aspects of landscape magnitude vary from the rapidly adjusting features, like the parameters of hydraulic geometry (Leopold and Maddock 1953) to the slowly adjusting relief (H) aspects, the latter therefore providing much of the quantitative data used by the landscape historians.

The final classes of geomorphic phenomena which are susceptible to expression in a quantitative manner are illustrated in Fig. 1 with reference to the historical plane (XY). These involve information some of which, like time, may be easy to measure and regarding which much work has been done; some of which, like rates of change, in which some investigation has proceeded (e.g. rates of erosion— see Schumm 1956); and, finally, some of which, like degree of form adjustment, has not yet been seriously considered. (Strahler's 'hypsometric integral' probably represents the closest approach to such a measure of form adjustment.)


## II. MEASUREMENT, SAMPLING, AND ERRORS

### Units and Scales of Measurement

Great care is needed in the process of measurement, which involves the assigning of a numerical value to some quality of an object, so as to represent some fact or convention about it, in accordance with definite rules (Stevens 1946, Krumbein 1958, 1960c). These rules are laid down in the *operational definition* employed. Such definitions should be clearly understood, and most of these definitions in geomorphology revolve around a precise statement of the isolation and measurement of the particular attribute concerned; for example, whether measured stream velocities relate to surface, maximum, mean or bed velocities. It is important to recognize that the properties of a number obtained 'when a specified measurement operation is performed on an object under fixed rules' partly depend on the kind of 'yardstick' used in making the measurement (Krumbein 1958, pp. 176-7). Krumbein (1958, 1960c) has set out some rules to assist in the establishment of a well-defined and meaningful operational definition:

1. 'It is the responsibility of the originator of the operational definition to demonstrate that his number has the meaning he intends' (Krumbein 1958, pp. 176-7). This meaning usually relates to some specific physical or geometrical quality directly concerned with the subject-matter of the investigation.
2. The number is obtained by an objective, rather than by an intuitive, process, so as to eliminate *operator variations* (see later section) resulting from subjective judgments.
3. It is recognized that the form and character of the resulting number depends on the *scale of measurement* (i.e. the 'yardstick'). This scale must be chosen, therefore, such that the number possesses versatile properties which make it available for all convenient mathematical and statistical manipulations.

Stevens (1946), Krumbein (1958) and Griffiths (1960) have identified four kinds of scales of measurement, which are listed in increasing order of importance, general application and meaning:

1. *The Nominal Scale.* This represents a simple classification designed 'to establish *equivalance* between objects in terms of some quality they possess' (Krumbein 1958, p. 177). Numbers are merely used instead of names to designate the classes, and a good example of this is Price's classification of coasts (McGill 1959). This is the least versatile of all numerical scales because there is no necessary relationship between the numbers and, for example, any class may be designated the first (i.e. $5 \neq 3 \neq 9$). Virtually no operational definition has any meaning in this context, except—'Do not assign the same numeral to different classes or different numerals to the same class. Beyond that, anything goes with the nominal scale' (Stevens 1946, p. 679). Numbers assigned according to this scale are of very restricted value and are not susceptible of any mathematical or statistical manipulation. The only information which they assist in yielding is the number of items (i.e. *frequency*) in each class and the identity and magnitude of the class possessing domi-

nance or the greatest frequency (i.e. *modal class*). Some early work in fluvial geomorphology was attempted within this nominal framework (notably the landform classification of Von Richthofen 1886, pp. 652–85), and even Davis' classification of landforms under such divisions as 'normal' and arid was a purely nominal one. The rigidity, lack of opportunity and stultification associated with nominal-scale thinking is especially apparent when one views attempts by scholars in a qualitative discipline, hitherto based on classification, to rise above this primitive scale of measurement. In this connexion, recent attempts to quantify some branches of urban geography, notably those associated with hierarchical ranking of towns (e.g. Bracey 1953) are instructive. Mathematically the value of the nominal scale falls far below the kindergarten concept of 'Jack has 6 apples and Jill has 4 apples', for it was at least possible for Jack to take 2 of Jill's apples and add them to his own. Viewed on the level of the nominal scale, Jack would be a Zen Buddhist and Jill a lady wrestler.

2. *The Ordinal Scale.* Such scales possess both equivalence and sequence (i.e. *order*), and their use is designed to allot numbers according to the relative amount of some quality possessed by objects. These numbers preserve relative rank, wherein 'there is a logical sequence to the numbers assigned to the ranked classes' (Krumbein 1958, p. 177), and the numbers themselves are only significant in that they indicate relative order or sequence (i.e. $9 > 5 > 3$). The only additional statistical techniques introduced by the use of the ordinal scale are those involving the recognition of relative position in a sequence. Thus the concept of the *median* (i.e. the middle-most item in a set of ranked items) and that of the various *percentile* measurements can be applied here. The type example of an ordinal scale is found in the Mohs scale of mineral hardness (Stevens 1945), or in numerical scales for measuring intelligence. Davis' divisions of youth, maturity and old age possess certain features of an ordinal nature. The numerical concept of stream ordering (Horton 1945, pp. 281–2, as modified by Strahler 1952a, p. 1120) provides numbers derived according to an ordinal scale, in that order two is greater in magnitude than order one, but an order two is not twice as large as an order one, order one and a half has no meaning, neither does the addition of an order one to an order two comprise an order three.

3. *The Interval Scale.* This possesses equivalence, order and *ratio of intervals*, in that there are equal intervals or differences between successive numbers. With this, one attains what has been termed the first quantitative scale (Stevens 1946), implying that it is 'the

minimal scale for obtaining numbers that can be manipulated in terms of computing the *mean* and *standard deviation*' (Krumbein 1960c). A considerable limitation, however, derives from an important property of interval scale numbers, in that they are referred to a purely arbitrary zero value. A general example of such a scale is the Centigrade scale of temperature which is related to a zero value of pure convenience—i.e. the melting-temperature of ice. This implies that such numbers are limited to linear transformations (Krumbein 1960) in that constants may be added (as in translating the Centigrade into the Fahrenheit scale). However, 'on these scales . . . it is meaningless to say that one value is twice or some other proportion greater than another' (Stevens 1946, p. 679) and no absolute concept of size ratios can be applied in a comparative sense. Thus no one would suppose that a temperature of 20°C is twice as 'hot' as one of 10°C. Interval scales are not common in geomorphology but the most obvious one, namely elevation above present sea-level, is very important in studies relating to denudation chronology.

4. *The Ratio Scale* is the most powerful and versatile of the four types, possessing equivalence, order, ratio of intervals and *ratio of values* (Stevens 1946, Krumbein 1958). This latter property results from their reference to an absolute zero value, such that correct ratios are preserved between the magnitudes of numbers (i.e. $\frac{3}{5} = \frac{9}{15}$). It is meaningful to multiply such numbers by constants and, taking as an example the Absolute temperature scale, a body having a temperature of 20°K is really twice as hot as one of temperature 10°K. These numbers are susceptible of treatment by virtually all types of mathematical and statistical procedures (Krumbein 1960c), and most of the numerical values employed by quantitative geomorphology fall into this category. The addition of ratio of values completes the requirements for adequate measurement, involving firstly the selection and establishment of a unit and secondly the development of a process of numerical comparison with the unit (Duncan 1953, p. 5). The units obtained with reference to the ratio scales are capable of further subdivision into two classes—fundamental units (the 'primary quantities' of Bridgman 1931, p. 18) and derived (secondary) units.

*Fundamental units* are those related to basic qualities which can be defined independently of all other units (Murphy 1949, p. 5), and which can be 'regarded as fundamental and of irreducible simplicity' (Bridgman 1931, p. 18). These are the units of *length* (dimensionally equal to L—i.e. $\overset{d}{=}$ L), *mass* ($\overset{d}{=}$ M), *time* ($\overset{d}{=}$ T) and *temperature* ($\overset{d}{=}$ t), in terms of which the dimensions of all other units can be expressed (Strahler 1958). However, in the most rigid sense it is possible to regard some of these units as derived in that, for example, the Newtonian concept of mass is really a definition of constant ratio of the masses of two bodies—one being the earth (Murphy 1949). For practical purposes, however, it is possible to regard these four unit qualities as basic, together with that of numerosity which relates to pure numbers which are dimensionally equal to zero (Stevens 1946, Krumbein 1960c). Thus such properties as stream length, relief and the number of streams of a given order (Strahler 1958, p. 282) may be regarded as expressions in terms of fundamental units. *Derived units*, as their name implies, are obtained from combinations or ratios of fundamental units and expressed in terms of them. These units are of great diversity and relate to a wide variety of properties of geomorphic interest. Such properties as basin area ($\stackrel{d}{=} L^2$), hydraulic radius (R) ($\stackrel{d}{=} L^2/L = L$), drainage density (D, or $D_d$) ($\stackrel{d}{=} L/L^2 = L^{-1}$), stream velocity (V) ($\stackrel{d}{=} LT^{-1}$), discharge (Q) ($\stackrel{d}{=} L^3T^{-1}$), force ($\stackrel{d}{=} MLT^{-2}$), surface resistivity ($\stackrel{d}{=} ML^{-1}T^{-2}$), absolute viscosity ($\mu$) ($\stackrel{d}{=} ML^{-1}T^{-1}$), density ($\rho$) ($\stackrel{d}{=} ML^{-3}$) and the acceleration of gravity ($g$) ($\stackrel{d}{=} LT^{-2}$) are obviously derived (Strahler 1958). The derived units listed above, however, all possess dimensional characteristics in that they are expressed in units of the form of square miles, miles per square mile, feet per second, cubic feet per second, dynes per square centimetre, dyne-seconds per centimetre squared, pounds per cubic foot, and feet per second per second, respectively. A second group of derived units are quite different from these, and are those which result from ratios which resolve themselves into units or numbers which have no dimensions—i.e. *dimensionless numbers* (Strahler 1958, p. 284). These dimensionless numbers vary greatly in complexity. Numbers relating to angles (S) (i.e. stream entrance angle ($\xi$), land slope ($\theta_g$) or channel slope ($S_c$)) are dimensionless (being trigonometrical ratios of length $\stackrel{d}{=} L/L = O$), as are relief ratios (e.g. basin relief/basin length $\stackrel{d}{=} L/L = O$) (Schumm 1956, p. 612) and hypsometric integrals (e.g. relation between percentage area and percentage height $\stackrel{d}{=} O/O = O$) (Strahler 1952a). Much more complicated dimensionless ratios are represented by the Reynolds Number ($N_R$) (Reynolds 1883) which expresses the relationship between the forces of inertia and viscosity in describing the state of fluid flow

$$(N_R = \frac{\rho VR}{\mu} \stackrel{d}{=} \frac{ML^{-3}.LT^{-1}.L}{ML^{-1}T^{-1}} = \frac{ML^{-1}T^{-1}}{ML^{-1}T^{-1}} = 0),$$

and the Horton Number ($N_H$) (Strahler 1958) which is a measure of the intensity of erosion on the slopes of a drainage basin

$$(N_H = \text{run-off intensity} \cdot \frac{\text{erosion intensity}}{\text{eroding stress}} \overset{d}{=} LT^{-1} \cdot \frac{ML^{-2}T^{-1}}{ML^{-1}T^{-2}} = )0.$$

The character of dimensionless numbers is illustrated diagrammatically in Fig. 4. The numerical magnitude of a dimensionless number does not change with, and is independent of, the fundamental units of length, mass and time (Bridgman 1931, p. 19,

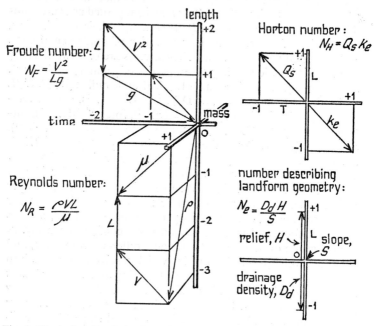

Fig. 4. Illustrating the derivation of some dimensionless numbers with the aid of the D-space diagram (from Strahler, 1958).

Duncan 1953, pp. 3 and 12). One of their values in geomorphology is that they can express valuable ratios of force and resistance; another is that they permit and encourage the comparison of the fundamental character of phenomena associated with systems of differing absolute magnitude. On a simple level, the use of angular measurements allows the geometry of large and small slopes to be compared, the hypsometric integral allows drainage basins of all sizes to be compared on the basis of unconsumed volume of mass, and the relief ratio permits comparison of the mean slopes of drainage basins of different magnitudes, opening the door to dynamic analysis (Schumm 1956). On a more sophisticated plane, the Reynolds Number enables a comparison of the fundamental flow qualities of liquids differing in density, flow velocity, depth and viscosity.

Finally one must refer briefly to a topic to which it will be necessary to return under a subsequent section entitled *operator variation*. In addition to the subjective elements regarding measurement which are involved in the setting up of operational definitions and in the selection of scales and units of measurement, it is obvious that one must examine the possibility of *errors of measurement* themselves (Krumbein 1934, Griffiths 1953). Krumbein (1958, 1960c) has recognized both non-compensating errors, which are in some sense systematic in that one set of errors of measurement do not necessarily cancel out another set, and compensating errors, which are random and mutually effacing. For this reason it is important to be able to recognize the possible sources of measurement errors in that, for example, non-compensating errors can seriously distort any calculations involving mean values. There are two, quite separate, sources of possible measurement error:

1. Errors of judgment. These often arise from inadequate operational definitions, involving such problems as incorrect identification of phenomena, and that measurements designed to isolate one property actually become involved with another. These errors of judgement may be either non-compensating (e.g. incorrect identification, outright mistakes, etc.) or compensating (e.g. incorrect estimates of magnitude performed by a number of different people).
2. Errors of measurement, proper, resulting from errors in measuring, counting, computing, etc. These may also tend to be either non-compensating (e.g. due to a faulty instrument) or compensating (as repeated linear and areal measurements tend to be).

It is only possible to judge the true importance of errors of measurement in the light of whether the variability of measurement produced is much greater or much less than the inherent variations in the geomorphic data (Krumbein 1960c). As Krumbein has elsewhere pointed out, these inherent variations are of very different orders of magnitude, in that:

Geological factors operate at more than one level temporally and geographically, so that many small-scale fluctuations are superimposed on broader large-scale effects, giving rise to high degrees of variability in some geological measurements (Krumbein 1960b, p. 83).

*Sampling*

An aggregate or class of objects or events which have one or more attributes in common is termed a *population* (or a 'universe') (Strahler 1954b, Krumbein 1960a, p. 348). The nature of any population is obviously determined by the operational definition, the geomorphologist being quite free to set up his conceptual population, and a geomorphological population may be defined (by paraphrasing Krumbein 1960a, p. 349) as a class or aggregate of geomorphic objects or events from which samples are taken for the purpose of drawing geomorphic inferences and making geomorphic predictions about the class, through statistical analysis. Some geomorphic populations may be almost infinitely large (i.e. *infinite population*), like the number of sand grains on a beach or the possible number of point slope angle measurements in a given area (Strahler 1954b), other populations (e.g. number of streams or sinkholes) may be quite large. For most purposes, however, the idea of the infinite population can be applied, in that, for example, sinkholes formed under given conditions might be expected to occur at any time throughout the total span of geological time—past and future, as well as present. Cochran, Mosteller and Tukey (1954) have pointed out that in many instances the total population is not available for sampling (Krumbein 1960a, 1960b), as, for example, when measurements are made in scattered excavations; but when the geomorphic population relates to surface conditions one may consider that the available population (*target population*) is virtually identical with the total population. It is also apparent that it is necessary in many instances to select parts of the target population to be sampled (i.e. a *sampled population*), as would be the case in selecting certain open sites at which to measure soil shearing resistance in a partially built-up area. As Krumbein (1960a, p. 353) has stated '. . . it becomes a matter mainly of geological judgment whether the sampled and target populations are nearly enough identical that inferences about the sampled population can be applied without qualification to the target population.'

Now, no two similar attributes relating to two items (*individuals* or *variates*) of a given population are ever absolutely identical, and variations within a population always occur (i.e. no two first-order streams in a given homogeneous region are quite the same length (Krumbein 1953a)). Inherent variability is therefore a basic idea in earth science, where every phenomenon is a little different from another (Strahler 1954b, p. 2), 'even though the two occur side by side and were formed at the same time by the same process' (Manning 1953, p. 544). However, within a given population, this natural variation (which is akin in character, but not of course in mechanism, to that relating to biological species) is random, non-systematic and generally tends to lie within a relatively small range (Krumbein 1953a), such that, for example,

> all geomorphologists recognize the general tendency of forms produced by the same group of processes within a given area to show a general uniformity which provides the basis for statements concerning the facies, or texture, of a region and for the demarcation of physiographic subdivisions (Strahler 1954b, p. 2).

The technical term *variance* is applied to the quality of variability, and the calculation of the inherent variance of a body of data gives one a most important *parameter* by means of which the sample (and, by inference, the population from which is was drawn) can be described. Another such parameter is the average value, or the *arithmetic mean*. The inherent variation which one expects to encounter within any single population is, however, not the only type of variance which is of importance. Variations between different populations generally tend to be on a larger scale and much more significant than variations within a single population (Krumbein 1953a), and it is vital that sampling should be carried out in such a manner that the true sources of variance can be identified (Krumbein and Miller 1953, p. 512); in other words, such that it may be recognized whether one is dealing with an attribute which relates to one or more populations.

Most geomorphic populations are extremely, possibly infinitely, large, and therefore it is not actually or physically possible to measure every manifestation of a given phenomenon (Krumbein 1960a, p. 347). The aim of the quantitative worker must be to select a relatively small sample which may be considered to approximate very closely to some of the characteristics of the population from which it was drawn, such that one may arrive at some valid conclusions regarding that population (Croxton and Cowden 1955, p. 26, Hansen, Hurwitz and Madow 1953, p. 4). This being so, the manner in which the sample is drawn from the population is of great importance, and Krumbein (1960a, p. 350) has stated that 'a sample may be defined as a group of individuals drawn from a population in accordance with a specific procedure'. There are three main procedures, of very different statistical significance, whereby samples may be selected:

1. Purposive selection. This is made purely on the basis of convenience, ranging between a subjective and arbitrary selection of items

which commonly 'tends to over-emphasize extreme variants rather than major . . . attributes' (Krumbein 1960b, p. 84); and a 'grab' sample of limited proportions arbitrarily selected in space or time, leading generally to an under-estimation of the inherent variability of the total population (Cochran, Mosteller and Tukey 1954, p. 13). The problem with a purposive sample is that there is no absolute idea of what chance each individual item in the population has of being selected—all one can say is that this chance is not the same for every item. The generation of such a biased sample on a purposive basis might result, for example, from sampling stream gradients in a given region simply on the basis of being most accessible from a main road running through the area. One would expect a smaller variation in the measured gradients than might be obtained from more widespread sampling, but would be unsure of the relationship between these two variances, as also between the mean values of stream gradient with respect to the sample and the region as a whole. It might be expected that the mean gradient of the sample would be different from that of the total population, but whether it is less on account of the road following the terrain with the least gradient, or whether it is greater on account of the road avoiding marshy, low-lying valleys, one could not be sure.

2. Random selection, which is made such that each individual in the population is separately drawn and has an equal chance of being included in the sample (Krumbein 1960a, p. 351). This is naturally the best means of selecting a representative sample, and the sampling designs and plans which follow are based on random selection. It is advisable to mention, however, that some so-called objective sampling techniques are

> unwarranted shotgun marriages between the quantitatively unsophisticated idea of sample as 'what you get by grabbing a handful' and the mathematically precise notion of a 'simple random sample' (Cochran, Mosteller and Tukey 1954, p. 13),

and that

> such terms as 'select at random', 'choose at random', and the like, always mean that some mechanical device, such as coins, cards, dice, or tables of random numbers, is used (Cochran, Mosteller and Tukey 1954, p. 16).

3. Probability selection. This is a highly specialized branch of sampling where the chances of inclusion of each individual are not equal but of known probability, or if the chance of selection depends on whether another particular individual is selected (Krumbein 1960a).

It must have become increasingly obvious that it is impossible to set about the collection of data in the form of representative samples without a very good idea as to the precise way in which they will be analysed so as to yield the desired information (Moroney 1960, p. 120). For example, many sampling techniques depend on some previous knowledge of the general population characteristics (see later sections on analytic statistics) (Olsen and Potter 1954, p. 29), but a special branch of statistical methods (*non-parametric statistics*) has been developed to deal with instances where such prior knowledge is not available. As will appear later, there is an increasing fund of information regarding the characteristics of geomorphic populations. Such an overall plan (or 'model') for the collection and analysis of information is termed an *experimental design* (Cochran and Cox 1950, Krumbein and Miller 1953, Krumbein 1955a, Fisher 1960), and naturally includes the interlocked *sampling design* and *statistical design*. Statistical design, involving the selection of a suitable statistical technique, is considered in the third part of this chapter. Sampling designs involve plans for the collection of data through time, or over area, or both (Krumbein 1955a, p. 9), such that they satisfy the requirements of the experimental design. This generally involves the necessity that sampling designs have to be so arranged that the data collected falls naturally into a framework such that 'the variances due to different causes can be sorted out and evaluated' (Krumbein 1953a, p. 858). It is important to recognize that the proper statistical treatment of objectively collected data provides a means whereby the very fine nuances of a body of information can be revealed. To employ an experimental design to investigate a phenomenon which is perfectly obvious anyway is not only a waste of effort, like cracking a walnut with a sledgehammer, but brings the employment of statistical methods into disrepute. As Moroney (1960, p. 122) has put it:

> Many investigations are extremely loose in design. They are like nets which are indeed spread wide but have a mesh so large that all but the most giant fish escape. In statistical work, the giant fish is the one that everyone can catch for himself, without the statistician's tackle.

Sampling designs require decisions of three sorts (Strahler 1950, pp. 677–9); (1) the type of data required (already considered under 'operational definitions'), (2) the rules of sampling to be followed (see the description of 'sampling plans' which follows), and (3) the size of the sample.

In deciding on the size of the required sample, the operator has to steer a middle course between the minimum number of variates giving a truly representative sample of sufficient size such that some inferences regarding the parameters (such as the mean and the variance) of the total population may be made (Strahler 1954b), and the point beyond which too much information is unnecessary or even so overwhelming 'as to be almost as much a limiting factor in research as too little data' (Peltier 1959). Determining the optimum size of a particular sample is very much a matter of experience, but it is important to realize that a smaller sample is generally needed to approximate the true mean value of the population than to fix the variance. For example, in recommending sample sizes between 20 and 200 for maximum slope angle readings, Strahler (1950, p. 679) stated that 'a sample of 50 slopes is adequate to reveal the characteristics of the distribution

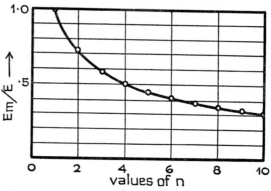

Fig. 5. Graph showing the decrease of the error of the mean (E$_m$), as a ratio of the error of a single observation (E), as the number of observations (n) increases (from Krumbein and Pettijohn, 1938).

in a homogeneous region of 6 to 12 first-order drainage basins; while a sample of 25 will closely fix the mean'. It is interesting that a random sample of 25 varieties yields significant mean values in some biological work (e.g. Anderson 1947, pp. 434–6), whereas Godwin (1941, p. 330) suggests that a sample of 150 tree pollen grains be selected from a sampled population to give an indication of the local variation of tree species. It has been found (Krumbein and Pettijohn 1938, p. 41) that the 'error of the mean' (i.e. the average difference between the sample mean and the mean value of the population) of a set of observations varies inversely as the square root of the number of observations (e.g. the size of the sample) (Fig. 5). The question of the validity of the sample size can only be finally settled, however, by employing some rigorous statistical test designed to compare certain characteristics of a given sample with those which are known to obtain for the population as a whole (see, for example, the *chi-square* test). It will be seen shortly that sampling on the basis of areas is often important in obtaining geomorphic data, wherein small areas are randomly selected to obtain information considered to be representative of much larger areas. Peltier (1959) has shown that the size of these sampling areas depends very much on the type of information re-

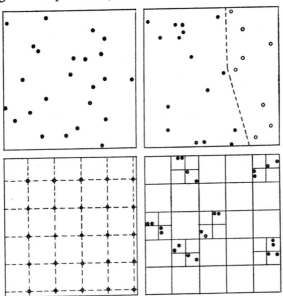

Fig. 6. Examples of areal sampling plans (from Krumbein, 1960a):

*Upper left:*   Simple random sampling. N = 24.
*Upper right:*  Stratified sampling. $n = 16$ points in left stratum and $m = 8$ in right. N = $n + m$ = 24.
*Lower left:*   Systematic grid sampling. The grid of N = 25 intersections was located by randomizing one grid point.
*Lower right:*  Multi-stage (nested) sampling at three levels. This involves the random selection of $n(=6)$ major units of the 25, $m(=2)$ out of the 4 minor units comprising each major unit, and $k(=2)$ out of 9 points of observation within each minor unit. N = $nmk$ = 24.

quired, and that, for example, 50-ft squares present fairly uniform sampling conditions for such properties as soil type, vegetation and parent material, whereas sampling areas of one square mile may be used for regional sampling of mean slope, relief and texture of dissection. Sampling frameworks in geomorphology can be of very different orders of magnitude—a stream channel for one purpose being one individual and for another it may embrace a large number of variates (e.g. pebble sizes, velocity readings, slope angles, etc.). For a test of slope sampling methods Strahler (1956, p. 589) selected a sample area 2200 yards square within which about 2000 random slope readings were made. Sometimes, particularly in geographical work where the areal sampling units are of arbitrary and differing size, it is necessary to 'weight' the values obtained by sampling according to the relative sizes of the areas to which they refer (Robinson 1956).

The rules of sampling (Cochran, Mosteller and Tukey 1954) most usually involve the geomorphologist in selecting a sampling plan of a geographical, or areal, type, for even variations of a temporal kind must commonly be studied in a spatial context. There are five general types of random geographical sampling, of which all except the first are illustrated in Fig. 6.

1. Random serial sampling, involving the collection of data in accordance with some pre-determined plan at arbitrary, but usually equal, interval spacing (Krumbein and Pettijohn 1938, p. 14). This method is ideal for linear sampling—i.e. pebble size along a narrow stream or maximum angles of slope along a valley side. Strahler (1950, pp. 677–9) employed this plan in sampling maximum valley-side slope angles in the Verdugo Hills, suggesting that the interval spacing should be 5–10 feet in fine-textured badlands (i.e. $\frac{1}{4}-\frac{1}{2}$ the average slope length) and 100–150 feet in medium-textured topography (i.e. $\frac{1}{3}-1\frac{1}{2}$ the average slope length). The question of how far apart individual samples must be taken on a continuous surface to be considered as 'different' readings obviously varies with the magnitude of the phenomena measured, and in this instance each sample was a complete orthogonal profile from which the maximum angle was measured. In another sampling programme, Strahler (1957) measured ground slope, soil strength, surface roughness and vegetation characteristics along 100-ft transit lines randomly selected in central Maine.

2. Simple random sampling, where all parts of a given area are equally accessible and equally relevant to the sampling programme. This implies that the required number of items is selected such that each is drawn independently and has an equal chance of being selected. Normally the locations at which the data are to be collected are chosen by the random co-ordinate method (Krumbein 1960a, p. 360). Strahler (1954b, pp. 3–4 and 1956, pp. 589–91) describes this method with special reference to slope angle sampling, wherein the square to be sampled is divided into 100 equal units on a side, forming an abscissa and an ordinate each designated by two digit numbers 00–99. Used in pairs, to represent X and Y co-ordinates,

these numbers give a possible 10,000 points within the sampling area (which may be further increased for large areas by further sub-division of the sides) (Fig. 7). Using a *table of random numbers* (Dixon and Massey 1957, pp. 366–70; use explained by Dixon and Massey 1957, pp. 33–5), random pairs of co-ordinates are selected, the 100 X values first and then the 100 corresponding Y values. This method ensures completely random selection of sampling locations, an example of which is given in Fig. 7. A sampling plan partaking of elements of both the random serial and simple random types is the 'operational experiment' which 'consists of assuming an initial point of departure which may be random or

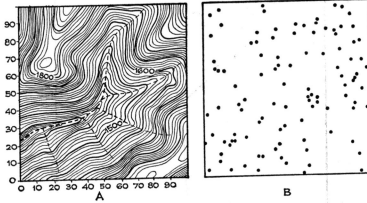

Fig. 7. Random selection of 100 points (B) at which slope measurements were taken in a portion of the Emporium, Pennsylvania, quadrangle (A). The area shown is about 4,000 feet square (from Strahler, 1954b).

rational, therefrom assuming an action and then following out that action with the accumulation of measurements of the magnitude and frequency of significant or critical conditions that are encountered' (Peltier 1959). Such a method includes 'random walk' sampling (Krumbein 1955a, p. 10), where an operator takes a chosen number of paces (equal to one leg = L) in a number of different directions (n), the azimuths being drawn from a table of random numbers. Figure 8 shows the pattern of such a random walk and gives an equation for the average straight line distance (d) travelled from the starting point. Strahler (1957) employed a somewhat similar sampling method for measuring tree size and frequency with 40-ft diameter random circles.

3. Stratified sampling. This can only be based upon some specialized knowledge regarding the population to be sampled (Krumbein

1953a). This commonly involves the assumption that the area to be sampled embraces phenomena which fall naturally into sub-groups or possibly compose different populations altogether. Krumbein (1953a), for example, considered a given beach from the point of view of particle size, shape, beach firmness, etc., to represent a series of homogeneous populations, grading and merging into one another, aspects of which might be sampled in a random manner to elucidate the nature and variation of a given aspect

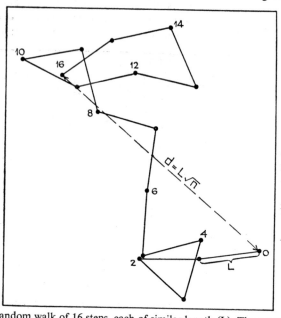

Fig. 8. Random walk of 16 steps, each of similar length (L). The equation gives the average expected straight-line distance (d) travelled from the starting point (from Krumbein, 1955a).

within a population or between different populations. To allow for, and to investigate, this possibility, the occurrence of this phenomena is divided into natural groups (or *strata*) for the purposes of sampling. The strata for sociological sampling are delimited not only on a geographical basis, but on those of sex, size of community, income group, colour, age, occupation, etc. (Croxton and Cowden 1939, p. 30). Geomorphic sampling strata are most usually geographical ones (although Curray and Griffiths (1955) have applied stratified sampling to laboratory material), where the sampling area is divided into natural segments, each of which is sampled individually. Such segments might involve, for example, the division of the beach foreshore from the backshore (Krumbein 1953a, 1960a), an outcrop of sandstone from one of limestone, pools from riffles (Leopold and Wolman 1957) in a stream bed, north-facing slopes from south-facing slopes, etc. From each of these segments a random sample of individuals is drawn, the size of the sample being proportional to the area of the segment (Krumbein 1960a), either by the method of random co-ordinates (Fig. 6) or by systematic grid sampling (Fig. 12).

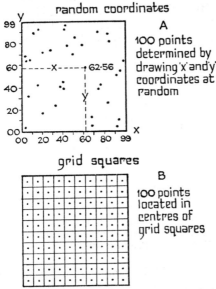

Fig. 9. Systematic grid sampling (B) of 100 points, compared with simple random sampling (A) of the same area (from Strahler, 1956).

4. Systematic grid sampling. The simplest instance of this type is when a regular grid (usually rectangular), with equal grid spacings, is laid in a random manner over the area to be sampled, such that the number of grid squares or intersections is equal to the size of the sample required (Strahler 1956, Krumbein 1960a). The advantages of this method over that of random co-ordinates (Fig. 9) are that the sampling points are obviously less tedious to locate, and the sampling coverage is more uniform; but there are also a number of disadvantages. In some instances a regular pattern of sampling may not give as representative a sample as a truly random

pattern, there is also the disadvantage that there is a limit imposed by the grid to the size of the sample which can be selected (Strahler 1956), and, finally, a completely unrepresentative sample will result if there is a similar regular pattern to the spatial distribution of the phenomenon to be measured, which either coincides exactly with the grid pattern or deviates entirely from it. The size of the grid mesh is largely determined by experience, and is controlled partly by the size of the area to be sampled and partly by the magnitude of individual phenomena. Krumbein (1953a) has suggested a beach sampling grid mesh size of 25 or 50 feet (for a more precise indication of the suitability of a selected grid mesh see Krumbein and Miller 1953, p. 516). Grids are not always rectangular, however, nor is their spacing always arithmetic. Figure 10 illustrates a

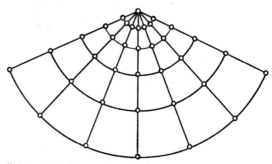

Fig. 10. Radial logarithmic sampling grid, designed to give more detailed data near the source of sediment (i.e. the apex of an alluvial fan) (from Krumbein and Pettijohn, 1938).

radial logarithmic grid for sampling the surface slope or pebble size of an alluvial fan (Krumbein and Pettijohn 1938, p. 15), where distance from the fan head is important, and pebble characteristics are believed to vary logarithmically with distance.

Two types of systematic grid methods especially useful in geomorphology are the 'two-factor' and the 'three-factor' basic forms (Krumbein and Miller 1953)—the single-factor basic form is that described under simple stratified sampling. A two-factor form is that, for example, designed to study the variation of a particular attribute in two directions. Figure 11 illustrates such a grid for sampling conditions within a stream channel (Krumbein and Miller 1953, Wolman 1954), orientated to give random sampling locations normal and parallel to the direction of flow in order to compare such local variations as those due to the sorting action of cross fluctuations of the currents with regional variations in a downstream direction. An elaboration of the two-factor form is provided by Fig. 12, showing its adaptation to stratified sampling

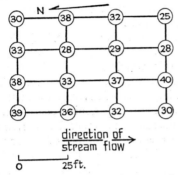

Fig. 11. Two-factor systematic sampling grid, Arroyo Seco, showing the percentage of granodiorite pebbles at each sampling point (from Krumbein and Miller, 1953).

of the moisture content along and across a beach, the whole being divided into two possible populations by the berm line which equally divides the grid. The three-factor basic form is most useful in that it may combine areal with time sampling (Krumbein and Miller 1953, pp. 521–3) such that a grid may be placed to allow sampling in two significant directions, and such that samples can

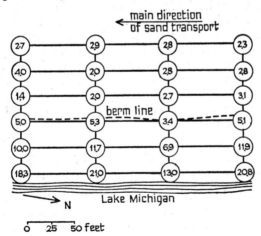

Fig. 12. Two-factor systematic sampling grid stratified across the berm line at Wilmette Beach, Lake Michigan. The numbers indicate the sand moisture content at each sampling point (from Krumbein and Miller, 1953).

be taken at different times from the same location. An example of this would be a grid placed over a rapidly-eroding badland valley at the intersections of which height measurements are taken at different times to separate the erosion rates parallel with and normal to the valley axis.

5. Multi-stage (nested) sampling (Fig. 6). This hierarchical or multi-level technique is commonly applied when a large area is to be investigated, within which significant local variations are also thought to occur (Krumbein and Slack 1956). To combine close sampling with a large area of coverage the method employed is to divide the total area into major, minor, sub-minor, etc., units, and then select in some random manner first a given number of major ('upper level') units, then a number of minor units from within these, and so on until finally a number of random locations are selected from the smallest areal sampling units (Krumbein 1960a). Olsen and Potter (1954) have applied this nested sampling method in field investigations of sedimentary petrology, as have Krumbein and Slack (1956), who employed 11 master units, each subdivided into 9 sub-units (townships) from 22 of which 44 individual mines were selected at which measurements of shale radioactivity were made (Fig. 13). An obvious application of this technique in geomorphology is in the sampling of Pleistocene deposits from open excavations, but in this, and other like instances, it becomes obvious that it is not always possible for geomorphologists to control the upper level of sampling (Krumbein 1960b)—in that the primary selection of locations is governed by the availability of suitable sites. However, it is possible for random sampling techniques to be applied on the lower levels (i.e. within individual excavations), and this has been termed 'lower semi-probability' sampling (Cochran, Mosteller and Tukey 1954). Finally, a very crude type of multi-stage sampling ('cluster sampling' (Krumbein 1960a)) consists of the two stages of, first, selecting a number of random locations and, secondly, making an *en masse* collection of individuals at each point without any attempt at randomization.

A last word regarding the significance of the original data (*raw data*) collected belongs to Manning (1953, p. 556):

The problems involved in obtaining sufficient precision in the data to warrant the use of statistical methods must, however, be left to specialists concerned with collection of data. It should be remembered that, whereas statistics provides a method for analysis, no method can ever be a substitute for common sense. The reliability of the original data cannot be improved upon by the most refined

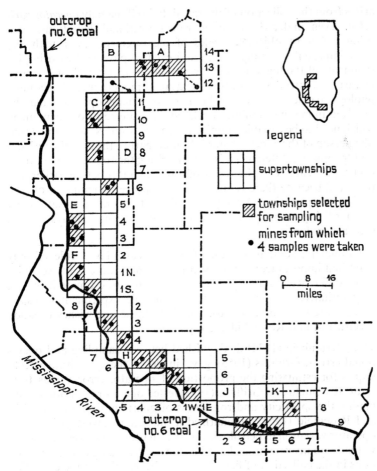

Fig. 13. Multi-stage (nested) sampling design applied to the investigation of low-level radioactivity in shale in southern Illinois (from Krumbein and Slack, 1956).

statistical analysis. On the other hand, the experimenter must exercise the same judgment in applying statistical methods to his data as he did in assembling the data in the first place.

## Operator Variation

In addition to the expectable natural variation encountered in a given population attribute and the significant variation occurring between essentially different populations, a further source of variation

arises from the collection of the raw data itself, namely *operator variation*. Even under the most rigorous operational definitions, even
using the most objective scales of measurement, even with the
most impartial sampling design and even employing measuring in-
struments of the highest accuracy, this additional unwelcome source
of variation intrudes itself. It is a feature of modern work in geomorphology, particularly in morphometry, that many operators may be
involved in making similar, or related, measurements of phenomena
which need to be capable of objective comparison. Now, granted that
'the person of the experimenter is himself part of the experiment' and
that 'people are different', it is not surprising that operator variations
occur, particularly as the result of individual errors (see earlier section) and because there is always room for a certain amount of subjective interpretation. Attempts to eliminate operator variations by
standardizing techniques and equipment have not always proved
satisfactory for

> Ultimately, standardization of process can play a role of only
> limited importance; a more satisfactory procedure is to recognize
> the difference among operators and arrange to estimate its effect,
> quantitatively if possible, and, by suitable experimental design,
> segregate the source of variation from those one wishes to study
> (Griffiths and Rosenfeld 1954, p. 75).

Thus, Krumbein (1934) distinguished between sampling and operational errors, Griffiths (1953) gave in detail the quantitative techniques for estimating the proportion of operator error versus total
error, Rosenfeld and Griffiths (1953) tested operator variation in estimating the sphericity and roundness of quartz grains, and Griffiths
and Rosenfeld (1954) summarized a number of investigations into
operator variation in petrological work. In geomorphology, however,
virtually no investigations have been made regarding operator variations in the collection of field data, and few relating to the collection
of information from topographic maps. Part of the latter deficiency
undoubtedly stems from a certain distrust of the accuracy of such
maps as sources of morphometric data (this has been discussed by
Strahler 1950, p. 679, Morisawa, 1957, 1959, p. 5, Clarke and Orrell
1958, Broscoe 1959, p. 2, and Coates 1959: in addition, Ray and
Fischer (1960, pp. 144–5) have investigated the variation between the
drainage density shown on aerial photographs of a given area and
the scale of the photograph), but, for this reason, it is all the more
important to determine what morphometric features are shown with
accuracy on maps of different scales and what are the sources of
operator variation in the identification and measurement of these

features. In other words, an answer must be sought to the question: 'What operations give rise to the largest sources of operator variation?' Chorley (1958a) attempted a preliminary answer to this question in comparing the results of two groups of inexperienced operators required to delimit and measure certain morphometric features from identical maps, and concluded that

> using maps on a scale of 1: 25,000 of drainage basins having a texture of dissection represented by a drainage density of about 3·50, two groups of relatively unskilled operators collectively showed no significant difference between their group delimitation and measurement of the mean values of linear, areal and channel gradient aspects of landscape geometry—except where the recognition of first order stream segments was concerned (Chorley 1958a, p. 217).

Griffiths and Rosenfeld (1954) considered the general implications of the above question in terms of the two basic types of experimental investigations:

1. Classifications based on a difference in kind. These may have a certain qualitative basis (e.g. the visual identification of minerals) and exhibit a greater operator variation.
2. Classifications based on a single quality. These are concerned with degree, based on a continuous scale (e.g. measurements of stream length), are commonly quantitative and exhibit lower operator variation.

Another significant feature of operator variation is that it is always present to some degree, not only between different operators, but also due to inconsistencies associated with one operator 'over different experiments or over the same experiment at different times' (Griffiths and Rosenfeld 1954, p. 76). It is particularly important in quantitative geomorphic work, therefore, for attempts to be made to recognize the character, sources and magnitudes of operator variation, so as to be able to disentangle them from the other variations the existence of which is the sole excuse for the employment of statistical methods.

# III STATISTICAL ANALYSIS OF GEOMORPHIC
## DATA

**The Characteristics of Geomorphic Populations**

It is most important to determine the characteristics of geomorphic populations because:

1. This knowledge assists one in determining the size of a representative sample. Figure 14 illustrates how a progressive increase in

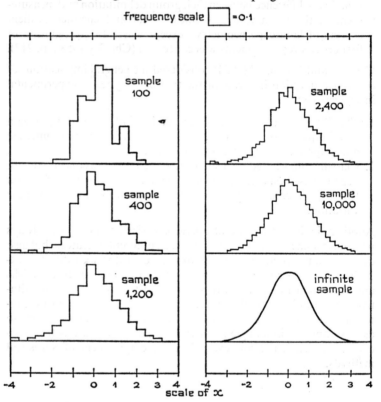

Fig. 14. An illustration of the progressive approach to a normal distribution with increasing sample size (from Tippett, 1952).

sample size causes a sample distribution to assume a form more and more characteristic of that of the total population (Tippett 1952, p. 5).

2. A knowledge of the population characteristics enables one to estimate the importance, or 'weight', which should be placed in such sample parameters as the arithmetic mean and the standard deviation (see later section regarding *skewness*).
3. It permits one to generalize concerning the proportion of variates which should be expected to fall above, or below, or between certain values (Croxton and Cowden 1955). This concept represents the basis of *probability statistics*, the most valuable analytical branch of the subject.

The precise methods by which it is possible to associate geomorphic samples with the population from which they were drawn will form the subject of the succeeding section of this chapter.

Geographers and geologists are most accustomed to presenting their data in the form of located points on a map, and a later section will refer to the contemporary attempts to render such a presentation susceptible to a more rigorous statistical treatment (Duncan, Cuzzort and Duncan 1961). For simple statistical purposes, however, the most useful form of presentation of data is as the *histogram*—a bar graph representing the percentage frequency of variates falling within equal class intervals. Figure 15A shows histograms of maximum valley-side slope angles for six different localities, and Fig. 15B represents the same data as *cumulative frequency distributions*. Figure 14 illustrates how the adoption of infinitely small class intervals transforms the stepped histogram into a smooth distribution curve.

A great variety of population distributions are possible, but in geomorphology two are of especial importance (the *normal* and the *lognormal* distributions) (Strahler 1954b) and a third (the *circular normal distribution*) is of increasing significance.

The normal distribution is represented in a frequency-distribution diagram by a symmetrical, bell-shaped curve, wherein most of the individual variates lie close to the central value and become progressively infrequent above and below this value, such that the curve extends infinitely far in both positive and negative directions (Croxton and Cowden 1939, pp. 265–87, Strahler 1954b, Dixon and Massey 1957, pp. 48–66). A normal, or *Gaussian* distribution is shown in Fig. 16A, and this is sometimes alternatively termed the *normal curve of error* because it would be produced, for example, by a large number of measurements of an identical object (Fig. 16B). Because such a distribution might be thought to represent the probability of the occurrence of a variate of given magnitude, this curve is also described as the *normal probability curve*, or simply the *normal curve*. The normal distribution is quantitatively described by certain parameters,

L

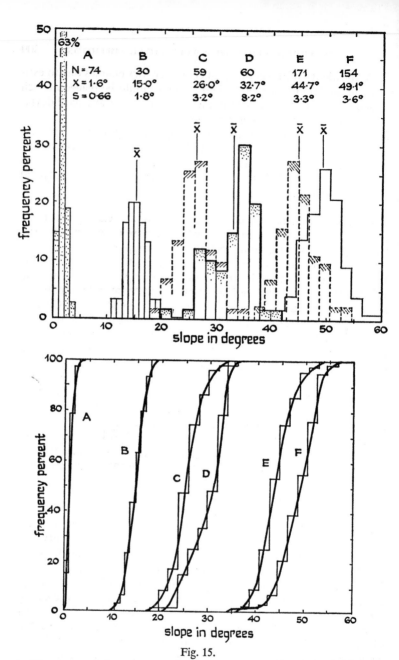

Fig. 15.

A. Histograms of six maximum valley-side slope frequency distributions (from Strahler, 1950):
(A) Steenvoorde, France; (B) Rose Well Gravels, Arizona; (C) Santa Fe formation, Bernalillo, New Mexico; (D) Hunter-Shandaken area, Catskill Mts., New York; (E) Kline Canyon area, Verdugo Hills, California; (F) Dissected clay fill, Perth Amboy, New Jersey.
B. Cumulative percentage frequency distributions of the data shown in Fig. 15A.

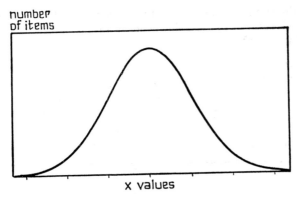

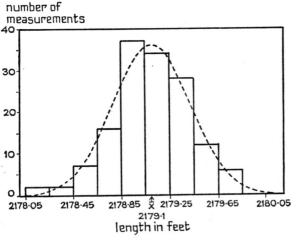

Fig. 16.

A. An example of the normal curve of error (from Croxton and Cowden, 1939).
B. A normal curve fitted to 144 measurements of the length of a single line (from Croxton and Cowden, 1939).

including the *arithmetic mean* ($\overline{X}$) and the *standard deviation* (S or $\sigma$). The arithmetic mean is the most useful 'measure of central tendency' and is obtained by dividing the sum of the variates ($\Sigma X$) by the number of variates (N):

$$\overline{X} = \frac{\Sigma X}{N}$$

A short method of obtaining the arithmetic mean for grouped data is described by Croxton and Cowden (1955, p. 181). The importance of the arithmetic mean, as applied to a normal distribution, is greatly enhanced because of its coincidence with two other measures of central tendency:

1. The *mode*—the value at the point around which variates tend to be most heavily concentrated. Thus the *modal class* is the class into which most variates fall.
2. The *median*—the value which lies in the middle of the variates when they are ranked in order of magnitude.

The standard deviation is a statistic which indicates the 'dispersion'

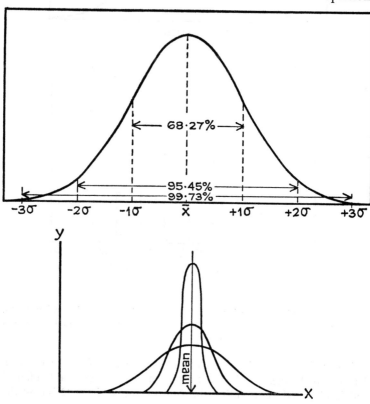

Fig. 17.

A. Proportion of variates included within $\pm 1$, 2 and 3 standard deviations ($\sigma$) of the arithmetic mean in a normal distribution (from Croxton and Cowden, 1939).
B. Three normal distributions with the same arithmetic mean, but different standard deviations (from Moroney, 1960).

qualities of the variates, or the 'spread' of the distribution (Strahler 1954b, p. 5, Croxton and Cowden 1955, pp. 215–19). It is a measure of the average deviation of the variates from the arithmetic mean, and may be calculated by employing the sum of the squares of the differences between each variate and the arithmetic mean:

$$\sigma = \sqrt{\frac{\Sigma(X-\overline{X})^2}{N}}$$

Obviously, these individual differences must be squared (and this subsequently rectified by taking the square root) because otherwise the values for a normal distribution, being equally positive and negative about the mean, would cancel out to zero. A short method for calculating the standard deviation for grouped data is given by Croxton and Cowden (1955, pp. 217–19). Closely allied to the standard deviation is the *variance* ($\sigma^2$) which is simply the square of the standard deviation (Strahler 1954b, p. 6), the significance of which will be referred to in a later section. The proportions of variates which lie within one, two and three standard deviations on either side of the arithmetic mean of a normal distribution is shown in Fig. 17A, and Fig. 17B illustrates several normal distributions having different standard deviations. Geomorphic populations which have been found to exhibit normal distributions include:

1. Maximum angles of valley-side slopes in a given region. (Strahler 1950) (Fig. 15A).
2. Mean angles of valley-side slopes in a given region (Carter and Chorley 1961) (Fig. 18A).
3. Elevations in a mature drainage basin (Strahler 1952a).
4. Beach firmness (Krumbein 1955a) and the shearing resistance of well-sorted, fine-grained soils (Chorley 1959) (Fig. 18B).
5. Natural moisture content of beach sands (Krumbein 1955a).
6. Entrance angles between tributaries and the main channel in a drainage basin where structural control over drainage lines is absent (Schumm 1956) (Fig. 18C). This latter distribution might be better treated, however, as a circular normal one (see later).

It is of interest that Melton (1958a) has listed characteristic values of parameters describing certain geomorphic distributions encountered in differing geological and climatic environments.

Many geomorphic populations, however, are characteristically asymmetrical, or *skewed*. By far the most common of these is the right-skewed, logarithmic-normal distribution, which constitutes the second important type of geomorphic distribution (Croxton and Cowden 1939, pp. 293–9). It is obviously of great value to determine

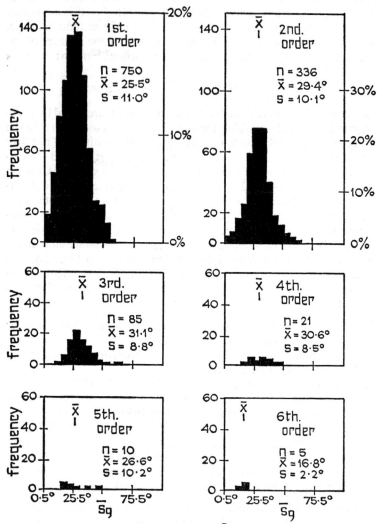

Fig. 18A. Mean angles of valley-side slopes ($\bar{S}_g$) of different order for Lighthouse Hollow, Connecticut (from Carter and Chorley, 1960).

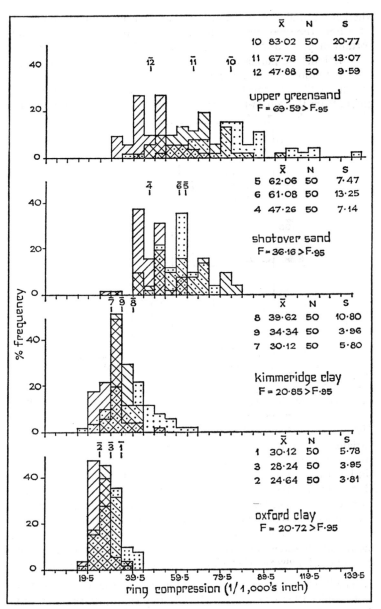

Fig. 18B. Histograms of Vicksburg Penetrometer needle penetration readings (in terms of bearing ring compression) for four soils in the vicinity of Oxford, England (from Chorley, 1959).

whether a population is skewed, in that the arithmetic mean departs from both the mode and the median, and is therefore a far less important measure of central tendency than when applied to a normal distribution. The standard deviation, implying as it does a symmetrical distribution of variates about the mean, loses all its value as a parameter. Skewed data therefore have to be treated in a manner which differs from that given to normal distributions (as, for example, the

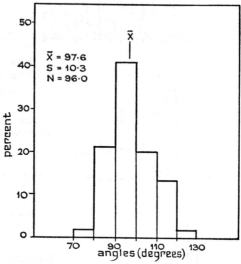

Fig. 18C. Histogram of entrance angles between tributaries and segments of the main channel, clay fill badlands, Perth Amboy, New Jersey (from Schumm, 1956).

highly skewed 'gamma' distributions—see later), or the individual variates have to be treated in such a manner as to normalize the distribution. This can be achieved for log-normal distributions by taking the logarithms of the individual variates (Miller 1953, Strahler 1954b) (Figs. 19A and B) so as to produce a normal distribution which can be treated in a simple manner such that parameters like the mean and the standard deviation are meaningful. It should be noted that not all skewed distributions are logarithmic in character, and that very occasionally left-skewed distributions (i.e. tailing off to the left) are encountered. Examples of log-normal geomorphic distributions are:

1. The lengths of stream segments of given order in a drainage basin (Strahler 1954b, Schumm 1956, Chorley 1957a, 1958a) (Fig. 19A).
2. Drainage basin areas of given order within a major basin (Schumm 1956, Chorley 1957a, 1958a) (Fig. 19B).

3. Mean channel slopes for streams of a given order (Chorley 1958a)
   (Fig. 20A), although Broscoe (1959) believes them to be normally
   distributed (Fig. 20B).

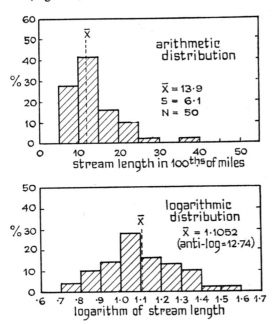

Fig. 19A. Frequency distribution histograms showing:

*Above.* Arithmetic distribution of lengths of first order streams developed on
the Copper Ridge Dolomite, Virginia (data from Miller, 1953).

*Below.* Distribution of logarithms of the first order stream lengths shown
above (from Strahler, 1954b).

4. The altitude differences (H) between each end of stream segments
   of a given order within a homogeneous area (Broscoe 1959) (Fig.
   20B).
5. The permeability of some sediments (Law 1944).

Both the normal and the log-normal distributions apply to data
wherein the values of the variates are referred to linear scales—i.e.
where increased values are progressively divorced from lower values.
However, there are classes of phenomena which are repetitive or circular in character, and these special distributions demand treatments
different from those described above. Obvious examples of circular
data are readings of azimuth (where 0° and 360° are coincident) and
those relating to repeating time periods (e.g. mean monthly figures,

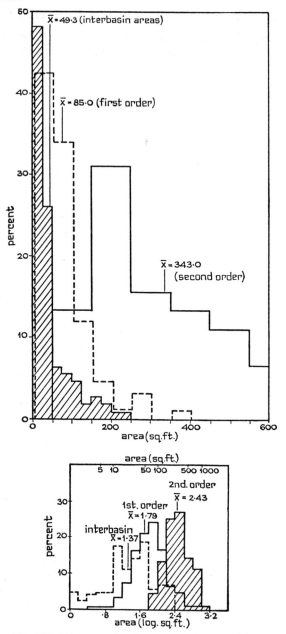

Fig. 19B. Frequency distribution histograms showing:

*Above.* Arithmetic distributions of first and second order basin areas and interbasin areas in clay fill at Perth Amboy, New Jersey.

*Below.* Logarithms of the areal data given above (from Schumm, 1956).

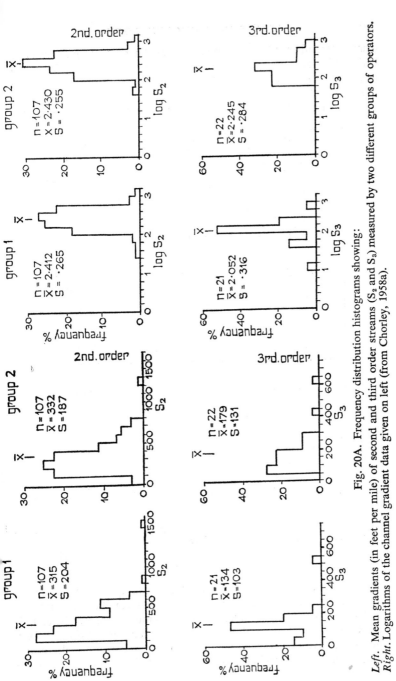

Fig. 20A. Frequency distribution histograms showing:

*Left.* Mean gradients (in feet per mile) of second and third order streams ($S_2$ and $S_3$) measured by two different groups of operators.
*Right.* Logarithms of the channel gradient data given on left (from Chorley, 1958a).

320     ESSAYS IN GEOMORPHOLOGY

where December is followed by January). There is no simple way in which this data can be normalized, although Krumbein (1939) minimized the effect of circularity by adjusting the distribution so that the modal class fell in the centre of the abscissa rendering the distribution roughly susceptible to normal linear methods. Pincus (1953, pp. 493–

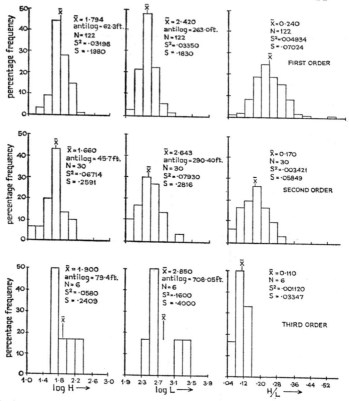

Fig. 20B. Logarithms of altitude differences (H) between each end of stream segments and of their lengths (L) for first, second and third order channels, Mount Deception quadrangle. Arithmetic values of the ratio H/L are also shown (from Broscoe, 1959).

494) has further pointed out that where, for example, ranges of angles are quite small (i.e. Figs. 15A and 18C) methods applicable to normal distributions can be employed without too much danger. The techniques to be properly applied to these *circular normal distributions*, however, have been developed by Gumbel, Greenwood and Durand (1953) and by Gumbel (1954) who describe the fitting of such ideal

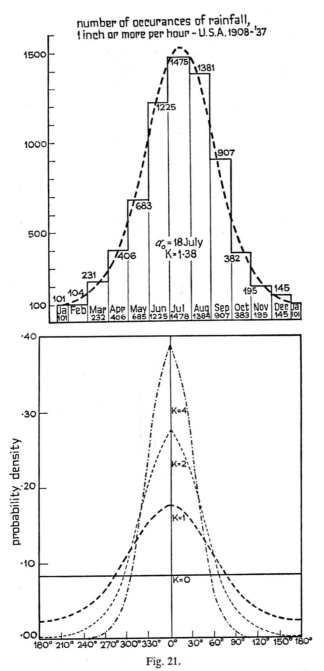

Fig. 21.

A. Circular normal distribution fitted to the number of occurrences of one inch or more of rainfall per hour in the U.S.A. during the period 1908–37. The mean occurrence date is 18 July (from Gumbel, 1954).

B. Examples of circular normal distributions related to azimuthal data having different values of K (from Gumbel, Greenwood and Durand, 1953).

curves to these distributions (Fig. 21A) and their description by a parameter '*k*' which approximates to the standard deviation (Fig. 21B). There are two distinct classes of circular data:

1. Two-dimensional: Involving variates with one 'circular' value— i.e. monthly rainfall figures (Gumbel 1954), orientation of rock fractures (Pincus 1953), angle of wave approach (Court 1952), azimuth of slope orientation, etc. Treatment of this data in geology has been described by Chayes (1942a) and Pincus (1953, 1956).

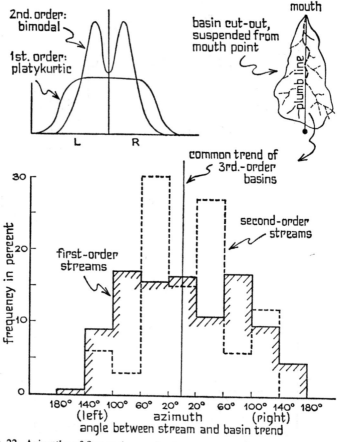

Fig. 22. Azimuths of first and second order stream segments plotted relative to the trend of the main third order basin. Combined data of 10 third-order basins developed on cherts and cherty limestones in the Wolf Lake, Illinois, quadrangle of the Ozark Plateau Province (from Strahler, 1954a).

2. Three-dimensional: These are much more complex and involve data wherein each variate has two 'circular' values—i.e. angular measurements of slope orientation and inclination. Chayes (1942b) and Pincus (1953) have again outlined the treatment of such data.

In addition to these three population distributions which are of importance to the geomorphologist there are several others which are worthy of mention:

1. *Bimodal Distributions*—where the nature of the data implies two separate concentrations of variates, or modes (Strahler 1954a) (Fig. 22). In most instances, however, bimodal distributions indicate the unintentional mixing of two populations with differing mean values.

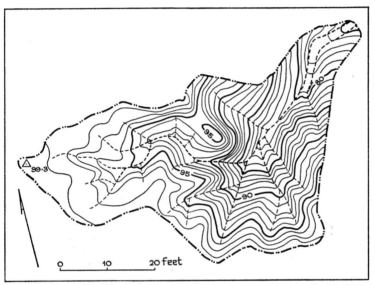

Fig. 23A. Contour map (contour interval 1 ft) of a drainage basin developed in clay badlands at Perth Amboy, New Jersey (from Strahler, 1956).

2. *Binomial Distributions*—which are 'normal' in character, but apply to discrete, non-continuous data such as combinations of heads and tails in groups of tossed coins (Croxton and Cowden 1939, pp. 268–70 and 287–92, Krumbein 1955a). Closely allied to this is the *Poisson Distribution*.

3. *Gamma Distributions*—being those which exhibit a much greater right-skewness than can be rectified by a logarithmic transformation (Krumbein 1955a). Size of raindrops, the roundness and

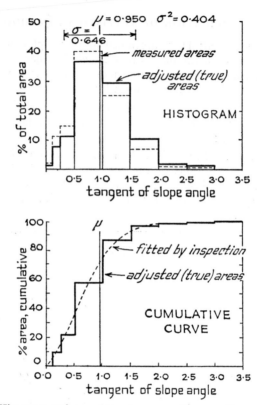

Fig. 23B. Histogram and cumulative frequency diagram of tangents of slope angles measured by planimeter from an isotangent map produced from the topographic map shown in Fig. 23A (from Strahler, 1956).

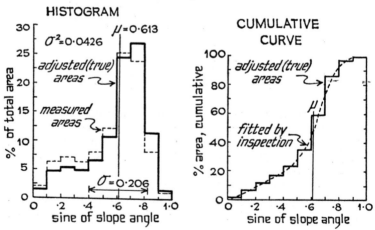

Fig. 23C. Histogram and cumulative frequency diagram of sines of slope angles measured by planimeter from an isosinal map produced from the topographic map shown in Fig. 23A (from Strahler, 1956).

spericity of particles in some sediments, as well as the relief and number of hilltops within unit areas within widely different geological and climatic environments (Wood and Snell 1957a, 1957b) all exhibit this exaggerated right-skewness. Within a single basin of the monadnock type elevations would tend to be extremely right-skewed (Strahler 1952a, p. 1131), as were the tangents of slope angles measured in the Perth Amboy drainage basin (Strahler 1956, p. 582) (Fig. 23B). It is interesting that the rare left-skewness was presented by the sines of the slope angles from Perth Amboy (Fig. 23C) and might be expected from elevations in a very youthful drainage basin (Strahler 1952a, p. 1129).

Krumbein (1955a) also refers to distributions of the *cube-root-normal*, *extreme values* and *Rayleigh* type, and mentions that the height of ocean waves conforms to the latter two types (Longuet-Higgins 1952).

## The Precise Description of Geomorphic Samples

It is usually not sufficient, however, to guess at the character of the parent population by a visual inspection of the sample distribution, unless the sample is very large (Fig. 14). More rigorous methods are required, therefore, to give an indication of the population distribution, as mirrored by that of the sample, and some of these methods have been well described by Strahler (1954b, pp. 7–10).

A simple, visual method of crudely testing the normality of a sample distribution is by plotting the percentage cumulative frequencies on the ordinate (Y axis) against the class mid-values on the abscissa (X axis) of *arithmetic probability paper*. This graph paper has the values of the ordinate so adjusted that normal distributions appear as straight lines, the angle of inclination of which is inversely related to the standard deviation of the distribution (Croxton and Cowden 1939, p. 285, Dixon and Massey 1957, pp. 55–7, Strahler 1954b, Chorley 1958b, p. 371). Figure 24A shows the distributions for certain beach properties plotted on arithmetic probability paper, and in Fig. 24B the normally distributed maximum slope angles already referred to (Fig. 15) are similarly plotted. Log-normal distributions naturally appear as curves on arithmetic probability paper (Figs. 25A and B), but these can be visually tested in a similar manner either by employing *logarithmic probability paper* which has a logarithmic scale on the abscissa (Fig. 25A) (Croxton and Cowden 1939, p. 295), or when logarithmic values of the variates are used in conjunction with arithmetic probability paper (Fig. 25B). Tanner (1958, 1959) has employed

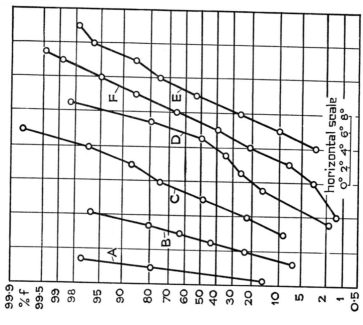

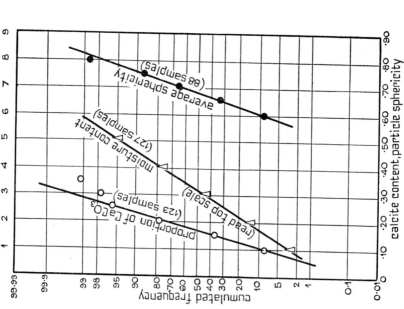

Fig. 24.

A. Arithmetic probability plots of cumulative frequency distributions of three beach properties; calcite content, moisture content and particle sphericity (from Krumbein, 1953a).

probability plots of some sediments to show that the 'zig-zag Gaussian components' may, in addition to indicating the mixture of two or more normally distributed populations, show explainable deficiencies in certain grain size ranges. He has also suggested that erosion surfaces might be recognized in a similar manner (Tanner 1959, p. 410).

If it is required to construct an appropriate normal curve for a

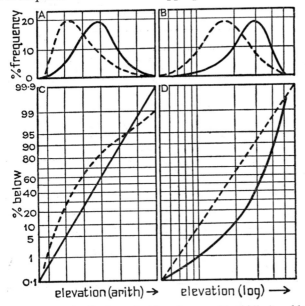

Fig. 25A. Frequency distributions of arithmetic normal (solid line) and logarithmic normal (pecked line) elevation distributions referred to (A) arithmetic and (B) logarithmic scales. The same distributions are also plotted in cumulative form on (C) arithmetic and (D) logarithmic probability paper (from Chorley, 1958b).

sample distribution—i.e. one having the same arithmetic mean and standard deviation as the sample—it is not sufficient to sketch a curve through the sample histogram. Precise methods for fitting the normal curve (Fig. 26) are given in Croxton and Cowden (1939, pp. 271–82, 1955, pp. 599–603) and Dixon and Massey (1957, pp. 61–2), involving a consideration of the ideal frequencies which might be expected to occur within the given class limits of a normal distribution having the same mean, standard deviation and class limits as the sample.

Now, of course, any sample distribution can be described by the most appropriate normal distribution, but before too much reliance can be placed on this association it is often necessary to determine quantitatively just how well the normal curve fits the sample data. To

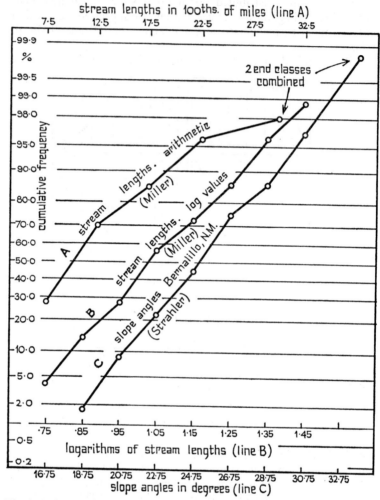

Fig. 25B. Cumulative frequencies plotted on probability paper of (A) arithmetic and (B) logarithmic values of the stream lengths given in Fig. 19A. Slope angles from Bernalillo, New Mexico, are plotted on (C) (from Strahler, 1954b).

tackle this kind of question in a statistical manner it is necessary to investigate whether the apparent visual resemblance between the sample distribution and one of the type distributions (i.e. the normal distribution) is merely due to chance vicissitudes of sampling and whether other similarly sized samples drawn from the assumed parent population would have different forms (Strahler 1954b, p. 9). Thus, the important statistical concept of *probability*, or likelihood (Dixon and Massey 1957, p. 328) is introduced. Strahler (1954b, p. 9) poses the type of question which a 'test of goodness of fit' sets out to answer: 'What is the likelihood (probability) that so poor a fit (or worse) of normal curve to sample data could be obtained by chance alone if the

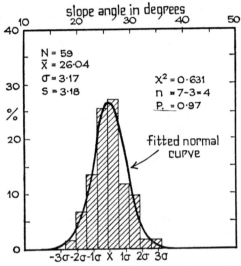

Fig. 26. Normal curve fitted to grouped data of maximum valley-side slopes in dissected fan gravels near Bernalillo, New Mexico (from Strahler, 1954b).

population from which the sample is drawn has a normal distribution?' To determine this probability, the statistic *chi-square* ($\chi^2$) is calculated (Croxton and Cowden 1939, pp. 282–7, Strahler 1954b, pp. 9–10, Dixon and Massey 1957, pp. 221–2 and 226–7), testing the hypothesis that the total population has a normal distribution, where;

$$\chi^2 = \sum \frac{(f - F)^2}{F}$$

In this instance, $f$ is the actual, measured frequency of variates in each respective sample class, and F is the theoretical frequency in equivalent classes of a normal distribution. (Note the relationship between this calculation and that referred to above in connexion with the construction of the normal curve.) The probability (P) (per cent — i.e.

the number of times out of 100) that, if the parent population is normally distributed, we should expect to get this poor a fit or worse with repeated random sampling, simply because of chance variations due to taking samples of the given size (Strahler 1950, p. 683), is obtained from a prepared table (Croxton and Cowden 1939, Appendix I, p. 882). In this, the value of chi-square is employed with another statistic—the *number of degrees of freedom* (*n*). The concept of degrees of freedom has a rather complex rationalization, based upon pure statistical theory, but has been conveniently defined by Croxton and Cowden (1939, p. 312) as 'the number of deviations' (i.e. variates or classes, whichever is appropriate) 'minus the number of constants determined from the sample and used to fix the points from which those deviations are measured'. In the instance of the chi-square test the value of *n* is the number of classes employed minus three, because three degrees of freedom are lost in that the fitted data were made to agree in respect of the three sample parameters of $\overline{X}$, $\sigma$ and N (Croxton and Cowden 1939, p. 286). The percentage probability thus obtained from the chi-square table is then compared with an arbitrary probability level which has been previously selected (in natural science it is usually 95 per cent, or occasionally 98 per cent when refined work calls for a high level of probability) to determine whether one should accept the hypothesis of a normally-distributed parent population (Calculated $P \geqslant 95$ per cent), or reject it ($P < 95$ per cent). Logarithmic normal populations can be tested in the same manner, using the logarithmic values of the individual variates. Among the workers who have applied the chi-square test to geomorphic data are Strahler (1950, 1956) and Chorley (1957a, 1958a), whereas Pincus (1953, 1956) has developed its application to circular distributions.

Finally, mention should be made of the use of the methods of *nonparametric statistics* (Dixon and Massey 1957, pp. 280–303, Siegel 1956) where the characteristics of the parent population are unknown. Because this lack of knowledge usually stems from the small size of the target population or from an inability to obtain a very large sample, these methods have not been found to be of important application in geomorphology, where most of the target populations are very large or infinite and where usually there is ease in obtaining large samples. The methods of non-parametric statistics involve the testing of 'distributions', rather than their parameters (Dixon and Massey 1957, p. 280); the *ranking* of data, rather than classing it; and the use of the median, rather than the mean. Non-parametric methods might find importance as applied to large amounts of quantitative data forming a basis for a quick initial investigation in order to determine which ordinary programme of statistical methods might prove most appropriate (Melton 1958b). Non-parametric tests have proved of value in the initial reduction of large masses of interlocked data, where rapid correlations between many variables may indicate fruitful connections possible of exploitation by more rigorous tests and further fieldwork.

## Comparison of Two Samples

Up to the present we have been mainly concerned with *descriptive statistics*, involving the description of the properties and characteristics of single samples. With this foundation, however, one can pass on to the utilization of this information in order to make inferences and draw conclusions within explicitly stated limits of probability by means of *analytic statistics*.

As Strahler (1954b) has pointed out, in his excellent pioneer paper on the application of statistical methods to geomorphic data, much work in geomorphology involves the comparison of similar, measured attributes between different areas or between different times at the same location. Thus, for example, it is often required to compare maximum valley-side slope angles on different formations; the state of a beach under spring and neap tide conditions; the velocity of glacier flow during summer and winter; or the shearing resistance of soils covered with grass or crops. In the past it has been thought sufficient merely to average each set of values and see which is the greater, but the recognition of the existence of natural variation within a single geomorphic-attribute population, together with the problems involved in taking a truly representative sample, has cast a strong doubt as to the sufficiency of this method. As Strahler (1954b, pp. 10–11) has put it:

> But at this point a suspicion unhappily enters: just because one sample mean is greater than the other, can we be sure that the populations from which the samples were drawn are truly different? Most geomorphic attributes have considerable dispersion. In any particular sample of 25, 50 or 100 variates the investigator might just happen, by chance, to include many more of the low-valued variates than is proportionate to their actual occurence. Perhaps the next sample would favor the high-value variates. Could this not cause the mean of one sample to be lower than the mean of the other sample, even though their population means are actually in the reverse order of magnitude?

It can be demonstrated (Strahler 1954b, p. 11) that the range of expected variations in means repeatedly drawn from the same population will follow a normal distribution (Fig. 27) about the mean of the total population, but naturally possessing a much smaller standard deviation ($S_{\bar{x}}$) than that of the total population (S). In this instance:

$$S_{\bar{x}} = \frac{S}{\sqrt{N}} \text{ where } S = \sqrt{\frac{\Sigma(X - \bar{X})^2}{N - 1}}$$

N, as usual, is the size of the sample, and the number of degrees of freedom is equal to N — 1 because one degree of freedom is lost by assuming that the mean of the total population is equal to the mean of the sample. From the above formulae two important facts emerge:

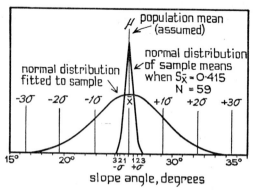

Fig. 27. Comparison of a normal distribution fitted to a sample and the normal distribution of sample means (from Strahler, 1954b).

firstly, that the range of variation of sample means from a given population decreases as the size of the sample increases; secondly, that this range of sample means depends directly on the standard deviation of the population. It is thus impossible to compare the significance of the difference between the means of two samples without considering their standard deviations.

Such a statistical test of comparison of means is the '*t*' *test* (Croxton and Cowden 1939, Chapter 12, especially pp. 330–1, Strahler 1954b, pp. 12–14, Dixon and Massey 1957, p. 119-24). This test typifies the conservative nature of statistical methods in that it adopts the proposition that no significant difference exists, and adheres to it 'until strong grounds are encountered for abandoning it' (Strahler 1954b, p. 12). This conservatism is achieved by setting up, and subsequently testing, a *null hypothesis* which states that: There is actually no real difference in the two populations from which the samples were drawn—the apparent difference between the sample means being due to chance sampling variations alone—and, thus, in effect we are dealing only with one population (Strahler 1954b, p. 12). This hypothesis is tested by the calculation of the statistic '$t$', which equals the difference between the two sample means divided by a combined value of their pooled standard deviations and number of variates ($N_1$ + $N_2$) of the two samples (Croxton and Cowden 1939, pp. 330–1, Dixon and Massey 1957, pp. 119–24). Using $t$ and a value of $n$ equal to ($N_1$ − 1) + ($N_2$ − 1), because two degrees of freedom are lost by assuming the sample means and variances to be equal, a value of the probability (P) is obtained from a prepared table (Croxton and Cowden 1939, Appendix F, p. 875) which gives the percentage of times in which this great a difference between sample means (or greater) might be expected to be encountered when repeated pairs of samples, of the given sizes, are drawn from one single normally-distributed population. This value of P is then compared with a previously-fixed acceptance level of probability (i.e. usually 5 per cent or 2 per cent, see previous section) and the null hypothesis accepted or rejected on this basis.

The nature of this test, involving the null hypothesis combined with a very conservative rejection level, well illustrates the 'above board' character of rigorous statistical investigations. As Strahler (1954b, p. 13) has put it:

> The odds of being right or wrong are stated forthrightly for all to see. The scientist cannot uphold an unwarranted conclusion on the strength of his opinion or prestige alone. Of course he can introduce a bias into his sampling, whether consciously or subconsciously, to ensure that the statistical test will prove favorable to his preconceived theory. This last doubt can be largely eliminated by randomized sampling or by having samples taken by two or more disinterested persons. . . .

This simple and important test has proved extremely popular with geomorphologists, both in original investigations (Strahler 1950, in a modified form; Schumm 1956, Smith and Flanagan 1956, Chorley 1958a, Smith 1958, Broscoe 1959) and in methodological tests such as that for operator variance (Strahler 1956, pp. 594–5). Figure 28 illustrates this test applied to four paired sets of samples relating to maximum valley-side slope angles of protected and basally corraded slopes (P<0·1 per cent; significant difference); slope angles measured in the field and from a map (P = 15 per cent; no significant difference at the 5 per cent confidence level); slope angles in badlands measured four years apart (P $\simeq$ 50 per cent; no significant difference); and angles of stream junction in youthful and mature basins (P $\simeq$ 0·01 per cent; significant difference).

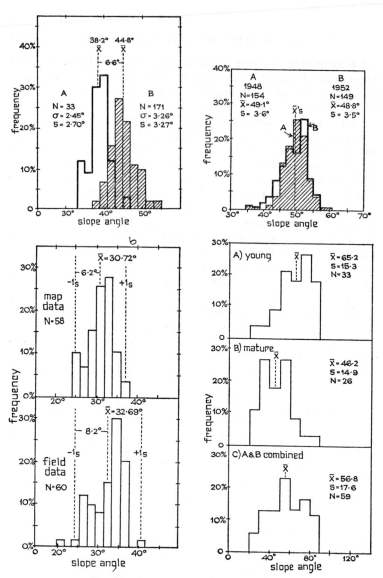

Fig. 28. The comparison of sample means:

A. Protected slopes (A) and basally corraded slopes (B) in the Verdugo Hills,
California (P < 0·1 per cent. Significant difference at the 5 per cent level)
(from Strahler, 1950).

B. Two samples of slope angles measured at an interval of four years (A, 1948;
B, 1952) on the same slopes in clay badlands at Perth Amboy, New Jersey
(P ≃ 50 per cent. No significant difference) (data by Schumm; from Strahler,
1954b).

C. Samples of slope angles from the same drainage basins in the Shandaken and
Hunter, New York, quadrangles obtained from map and field measurement
(P = 15 per cent. No significant difference) (from Strahler, 1950).

D. Samples of young, mature and combined angles of stream junctions, clay
badlands at Perth Amboy, New Jersey (comparison of young and mature
basins: P ≃ 0·01 per cent. Significant difference) (from Schumm, 1956).

It is of note that, because certain statistical tests (including the *t* test) assume that there is no significant difference between the variances ($\sigma^2$) of two samples which are being investigated from another point of view, it is sometimes necessary to test the significance of difference between sample variances (Strahler 1954b, pp. 14–16, Dixon and Massey 1957, pp. 102–10). In this instance a statistic 'F' is calculated and then compared with a tabulated value of F at the

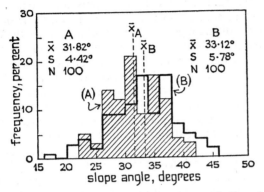

Fig. 29. Comparison of slope samples in homogeneous clastic rocks in western Virginia: A, Athens formation; B, Pennington formation (data from Miller, 1953; see also Strahler, 1954b).

selected critical level of probability. On the basis of the comparison between these two values of F the null hypothesis, that the variances are the same, is accepted or rejected. Figure 29 illustrates one of the few instances in which this test has been applied to geomorphic data, illustrating that there is a significant difference between the variances of slope angle data between the Athens and Pennington formations in the Appalachians (Miller 1953). The need for a reasoned assumption of similarity of variances further illustrates the value of Melton's (1958a) list of sample parameters.

## Comparison of three, or more, Samples

It is often useful in geomorphic work to be able to test the probability as to whether three or more samples of a particular attribute have been drawn from one population, or whether they represent significant differences. In this instance it is not good statistical procedure to perform multiple '*t*' tests between all possible pairs of samples, because this method invariably leads to the adoption of a larger measure of tolerance than that intended by the selected confidence level

(P) (Dixon and Massey 1957, p. 139). The statistical test used in this instance is the *analysis of variance* (Croxton and Cowden 1939, pp. 351–9, Krumbein and Miller 1953, Strahler 1954b, pp. 16–17, Krumbein 1955a, Dixon and Massey 1957, pp. 139–88).

The most simple version of this analysis is the 'single variable classification' or the 'single-factor basic form', in which one attribute or variable is sampled under three or more different conditions and the samples compared. Examples of this circumstance are not difficult to find, and include comparisons of samples of valley-side slope angles on a number of different geological formations (Miller 1953), of sampled stream discharges at different times of year, or of sampled beach firmnesses at various distances across a beach (Krumbein 1955a, pp. 5–6). As with the '*t*' test, it is required to determine whether the samples were drawn from essentially different populations, or whether they came from the same population and that the observed differences in means might be readily explained on the basis of chance variations in sampling (Strahler 1954b, p. 16). A null hypothesis is set up that the means and variances of all samples are homogeneous, in other words 'that there is no greater difference among them than may be expected among similar sets of samples drawn from a homogeneous population' (Krumbein and Miller 1953, p. 513), and this is tested by the calculation of the *F ratio*. This value of F is a ratio comparison of the variance between the groups or samples and the average variance within the groups or samples. Employing two values for the number of degrees of freedom, one referred to the number of samples or groups and the other to the total number of variates, a value of F is obtained from prepared tables (Croxton and Cowden 1939, Appendix G2, pp. 878–9, Dixon and Massey 1957, Table A-7a, p. 388) at a previously selected confidence level (say 5 per cent). The calculated value of F is then compared with the tabulated value of $F_{.95}$ and the null hypothesis retained or rejected on this basis. If, for example, the variance between samples exceeds the variance within samples by a value greater than that expressed by the F ratio at the selected confidence level (i.e. $F > F_{.95}$) the null hypothesis must be rejected and the samples considered to have been taken from different populations (Dixon and Massey 1957, p. 150). Although the analysis of variance is 'robust enough to apply to fairly skewed distributions' (Krumbein 1955a, p. 7), the test has been designed to apply to normal distributions and it is therefore necessary to be assured of this normality or to attain it by means of *transformations*. As discussed in a previous section, the log transformation is the most useful one applied to geomorphic data, but it is of note that the use of percentages or proportions in the analysis of variance must be prefaced by an arc sine transformation (Krumbein 1953b, p. 281, Dixon and Massey 1957, p. 183). It sometimes occurs that one of the samples is so obviously anomalous that it is desirable to eliminate it from consideration (Miller 1953, pp. 10–11), and this elimination of the most divergent mean is achieved by the Scheffé method of judging contrasts (Scheffé 1953) in order that the null hypothesis can be tested for the remaining samples.

With the 'two-factor basic form' of analysis of variance (Krumbein and Miller 1953, pp. 514–24, Dixon and Massey 1957, pp. 140–2 and 155–63) a most important step is taken in statistical analysis—for the first time the effects of two variables are introduced. In this each variate is classified according to two criteria with reference to each of which values of F are computed in order to determine whether variations in either are mirrored by variations (at a significant confidence level) in the measured attribute. For example, Krumbein and Miller (1953) have described a test to investigate the effects of stream sorting of granodiorite pebbles in downstream and cross-channel current directions, and Melton (1960) applied this analysis to determine whether aspect or erosional environment (i.e. presence of a basal alluvial fan, etc.) affects slope angles in the Laramie Mountains, Wyoming. The employment of two variables, however, introduces us to the most important limitation of the analysis of variance, in that an *additive property* of population variance must be assumed. In other words, the factors under investigation must have no mutual effect or interaction upon each other and, therefore, 'do not have an effect in combination different from the sum of their separate effects' (Dixon and Massey 1957, p. 162). Although a test for significance of interactions can be applied to the factors (Dixon and Massey 1957, pp. 161–5, Melton 1960, p. 136 and Appendix 1A, p. 144) if it can be demonstrated, for example, that aspect has a certain control over erosional environment in the Laramie Mountains, then the effect of the two variables cannot be evaluated separately by means of the analysis of variance. This restriction is a most profound one, for it is one of the most striking characteristics of natural factors that they tend to present such significant interactions (e.g. air temperature and humidity, soil moisture and clay content, mineral grain roundness and sphericity), and it will be necessary in a later section to describe a group of most important statistical tests designed to allow for and measure factor interactions.

A further variable can be introduced in the 'three-factor basic form' (Krumbein and Miller 1953, pp. 521–3), as for example by sampling the proportion of granodiorite pebbles in two directions under different conditions of stream discharge, but the restrictions referred to above, combined with the increased complexity of the computations and the fact that no relative importance can be ascribed to the various factors (only significant or non-significant control over the measured attribute), generally makes this statistical test of limited attraction. However, one more popular variant of the three-factor form involves the use of *the latin square* (Krumbein, 1953b, Krumbein and Miller 1953b, pp. 523–6, Dixon and Massey 1957, pp. 171–4). This is a random arrangement of letters ('treatments') so that each letter occurs only once in each column and row of the square (Fig. 30A). These letters can be substituted for by the measured values of the treatments referred to the other two variables of classification represented by the rows and columns, and a separate evaluation

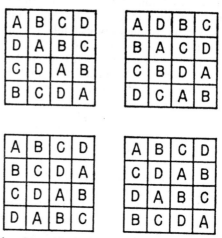

Fig. 30A. Examples of 4 × 4 Latin squares (from Krumbein and Miller, 1953).

carried out of the variance associated with each of the three factors involved (i.e. rows, columns and treatments). Figure 30B (Krumbein 1953b, p. 281) illustrates the percentages of garnets counted by four different persons (e.g. operators—treatments), from 4 different sandstone samples (e.g. rows), each employing 4 different total numbers of mineral grains counted (e.g. technique—columns). A null hypothesis is then set up to the effect that there are no significant differences between the garnet content of the sandstones, the skill of the operators or the counting techniques at the 5 per cent significance level, and that all observed differences can be explained by random sampling differences alone. The experiment is then performed and the hypothesis tested by comparing the variances of the three main effects (factors) with the *residual* variance left after the main effects are separated out, and if the F ratios of the main effects to the residual exceed the selected critical level for the appropriate degrees of freedom the hypothesis is rejected (Krumbein 1953b, p. 281). In this instance a significant difference was measured between the proportion of garnets in the 4 samples, but no significant difference between either the operators or the techniques employed. In other words, the operators and

**A. RAW PERCENTAGE DATA**

technique (no. of grains)

| | 50 | 100 | 200 | 400 |
|---|---|---|---|---|
| 1 | B 0.0 | C 17.0 | D 12.0 | A 10.2 |
| 2 | C 16.0 | D 18.0 | A 13.5 | B 13.4 |
| 3 | D 0.0 | A 1.0 | B 0.0 | C 2.0 |
| 4 | A 10.0 | B 8.0 | C 13.0 | D 8.0 |

letters are operators

samples

**B. TRANSFORMED DATA (ARC SINE)**

A = 64.3
B = 37.9
C = 77.2
D = 61.8
—————
241.2

| B 0.0 | C 24.4 | D 20.3 | A 18.6 | 63.3 |
|---|---|---|---|---|
| C 23.6 | D 25.1 | A 21.6 | B 21.5 | 91.8 |
| D 0.0 | A 5.7 | B 0.0 | C 8.1 | 13.8 |
| A 18.4 | B 16.4 | C 21.1 | D 16.4 | 72.3 |
| 42.0 | 71.6 | 63.0 | 64.6 | |

**ANALYSIS OF VARIANCE**

| SOURCE | SS | D.F. | VARIANCE | F | |
|---|---|---|---|---|---|
| Technique | 122.09 | 3 | 40.70 | 2.38 | NS |
| Samples | 826.88 | 3 | 275.63 | 16.13 | ** |
| Operators | 201.41 | 3 | 67.14 | 3.93 | NS |
| Residual | 102.51 | 6 | 17.09 | | |
| ˙TOTAL | 1252.89 | 15 | | | |

$F_{.95}(3,6) = 4.76$; $F_{.99}(3,6) = 9.78$

Fig. 30B. Raw and transformed data on percentages of garnets counted in 4 different sandstone samples, by 4 different operators, employing 4 different techniques (i.e. numbers of mineral grains counted). A significant difference was observed only between the proportion of garnets counted in the different rock samples, not between the operators or the different techniques (from Krumbein, 1953b).

the techniques were not significant factors in controlling the number of garnets counted. Similarly, one might imagine that the results of 4 operators measuring the shearing resistance of soils associated with 4 geological formations with each of 4 different penetration methods might be analysed in the above manner. It must be kept in mind, however, that the usual analysis of variance restrictions apply to this test and it would be impossible to determine which method of resistance measurement might be expected to give the best results for a particular formation. Nevertheless, latin squares 'serve well as exploratory devices for rapid evaluation of main effects' in an experimental design (Krumbein 1953b, p. 280); they are useful in testing operator variation; and, because two of the three factors can be expressed in a non-quantitative manner, the method might well recommend itself to disciplines in which only part of the research data is of a quantitative kind (e.g. historical geography).

Reference should be made to the additional articles by the following authors in which the analysis of variance is applied to geomorphic and geological data—Carter and Chorley (1961), Chorley (1957a), Coates (1958), Curray and Griffiths (1955), Griffiths (1953 and 1959), Krumbein (1953a), Krumbein and Slack (1956), Melton (1957) and Rosenfeld and Griffiths (1953).

## Regression

A regression is the association, usually expressed in the form of a mathematical equation, between two attributes which are repeatedly measured simultaneously (Strahler 1954b, p. 18). A regression problem involves consideration of one variable when another is held fixed at each of several levels (Dixon and Massey 1957, p. 189). This method has long been employed to relate an assumed casual factor (i.e. independent variable $-X$) with an effect (i.e. dependent variable $-Y$) by means of a function of the form,

$$Y = f(X)$$

It is now readily apparent that the multivariate nature of most controls in natural science militates against the uncritical or unmodified employment of this simple relationship, except in those instances where one controlling factor is of over-riding importance. In the following two sections further restrictions will be set to the unbridled use of regressions in the drawing of causal inferences, but first it is appropriate to describe the different types of regression and their computation (Croxton and Cowden 1955, Chapters 12 and 13, Dixon and Massey 1957, Chapter 11), under their two major classes of *linear* and *non-linear* regressions.

Linear regressions (Strahler 1954b, pp. 18–20, Croxton and Cowden 1955, pp. 261–75) are those expressing straight line trends on plots employing arithmetic scales on both the ordinate and abscissa, and are of the form:

$$Y = a + bX.$$

In this instance, 'a' and 'b' are constants fixing the position of the line in two dimensions; 'a' being the point of intersection of the line with the Y axis (i.e. the value of Y when X equals zero), and 'b', the *regression coefficient*, expressed the slope of the line, its sign indicating whether there is a *direct* (+) or an *inverse* (−) relationship between

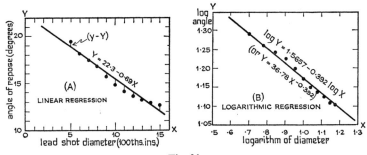

Fig. 31.

A. Linear regression of angle of repose versus diameter of lead shot (data from Van Burkalow 1945).
B. Logarithmic regression fitted to data given in Fig. 31A (from Strahler 1954b).

X and Y. A best-fit regression is calculated for a given plot of points by the *method of least squares* (Strahler 1954, pp. 19–20, Croxton and Cowden 1955, pp. 263–73, Dixon and Massey 1957, p. 193) (Fig. 31A). This is designed to accomplish two results:

1. The sum of the vertical deviations from the best-fit regression line ($(y - Y)$ in Fig. 31A) must be zero. This is not sufficient in itself, however, because any straight line passing through the average X and Y values (i.e. through the co-ordinate $\overline{X}$, $\overline{Y}$) would fulfill this requirement.
2. The sum of the squares of these deviations must be less than the sum of the squares calculated with reference to any other possible straight line. In meeting this second requirement the first is automatically satisfied.

Unfortunately, this simple linear relationship is seldom encountered in geomorphic work (Fig. 32), where almost all the relationships are of a non-linear kind. Although an infinite number of non-linear forms

M

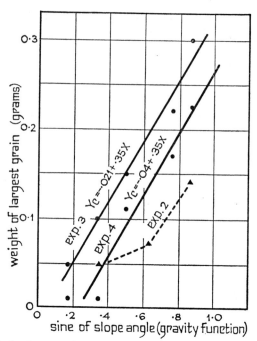

Fig. 32. Relation between the largest particle moved by experimental spraying (Experiments 2, 3 and 4) on a badland slope and the sine of the slope angle (from Schumm 1956).

are theoretically possible, three—*exponential, power,* and *polynomial* functions—have been found to apply commonly to geomorphic data.

An exponential function (Krumbein 1937) is one in which the dependent variable (Y) increases or decreases in geometical progression, as the independent variable (X) increases in arithmetic progression. This exponential (or *semi-logarithmic*) function is of the form

$$\log Y = \log a + \log b \cdot X \text{ (or; } Y = y_0 \cdot e^{ax}),$$

which gives a curved line on arithmetic graph paper because the rate of increase of one variable with the other is not constant (Croxton and Cowden 1955, pp. 93–116), as is the case with the linear regression, whereas it yields a straight line on semi-logarithmic graph paper (Fig. 33). The exponential regression represents a constant percentage rate of growth as a straight line (consequently it is often termed the *rate of growth curve*), in which the rate of change of the dependent variable is always proportional to the value of the independent variable at the point under consideration (Krumbein 1937, p. 595). The

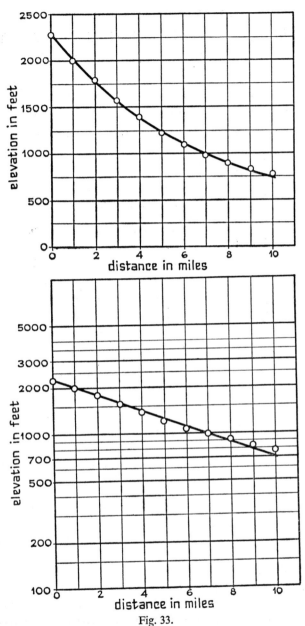

Fig. 33.

A. Arithmetic function fitted to the surveyed profile of San Antonio Canyon, California, alluvial fan.

B. Exponential function fitted to the data given in figure 33A (from Krumbein 1937).

exponential regression has wide application in expressing relationships in earth science, including: decrease in mean pebble size along a beach; variation of loess thickness with distance; elevation versus distance from the apex of an alluvial fan (Fig. 33); dispersion of debris in a glacial boulder train with distance (Krumbein 1937); sediment loss versus drainage basin relief (Schumm 1956, p. 615) (Fig. 34);

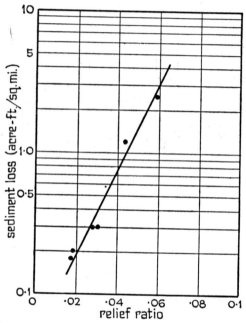

Fig. 34. Relation of mean estimated annual sediment loss (reservoir sedimentation) to the relief ratio (H/L) in selected New Mexico, Arizona and Utah drainage basins (from Schumm 1956).

erosion rate versus sine of slope angle (Schumm 1956, p. 627); elevation versus distance along a large river (Shulits 1941); unit weight of vegetation versus mean annual precipitation (Langbein and Schumm 1958).

Power, or *logarithmic*, functions have the form;

$$\log Y = \log a + b. \log X \ (\text{or}; \ Y = a\,X^b).$$

and appear as straight line relationships when the logarithms of both the X and Y values are employed (Fig. 31B), or where logarithmic scales are used for the ordinate and abscissa. As with the linear and exponential forms, best-fit regressions can be calculated by the

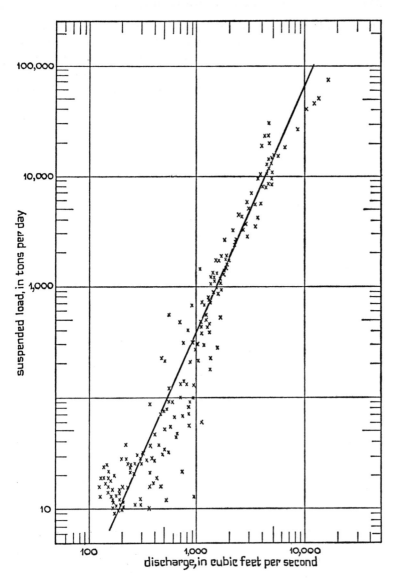

Fig. 35. Relation between suspended sediment load and discharge for Brandywine Creek at Wilmington, Delaware (from Wolman 1955).

method of least squares (Croxton and Cowden 1939, pp. 694–7), by using the logarithmic values of X and Y co-ordinates to calculate the constants 'log *a*' and '*b*' from simultaneous equations. Logarithmic regressions do not have any of the genetic overtones possessed by exponential relationships (Krumbein 1937), but they have been found

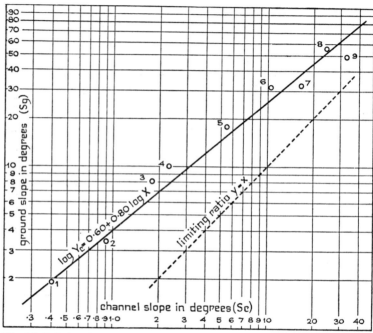

Fig. 36. Relation between mean maximum valley-side (ground) slope ($S_g$) and the associated basal mean channel slope ($S_c$) for nine maturely dissected regions (from map data): (1 and 2) Grant, Louisiana; (3) Rappahannock Academy, Virginia; (4) Belmont, Virginia (5) Allen's Creek, Indiana; (6) Hunter-Shandaken, New York; (7) Mt Gleason, California; (8) Petrified Forest, Arizona; (9) Clay fill, Perth Amboy, New Jersey (from Strahler 1950).

to describe closely many geomorphic relationships, including: the transport of bed material, suspended load (Fig. 35) and chemical load as a function of river discharge (see respectively Einstein 1950, Wolman 1955, and Wolman and Miller 1960); repose slope angle versus particle size (Fig. 31B); regional valley-side slope angle versus associated stream channel slope (Fig. 36). Students of hydraulic geometry have found logarithmic forms of particular value in relating channel characteristics with fluvial processes, for example; stream veolocity, depth and width versus discharge (Fig. 37); meander wavelength versus catchment area (Dury 1960); and stream width-depth ratio versus per cent silt-clay (Schumm 1960b).

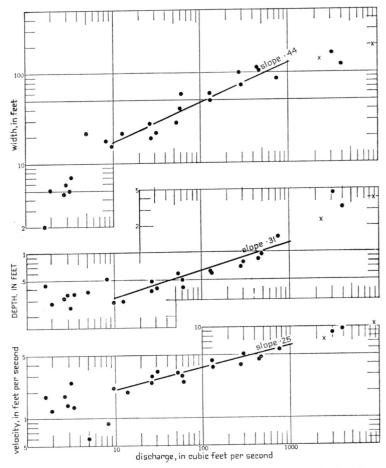

Fig. 37. Relation of width, depth and velocity to discharge at the Domingo, New Mexico, gauging station on the Rio Galisteo (crosses indicate slope-area measurements) (from Leopold and Miller 1956).

Polynomial functions express graphical forms possessing more complex, or compound, inflexions than the types of functions previously discussed. This large family is not capable of presenting linear

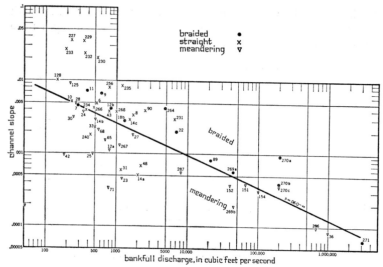

Fig. 38. Values of slope and bankfull discharge for various natural channels-
together with a logarithmic regression broadly separating braided from meander,
ing channels (from Leopold and Wolman 1957).

trends by the use of simple transformations, and two of the more
common forms are:

$$Y = a + bX + cX^2 \qquad \text{(Parabolic, quadratic, or second degree).}$$

$$Y = a + bX + cX^2 + dX^3 + eX^4 \qquad \text{(Quartic, or fourth degree).}$$

These regressions are also fitted by a rather more complicated use of
the least squares technique (Croxton and Cowden 1939, pp. 426–32)
but, because the number of simultaneous equations required exceeds
by one the powers of X involved, equations of third degree or higher
are usually calculated by using *orthogonal polynomials* (Croxton and
Cowden 1939, pp. 433–5). These are built up by the addition of new
constants, maintaining the existing constants, until a satisfactory fit is
obtained, and have been employed to approximate three-dimensional
areal distributions (see later section).

Finally, regressions can be useful for indicating boundary conditions between different phenomena, and Leopold and Wolman
(1957, p. 59) have thus distinguished between the combinations of
channel slope and bankfull discharge which produce braided or
meandering channels (Fig. 38).

## Correlation

In dealing with the relationships between two sets of paired numerical values it is not sufficient merely to calculate the regression which best approximates the data. The significance of this calculated regression depends to a large extent upon the closeness of fit between the regression and the points upon which it was based—in other words, a measure is needed of just how good a fit the best-fit regression is. After all, a 'best-fit' regression can be fitted to any plot of points, no matter how scattered they are.

A simple measure of this excellence of fit is the *scatter* ($\sigma_{y.x}$) (Strahler 1954b, p. 20), which is calculated from the squared departures parallel to the Y-axis of the plotted points from the best-fit regression (i.e. ($y - Y$) in Fig. 31A), such that

$$\sigma_{y.x} = \sqrt{\frac{\Sigma(y - Y)^2}{N}}$$

N, as usual, is the number of points, and the statistic $\sigma_{y.x}$ is analogous to the standard deviation of a sample. An estimate of the scatter of the whole population ($S_{y.x}$), or the *standard error of estimate*, is given by the equation:

$$S_{y.x} = \sqrt{\frac{\Sigma(y - Y)^2}{N-2}}$$

About two-thirds of the total items might be expected to fall within a band of $\pm 1\ S_{y.x}$ wide about the best-fit regression (Croxton and Cowden 1939, pp. 657–60).

The scatter, however, is measured in the units relating to the Y values, but a more versatile dimensionless measure of this property is the *correlation coefficient* ($r$), which allows direct comparison of plots involving different units. This expresses the relationship between the plotted points and the calculated regression on a scale ranging between zero, for a completely random scatter of points which might be equally well fitted by any regression through the co-ordinates $\bar{X}$, $\bar{Y}$; and + or − unity, referring to a perfect coincidence between points and regression line (the sign being governed by the sign of the regression coefficient). The value of $r$ can be calculated in a number of different ways. A simple rule of thumb, calculation is given by Croxton and Cowden (1939, p. 671–2), while Strahler (1954b, p. 23) expresses it by the formula:

$$r = \sqrt{b_{yx} \cdot b_{xy}}$$

Where $b_{yx}$ is the regression coefficient for the equation calculated

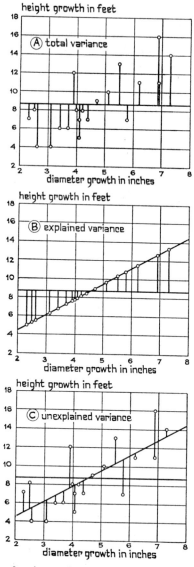

Fig. 39. Derivation of variance of height growth of 20 forest trees as explained by their diameter growth (from Croxton and Cowden 1939).

when X is assumed to be the independent variable, and $b_{xy}$ is the regression coefficient when Y is the assumed independent variable. For purposes of understanding the properties of $r$, as well as providing an introduction to the subsequent section on multivariate analysis, the derivation of $r$ explained by Croxton and Cowden (1939, pp. 660–6) proves most useful. In this instance the correlation coefficient is calculated by taking the square root of the ratio between the *explained variance* and the *total variance* (Fig. 39). The variances are defined as:

1. The total variance—the mean squared deviation of the Y values from the mean Y value (i.e. from the horizontal regression line $X = \bar{Y}$ in Fig. 39A). Symbolically, the total variance is expressed by

$$\frac{\Sigma (Y - \bar{Y})^2}{N}$$

2. The explained variance—the mean squared deviation of the calculated best-fit Y values ($Y_c$) from the mean value of $Y(\bar{Y})$ (Fig. 39B). It is expressed as

$$\frac{\Sigma (Y_c - \bar{Y})^2}{N}$$

3. The unexplained variance—the mean squared deviation of the actual Y values from those of the best-fit regression (Fig. 39C). The unexplained variance equals

$$\frac{\Sigma (Y - Y_c)^2}{N}$$

In the instance quoted, relating tree height growth to diameter growth (Fig. 39), the explained variance of 5·99, together with the total variance of 10·43 (i.e. unexplained variance of 4·44), gives a value of $r$ equal to 0·758 (i.e. $\sqrt{\frac{5·99}{10·43}}$). The correlation coefficient can therefore be looked upon as a square root measure of how much better the best-fit regression approximates the actual plot of points than does a line of zero slope (i.e. $X = \bar{Y}$), indicating no relationship between Y and X. It must be stressed, however, that the coefficient of correlation refers only to the points involved in the computation and tells one little about the probable degree of correlation of the total population from which the points were sampled.

This lack of direct population inference properties places a severe limitation on the employment of the unsupported correlation coefficient for purposes of causal inference, even allowing for the hazards besetting simple correlation which are set out at the end of this section. Kinsman (1957) has pointed out that the calculation of $r$ is strongly affected by the value of N, and that great caution should be exercised when dealing with correlation coefficients obtained from small samples. It is difficult to set a critical acceptance value for $r$, in that a value of $r = 0.6$ only accounts for 20 per cent of the standard error of estimate, and $r = 0.866$ only 50 per cent. For practical purposes, it is wise to set the lowest unsupported value of $r$ to be accepted as the basis for further investigation as 0.95 (i.e. accounting for 70 per cent of the scatter). The most profitable use for the correlation coefficient is in exploratory work, when a high coefficient between one of many assumed casual factors and an effect may point the way to the most productive future line of investigation. In short, $r$ is useful as supporting evidence or as an indicator, but can never alone play the role of a primary argument (Kinsman 1957, p. 413).

A test for the significance of the correlation coefficient is set out by Croxton and Cowden (1939, pp. 681–2) and Strahler (1954b, pp. 23–4); employing, once again, the statistic $t$, where

$$t = \frac{r\sqrt{N - m}}{\sqrt{1 - r^2}}$$

$m$ being the number of degrees of freedom lost; in this instance 2. This test of the correlation coefficient enables one to infer the probability that, if similar sets of sample pairs were drawn repeatedly from this population, this good a correlation might be expected to appear purely by chance if no correlation actually exists (Strahler 1954b, pp. 23–4). In the case of the plot of slope length versus slope angle (Fig. 40) Strahler (1954b) has shown that, although the value of $r$ is only 0.485, the $t$ value yields a probability of less than 0.1 per cent that this good a correlation might be due to chance. Thus, despite the low correlation coefficient, one is strongly disposed to accept the existence of a relationship between slope length and angle in this instance.

Finally, however, it is necessary to draw attention to the dangers of automatically drawing inferences from a high correlation to cause and effect, for the correlation coefficient is not a measure of proved causation but simply one of co-variation (Croxton and Cowden 1939, p. 678). Indeed, a high correlation coefficient may express any one of the following situations:

1. A variation of one variable caused by the other. This is an instance of a real cause and effect relationship. For example, there can be little doubt that Fig. 35 indicates that discharge exercises the most

important control over rate of suspended sediment transport. This type of single correlation need not imply that only one causal factor is operating, however, and the scatter in Fig. 35 is undoubtedly a measure of the interference of other less important factors (e.g. calibre of the sediment), although discharge undoubtedly is of overriding importance. The truth of a causal correlation cannot be established statistically, but only by the application of rational deduction.

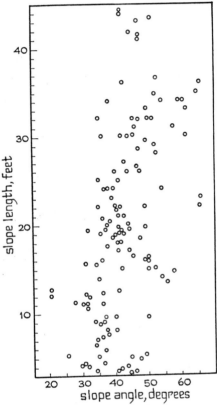

Fig. 40. Relation between slope length and slope angle on badland slopes bordering miniature pediments in the lower Brule formation, Big Badlands, South Dakota (from Strahler 1954b; data by Smith; see also Smith 1958).

2. A co-variation of two variables due to a common cause. In this instance both are yoked dependent variables, which cannot act dynamically upon each other, and no cause and effect relationship

obtains between them. A good geomorphic example of this is provided by high correlation plots of stream width to width of the meander belt (Bates 1939), when it is now obvious (Leopold and Wolman 1957) that both variables, together with their significant ratio, are functions of other mutual controlling factors of which discharge is the most important.

3. An interacting causal relationship between the two variables. Such a mutual relationship between valley-side slope and channel gradient is demonstrated in Fig. 36.

4. A purely chance correlation between two unconnected properties. Kinsman (1956, p. 412) refers to the correlation coefficient of 0·87 which was obtained between membership of the International Machinists Union and the death rate in the State of Hyderabad!

The application of correlation techniques to non-linear regressions is explained by Croxton and Cowden (1939, pp. 691–738, 1955, 282–319).

### Significance of Trend

In testing the significance of a geomorphic regression, besides considerations of the degree of scatter and the number of points used, Strahler (1954b, p. 20) has pointed out that the slope of the regression line ($b$) is of great importance. It is more than obvious that if one desires to investigate sympathetic variations between two variables this cannot be expressed by the correlation coefficient alone, for, even if the value of $r$ indicates perfect correlation (i.e. unity), a regression coefficient for the best-fit line not significantly different from zero (i.e. the regression line is parallel to the X-axis) indicates no connection whatsoever between the two variables. It is necessary, therefore, to test the significance of the trend of the regression (represented by the regression coefficient, $b$). This is accomplished (Strahler 1954b, pp. 20–2) by setting up the null hypothesis that $b$ is not significantly different from zero for the whole population, and calculating the value of the statistic $t$, where;

$$t = \frac{b\sqrt{\Sigma(X-\overline{X})^2}}{S_{y \cdot x}}$$

In this instance $\Sigma (X - \overline{X})^2$ equals the sum of the squared deviations of the X values from their mean value ($\overline{X}$). Using the $t$ table and the appropriate number of degrees of freedom (here equal to the number of points minus 2), the probability (P) is obtained that repeated sampling of a population showing no significant trend (i.e. $b = 0$) would

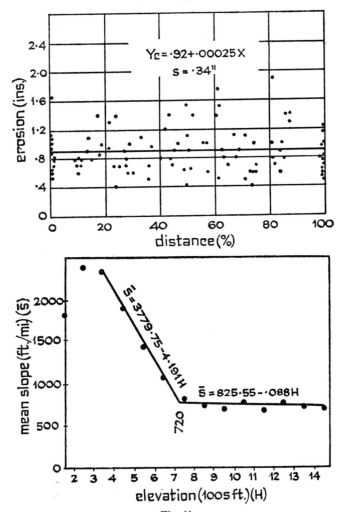

Fig. 41.

A. Regression fitted to a scatter diagram of depth of erosion versus per cent of distance from the top of straight slope segments in clay badlands at Perth Amboy, New Jersey (P > 65 per cent. Regression coefficient not significantly different from zero) (from Schumm 1956).

B. Plot of mean land slope versus elevation in the Heddon basin, north Devon (above 720 feet, 30 per cent < P < 40 per cent. No significant variation of land slope above this elevation) (from Chorley 1958b).

yield this great a *b* value, or greater, purely by chance sampling. As before, this hypothesis is accepted or rejected according to whether P is greater or less than the selected probability level (i.e. 0·05, or 5 per cent). A detailed calculation applying this test is given by Chenoweth (1952, pp. 540–3). If the null hypothesis is rejected, the slope of the regression line is considered significant, in other words that Y varies with X, although Strahler (1954b, p. 21) has given the following caution:

> Note that the door is left open to the remote possibility of obtaining this assemblage of paired observations by chance alone when no trend actually exists, and we shall never be absolutely positive that such is not the case here. The scientist must gamble in the final analysis, but he wants to be sure he has the odds overwhelmingly in his favor.

As Nagel (1939, pp. 3–4: quoted by Mahalanobis 1950) has put it, in a wider setting:

> The long history of science and philosophy is in large measure the history of the progressive emancipation of men's minds from the theory of self-evident truths and from the postulate of complete certainty as the mark of scientific knowledge.

This test has been employed by Schumm (1956, pp. 624–5) (Fig. 41A) in accepting the hypothesis of no significant difference in depth of erosion down badland slopes (P > 0·65) and by Chorley (1958b, p. 373) (Fig. 41B) in showing no significant variation of mean land slope with elevation above 720 ft in the Heddon basin, Devon (0·30 < P < 0·40).

Two other useful statistical techniques involving tests of the significance of regression coefficients are the *analysis of covariance* (Walker and Lev 1953, pp. 390–3, and Dixon and Massey 1957, pp. 209–19) and that for the fit of a given plot of points by a single regression line (Walker and Lev 1953, pp. 393–5). The analysis of covariance employs the statistic F, as in the analysis of variance, to determine the probability of significance of difference of trend for two or more regressions. Chorley (1957b) has used this analysis to demonstrate the similarity in slope of regressions expressing the laws of morphometry (e.g. Fig. 42) and, thus, the striking geometrical similarity between three erosional topographies of very different textures of dissection. The test of the applicability of one single regression line may prove useful in identifying and testing the significance of breaks in graphic plots (Chorley, 1958b).

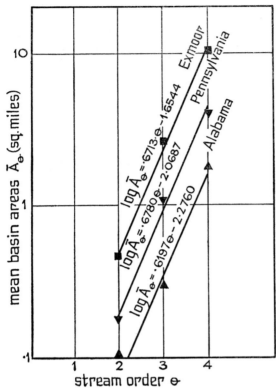

Fig. 42. Regressions, with not significantly different regression coefficients, illustrating the law of drainage basin areas in three sandstone regions of mature dissection in Exmoor, Pennsylvania and Alabama (from Chorley 1957b).

## Trend Surface Analysis

Just as a best-fit regression line can be fitted to a two-dimensional plot of points, so mathematical surfaces can be used to approximate three-dimensional, areal distributions of quantitative data. This concept has long been employed in geomorphology in a qualitative sense in such descriptions as 'the hilltops form a surface sloping gently seaward', but few attempts have been made to place this type of analysis on a more rigorous footing.

The most simple surfaces to fit to areal data are planes, which may be described as linear *multiple regressions* involving three variables, the two independent of which are areal co-ordinates. Walker and Lev (1953, pp. 318–20) have described the general method for obtaining a best-fit plane of the form $Y = a + b_1X_1 + b_2X_2$; Miller (1956, p. 427) has illustrated the fitting of a plane to sand size data on a beach (Fig. 43); Lippitt (1959) has fitted the plane $X = 45\cdot20 + 0\cdot4056Y - 1\cdot427Z$ relating the percentage of sand content (X) to the location (Y,

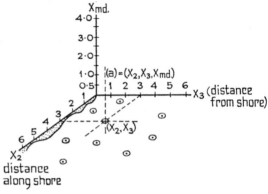

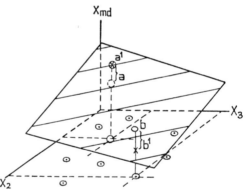

Fig. 43.

A. 3-dimensional co-ordinates applied to the areal description of near-shore sediment size. $X_2$ = distance along shore; $X_3$ = distance from shore; $X_{md}$ = median sediment size in phi units.

B. Illustrating a best-fit plane (i.e. first degree surface) fitted to the above situation. The observed value 'a' lies below its computed counterpart 'a¹' on the plane, and the observed value 'b' lies above its computed counterpart 'b¹' on the plane (from Miller 1956).

Z co-ordinate) of the Lower Cobourg Limestone; and Krumbein (1960d) has fitted the surface $X' = 131\cdot689 - 0\cdot619U - 0\cdot349V$ to the areal variation of thickness (X') of the Three Yard Cyclothem. In the last instance the plane was fitted by the use of an electronic computer (IBM 650; Programme number 60705) in under one minute to 19 measurements of thickness (X) at locations represented by the co-ordinates U, V. A recent geomorphic application of this technique has been made by Svensson (1956) who attempted to reconstruct an erosion surface in the Lofoten Islands by fitting the equation $ax + by + z + c = 0$ to 8 elevations (Z) of hilltops (Location X, Y). Svensson (1956, p. 2) gives the three simultaneous equations employed to solve for the constants $a$, $b$ and $c$, and explains how to obtain certain diagnostic parameters from these constants—namely, the inclination of the plane parallel to the X-axis ($\tan^{-1} a$), the inclination of the plane parallel to the Y-axis ($\tan^{-1} b$), the direction of true dip of the plane ($\tan^{-1} a/b$, measured from the Y direction), and the amount of true dip ($\tan^{-1}\sqrt{a^2 + b^2}$). A measure of the standard deviation of the points from this best-fit plane is given, and Svenssen suggests that this measure might be used for testing whether another elevation (i.e. of a nearby hilltop) might be correlated with this plane (see also Jones 1952).

Few maps, however, represent simple linear trends (Krumbein 1960d)—erosion surfaces may become warped as well as tilted, and the deposits of sandy facies may be patchy. Although Swartz (1954) has pointed out that most contour type maps 'may be considered as built up by the superposition of a double infinity of elementary undulating surfaces' into 'mosaic-type composite maps', it is common to approximate the areal distribution by successively more complex, higher degree polynomials, such as the second degree, parabolic, quadratic surface; the third degree, 'swell and swale', cubic surface; or the fourth degree, 'ridges and hollows', quartic surface (Fig. 44B). Gilchrist and Cressman (1954) have fitted second degree polynomial surfaces to meteorological data for forecasting purposes, and Simpson (1954) has employed higher order polynomials to describe areal gravity data. The fitting of non-linear surfaces can be accomplished by three methods:

1. The graphic method. If the areal data is abundant such that intervening values can be interpolated by eye, it is possible to sketch in approximating isopleths (Bishop 1960, pp. 134-7 and 153-8). In this way Wooldridge and Linton (1955, p. 110) have constructed generalized contours on the Chiltern dip-slope. Krumbein (1956, pp. 2167–71) has also described a simple profile method for surface fitting.
2. The use of a desk calculator for fitting quadratic surfaces (Miller 1956) by a method of successive approximations.
3. The mathematical fitting of quadratic and higher degree surfaces

(Grant 1954, 1957, Oldham and Sutherland 1955), or combinations of these surfaces, usually with the aid of an electronic computer (Krumbein 1959a).

Because of the infinity of three-dimensional surfaces of increasing degrees of complexity and differing attitude which could be theoretically fitted to an areal plot of data it is not realistic to think in terms of a best-fit surface, or combination of surfaces. It is possible, however, by progressively fitting linear, quadratic, and higher degree surfaces to the map data by the least squares technique, to determine, by the *reduction in the sum of squares*, the contribution to the explained variability contributed progressively by the addition of each higher degree polynomial term. This reduction in the sum of squares is a three-dimensional equivalent of the two-dimensional procedure illustrated in Fig. 39. It is calculated by expressing the ratio of the explained to the total variance as a percentage, this being an expression of how much better an approximation of the measured points the fitted surface is than is a plane surface of zero slope passing through the mean co-ordinate. (The unexplained variance equals

$$\frac{\Sigma(a-a^1)^2}{N},$$

as illustrated by Miller (1956) in Fig. 43.) This minimum variance principle (Brown 1955, 1956) has been explained by Krumbein (1960c) such that if the best-fit linear surface reduces the sum of squares by 92 per cent this means that any new value estimated from this fitted surface has 2 chances in 3 of being on the average of no more than 8 per cent in error. Whitten (1959, pp. 839–40) has calculated the progressive reductions in the sum of squares for linear and linear plus quadratic fitted trend surfaces to various properties of a granite. A very high level of reduction is rare, however, and sometimes a figure below 50 per cent has to be accepted in instances where there are marked local variations which tend to complicate the regional trend.

It is important to try to describe and approximate areal distributions by fitted, regular, geometrical surfaces because, as Krumbein (1956, p. 2164) has pointed out, these may represent *response surfaces* (Box 1954) generated by geological factors, operating on a geographical scale, controlling the depositional, tectonic, or erosional processes, such that an accurate description and analysis of the trend surface may give important clues regarding dynamics (Box and Youle 1955). Miller (1956) has thus recognized the diagnostic trend patterns of sediments, Whitten (1959, 1961) has related major petrological trend surfaces in a granite to the mechanism of granitization, and it is not unlikely that regional trend surfaces fitted to elevated erosion levels

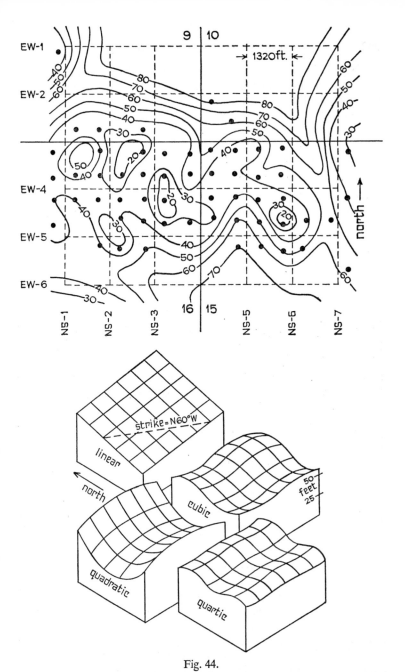

Fig. 44.

A. Net sand thickness, Reynolds zone, West Brock area, Carter County, Okla-
homa. Isopachs (isopleths of equal thickness) have been sketched in from
well drillings at the marked locations (data from Dapples and Sloss; from
Krumbein 1956).

B. Elementary best-fit linear, quadratic (second degree), cubic and quartic
surfaces fitted to the well data given in Fig. 44A. Each surface is expressed in
terms of mean sand thickness (from Krumbein 1956).

might yield important clues to the methods and agents of their deformation. It is not sufficient to rely in all instances upon sketched
contours, in that the eye can easily be deluded by the illusion of
complexity when apparently complex patterns are produced by
the superimposition of two or more very simple and highly diagnostic patterns. Referring to the apparent chaos of the ocean surface,
Johnson (1919, p. 20) wrote:

> Imagine several series of waves crossing each other at distinctly dif-
> ferent angles, and we have an adequate explanation for all the
> great irregularity in wave form observed in the open ocean. Only
> when the observer is stationed high above the tossing waters, and
> then only under favourable conditions, can he distinguish the
> several orderly systems of waves which are responsible for the
> apparent chaos.

Not only are the regional trend surfaces of diagnostic importance,
but local deviations from these surfaces, or *residuals* (represented by
a–a[1] in Fig. 43) are also of great interest when presented as an areal
distribution. After a satisfactory regional trend surface (Fig. 44C) has
been calculated by the fitting and testing of surfaces of successively
higher degree (Fig. 44B), a residual map (Swartz 1954) can be constructed (Fig. 44D) showing the contoured departures of the actual
measured values from the fitted trend surface. Just as the regional
trend surface may be diagnostic of a large-scale effect, so the residual
map may disentangle from the underlying broader patterns of variation both the effect of local factors and the non-systematic chance
variations (Krumbein 1956, 1960c). Thus, the local component is
etched out from the regional component (Krumbein 1956, p. 2165)
and may be considered separately in terms of local mechanisms or as
non-systematic departures from the regional trend surface. In geology, besides the obvious applications in oil prospecting, Whitten
(1959) has used residual mapping to show up the local 'ghost' stratigraphy which is barely perceptible in a region of subsequent granitization, and the geographers Robinson, Lindberg and Brinkman (1961)
have applied the principle of residuals to rural population deviations
from fitted population and rainfall associations in the Great Plains.
Doubtless, geomorphic applications of this method of residuals will
immediately spring to the mind of the reader, but one example might
be taken from an extension of the peneplain application considered
above. Supposing that the erosion surface possesses a number of
rather insignificant residual monadnocks the form of which might be
held to indicate the erosional mechanism under which they were
etched out (e.g. arid pediplanation) and the areal arrangement of

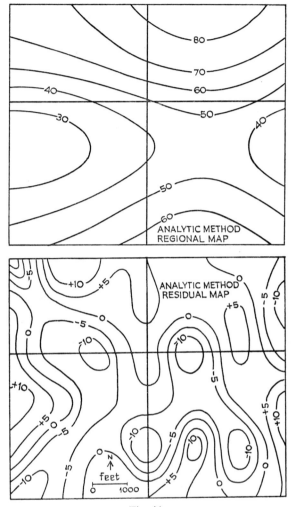

Fig. 44.

C. Best-fit linear plus quadratic plus cubic trend surface fitted to the data given in Fig. 44A (from Krumbein 1956).

D. Map showing local residuals of the observed Reynolds sand thickness from the regional trend fitted in figure 44C (from Krumbein 1956).

which is in response to subtle influences of the underlying bedrock. In this instance both these diagnostic features of geometry and arrangement might appear from a residual map of the subsequently uplifted, warped and eroded surface. It must be reiterated, however, that one square foot of datable deposits of known age is more valuable in the interpretation of the history of landscape than inferences of the most extensive erosion surfaces based solely on geometrical form.

An interesting geographical variation of the method of trend surface construction has been provided by Robinson and Bryson (1957) who have fitted linear surfaces to rural population and rainfall distributions in Nebraska and have expressed the correspondence between these trend surfaces by means of a correlation coefficient.

## Regional Analysis of Areal Data

Since the culmination of the studies in regional geomorphology by Fenneman (1931, 1938), notwithstanding the abortive attempt at a revival of interest by Linton (1951), geomorphologists have not shown any pronounced inclination to base their work on the region *per se*, in the sense that a geographer might organize his data. Of the many reasons for this reticence, two are probably paramount. Firstly, the two dominant morphometric parameters which control landscape geometry—relief and drainage density (Strahler 1950, pp. 684–6)—are extremely sensitive to tectonic, structural, lithological, climatic and vegetational controls. This is particularly so with drainage density, which exhibits a huge natural range of values (Smith 1950, p. 667). Thus it is, therefore, that the distinctions between regions of different morphometric character, and in many instances the boundaries separating them, are often so obvious as to provide little stimulation for further analytical work. Secondly, a regional framework is often implicit in geomorphic studies which are conducted from other points of view. For many scholars the coherent denudation chronology proposed by Wooldridge and Linton (1955) has given to southeast England a more subtle and significant regional character than previous geomorphic work was able to confer. In addition, many studies relating form and process in geomorphology are conducted within a rather rigid regional framework in order to eliminate excessive variables, and, for example, Strahler's (1950) slope studies in southern California have provided a vivid geomorphic description of the Verdugo Hills.

In the preceding section areal data was studied as a continuum, but a small minority of geomorphologists and a majority of geographers have found it necessary to stress those aspects of areal information which promote differentiation (Hartshorne 1959). This attitude has found a recent statistical expression in the work of Duncan, Cuzzort and Duncan (1961) who have identified four aspects of such an investigation, all of which have certain geomorphic applications:

1. The reliability of information relating to areal units as a sample of 'total population' characteristics. It will be remembered that reference has already been made to Robinson's (1956) warning regarding the composite use of unweighted averages, percentages and ratios obtained from sampling areas of different size, and the recent correspondence by Chisholm (1960) relating to conclusions regarding the incidence of commuting in West Germany by Dickinson (1959) further highlights this problem. Geomorphologists are not as inhibited in this matter as are the geographers who are forced to accept much of their basic data in arbitrary administrative parcels, but the low incidence of unchannelled interbasin areas (Schumm 1956, pp. 608–9) explains the abnormally high drainage density which is obtained from sampling smaller basins of lower order within a 'homogeneous' geomorphic region.

2. The measurement and statistical description of characteristics relating to an areal sample. This generally involves the application of the usual procedures of descriptive statistics employing an areal sampling framework.

3. The statistical analysis of spatial structures. In this instance one is interested in aspects of the internal distribution or structure within a given areal unit, such that factors representing precise location (Thompson 1957), linkage or azimuth are considered. A geographical example of such work can be found in the studies of Garrison (Garrison and Marble 1958, Garrison 1959–60) who has applied linear programming techniques to location, market, price and transportation relationships, as well as to minimize the joint cost of transportation and investment in a highway system such as to obtain 'optimal output under a set of restraints' (Garrison and Marble 1958, p. 10). Spatial structures have assumed importance in geomorphology partly as the result of the introduction of the system of stream ordering by Horton (1945, pp. 281–3), which was subsequently modified by Strahler (1952a, p. 1120) and rationalized by Melton (1959). However, no quantitative method has yet been specifically devised to replace the qualitative description of drainage patterns formalized by Zernitz (1932), although the bifurcation ratio may prove useful in this respect. The next step in such a spatial structural analysis is to compare either similar

structures between different areas (Judson and Andrews 1955) or
the structural patterns of different features within the same area
(Chadwick 1961).
4. The comparison of regional characteristics and the construction of
boundaries. In considerations of this nature the methods applicable by geographers and by geologists interested in facies mapping
have much in common. Zobler (1957, 1958), for example, has
tested regional differences by means of the chi-square test (for
details see Quenoulle 1950, pp. 86–8) and has compared differences
within and between regions by the analysis of variance. In geology
Potter and Siever (1955) have also employed the analysis of variance to investigate the areal variation of certain lithologic parameters in southern Illinois as exhibited by a hierarchy of sample
areal units from one square mile to the 'supertownship'. Similar
techniques have been used by Krumbein (1955b) to test 'facies
homogeneity', assisted by the employment of high-speed computers (Krumbein and Sloss 1958), and good reviews of facies mapping techniques have been given by Forgotson (1960) and Bishop
(1960, pp. 99–128). Earlier and less precise regional differentiations
of geomorphic attributes have been made by Smith (1935), by
Raisz and Henry (1937), and by Calef and Newcomb (1953).

## Multivariate Analysis

One of the most significant characteristics of geological, geographical and geomorphic phenomena is that they are the result of a
number of simultaneously operating variables which must be evaluated separately, relatively and in combination (Burma 1949, Krumbein 1960b). This type of complete analysis of causes has always
proved extremely difficult in natural science, where the conditions
favouring controlled experiment are often lacking, but, as Krumbein
(1960b) has pointed out, the method of multiple working hypothesis
(Chamberlin 1897) represents a qualitative attempt to consider simultaneously the implications of several lines of evidence. The problem
has often been intensified because many earth science phenomena
possess a high natural variability 'owing to the simultaneous activity
of numerous factors operating on different time and space scales'
(Krumbein 1960b, p. 87) producing 'fluctuations in data that cannot
be assigned to specific causes, and which, if large, may obscure the
meaningful information in the data' (Krumbein 1960b, pp. 88–9).
This high natural variability is termed *noise*, the presence of which
often results in the obscuring of significant relationships.

Until the comparatively recent spread of appropriate statistical methods, currently assisted by the use of high-speed computers, students were often forced to restrict artificially the number of variables under consideration, and were only able to analyse one or two factors of assumed importance in any detail. This restriction often resulted in an unrealistic concentration upon those factors which seemed obvious, or were easy to observe and measure, or those which seemed attractive on doctrinaire grounds. Needless to say, these factors have not always turned out to be associated with either the most subtle or the most significant relationships, and, in an extreme form, such restricted views can be held largely responsible for the various manifestations of uni-causal determinism from which the discipline of geography has repeatedly suffered. In geomorphology countless instances exist of over-importance being ascribed to a particular factor of structure, process or time in the explanation of landscape features; just as in the study of economic location the factor of distance has often been over-emphasized.

Fundamentally, once the multivariate character of most investigations has been recognized, it is important that the following questions be asked, and answered (Krumbein 1959b, p. 575):

1. How many controlling factors are involved? This primary step in any investigation can only be taken as the result of the experience or intuition of the investigator, and, although statistical methods are able to indicate the possible relative importance of these factors, they can never give an unequivocal answer as to whether these are the 'correct' controlling variables. Statistical methods are an adjunct to hypothesis, experience and intuition—not a substitute for them.

2. Are these factors inter-related in some way? Usually in nature controlling factors interact upon each other to produce *replication*, such that often one variable will repeat information already supplied by another. In short, any realistic multivariate analysis cannot assume the property of addivity among the factors.

3. For a given set of factors, which one or more are the most important controls? This question can only be answered in conjunction with the following question, in that there are few invariable factors which do not themselves change in importance in the presence of other factors.

4. Are these same factors most important under all environmental conditions, or may their relative importance vary from one situation, or one time, to another?

The above questions prompt one to attempt to determine what independent variables 'explain', or account for, most of the variability of the dependent variable, and what is the nature of the residual, or 'unexplained' variations (Krumbein 1959b, p. 575).

It is convenient to divide the techniques which have been adopted to achieve the above end into two categories—firstly, those involving empirically eliminating or holding certain factors constant while the effect of the ones remaining is examined; and, secondly, the true multivariate techniques which allow composite effects of a number of variables to be evaluated.

Under the first category, one important and popular method is exemplified by the controlled experiment. The detailed work of Gilbert (1914) on the laboratory evaluation of the factors controlling stream tractive capacity—namely, channel slope, discharge, debris size, mixtures of sizes, width-depth channel 'form' factor, and mean velocity—is the most obvious example of a geomorphic application of this technique. More recently Van Burkalow (1945) conducted a controlled experiment to estimate the individual importance of the factors assumed to control the angle of repose of fragmented material—particle size, range of sizes, density, shape, roughness, compaction, height of fall, moisture content, inclination of the slope base, and shape of the slope in plan. Such a technique is obviously limited in scope because relatively few geomorphic phenomena can be subjected to controlled experiment, and because this method is not easily adapted to answering questions 2 and 4, above, relating to factor interactions. Thus, Van Burkalow found that with perfectly sorted material angle of repose varies inversely with particle size, whereas mixtures of sizes assumed characteristic angles of repose directly related to the average size of the particles (Van Burkalow 1945, p. 703).

A second eliminative, empirical method of evaluating the individual effects of controlling factors might be termed 'eliminative field work'. An example of this can be found in Chorley's (1957a) attempt to remove the lithological factor in investigating the effect of climate and vegetation on morphometry in three regions of massive sandstone. However, as with controlled experimentation, questions 2 and 4 are largely unanswered, and question 3 very imperfectly treated.

The second group of multivariate techniques are employed in attempts to avoid the kind of ambiguity encountered by Van Burkalow in dealing with the individual effects of variables treated in isolation. In effect, the techniques described below attempt, at different levels of sophistication, to answer questions 2 and 4, as well as 1 and 3. As Fisher (1926) has elegantly expressed it:

No aphorism is more frequently repeated in connexion with field trials than that we must ask Nature few questions, or, ideally, one question at a time. The writer is convinced that this view is wholly mistaken. Nature, he suggests, will best respond to a logical and carefully thought out questionnaire: indeed, if we ask her a single question she will often refuse to answer until some other topic has been discussed.

The attempts by geomorphologists to present Nature with such a controlled questionnaire are here classified into: index number construction, the adaptation of univariate methods, multiple correlation, and multiple regression.

Index numbers (Croxton and Cowden 1955, chapters 17–18) represent an attempt to express collectively the composite magnitude of a group of related variables, against which an effect can be compared. Dimensionless numbers often represent the most effective index numbers, but usually this method is a cumbersome and crude attempt to represent a total effect. This is so because index numbers are basically ratios, and the components of these ratios need to be weighted in terms of their importance—a knowledge of this relative importance is often precisely the question which the index number constructor wishes to avoid by the use of these numbers. In geomorphology, the Index of Climate and Vegetation (Chorley 1957a) and the Index of Erodibility (Chorley 1959) represent examples of this unsatisfactory method of expressing the composite effects of multiple factors.

Adaptations of univariate methods to serve multivariate ends form another obvious approach to the analysis of multiple factors. In a previous section the two- and three-factor basic forms of the analysis of variance introduced the operation of a number of separate factors, but it is important to recognize that each univariate extension or adaptation involves limiting initial assumptions and often tortuous calculation. Thus, for example, unless special allowance is made, the use of the analysis of variance involves the limiting assumption of additivity (Krumbein 1953c). An extension of the analysis of variance was used by Burma (1949) to compare fossil forms on the basis of eight measured characteristics. This was followed by Krumbein and Tukey (1956) who, with the use of nested samples, employed the analysis of variance to test the areal variability of a number of geological parameters in order to investigate, for example, how to identify a single drift sheet, despite local variations of gross aspect, depth of leaching, dominance of particular lithologies or grain size distribution. Dawson (1958) used a similar technique in studying the mineralogical variation across a batholith. Although these techniques are multivariate in the sense that several factors are evaluated simultaneously, the problem which they are designed to attack relates to the characteristic association of factors, not to their relative evaluation. A most interesting recent adaptation technique of a similar sort is that developed by Williams and Lambert (1959, 1960) to distinguish significant plant species-associations. This rather complex modification technique uses the chi-square test as a hierarchical sorting method in order to reveal 'an underlying structure simpler than the raw matrix of associations' (Williams and Lambert 1959, p. 83). On the reasonable assumption that these plant associations are not independent, the problem assumes a multivariate character which also promises to have applications in the study of geographical regional associations, and in the recognition and analysis of hierarchical spatial structures.

The technique of *multiple correlation* together with the allied *multiple regression*, represents the first method to be described here which measures up to the optimum requirements set out in the four questions given earlier in this section. Multiple correlation (Croxton and Cowden 1939, pp. 739–89) involves the calculation of the *coefficient of determination* which equals the square of the coefficient of correlation (i.e. $r^2$, or the explained variance divided by the total variance. See Fig. 39). The coefficient of determination gives the percentage of total variation of the dependent variable $X_1$ which is 'explained', or accounted for, by variations in any other single variable (e.g. $X_2$, $X_3$, ... $X_n$) (Croxton and Cowden 1939, pp. 739–40). Thus the designation $r^2_{1.2}$ refers to the coefficient of determination linking $X_1$ with $X_2$, and so on. This method enables controlling factors to be considered individually and ranked according to their individual effects on the dependent variable. Now, the method of multiple correlation makes no assumption of additivity, and it is therefore necessary to compute coefficients of determination for combinations of independent variables in order to estimate their composite control over variations in the dependent variable ($X_1$). To this end, an extension of the coefficient of determination (i.e. the *coefficient of multiple determination*, $R^2$) is made. Coefficients of multiple determination representing all combinations of independent variables as controls over the dependent variable can be calculated with increasing tedium as the combinations get bigger. For example, with a three controlling variable system calculations of $R^2_{1.23}$, $R^2_{1.34}$, $R^2_{1.24}$ and $R^2_{1.234}$ might be made. In practice, the independent variable which most greatly reduces the sum of squares of $X_1$, might be held constant by computing the first order *partial correlation coefficient* (Croxton and Cowden 1939, pp. 742–3) and thus the second strongest independent variable be selected—and so on (Krumbein 1959b, pp. 586–7). In the more straightforward applications of multiple correlation an assumption is made as to the linear relationship between the variables.

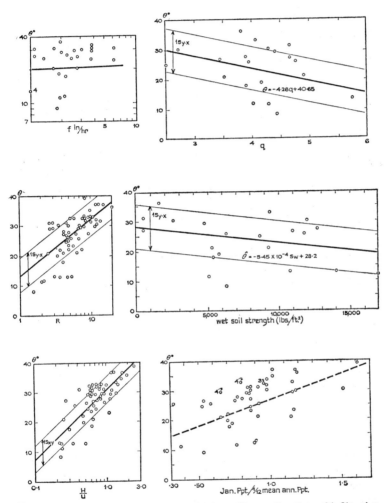

Fig. 45. Best-fit regressions of valley-side slope ($\theta$) as a function of infiltration capacity ($f$), runoff intensity ($q$), relative relief ($R$), wet soil strength ($S_w$), ruggedness ($H/u$) and the ratio of mean January precipitation to 1/12th mean annual precipitation (from Melton 1957).

In geomorphology, Melton (1957) employed this method in comparing variables relating to drainage basins in Arizona, New Mexico, Utah and Colorado. One of the relationships which he investigated was maximum valley-side slope $(X_1)$ as a function of wet soil strength $(X_2)$, infiltration capacity $(X_3)$, log. ruggedness number divided by basin order $(X_4)$, log. (P-E) index $(X_5)$, log. relative relief $(X_6)$, roughness number $(X_7)$ and a measure of rainfall intensity $(X_8)$ (Fig. 45). The results achieved were: $r_{1\cdot4}^2 = 0\cdot604$ (i.e. 60·4 per cent explained); $r_{1\cdot3}^2 = 0\cdot557$; $r_{1\cdot6}^2 = 0\cdot391$; $R_{1\cdot38}^2 = 0\cdot843$; $R_{1\cdot34}^2 = 0\cdot839$; $R_{1\cdot35}^2 = 0\cdot724$. Melton also investigated drainage density $(X_1)$, as a function of log. (P-E) $(X_2)$, log. infiltration $(X_3)$, per cent bare area $(X_4)$, log. roughness number $(X_5)$ and log. runoff intensity $(X_6)$ (Fig. 46). This yielded: $r_{1\cdot2}^2 = 0\cdot889$; $r_{1\cdot4}^2 = 0\cdot810$; $r_{1\cdot3}^2 = 0\cdot629$; $r_{1\cdot6}^2 = 0\cdot433$; $R_{1\cdot26}^2 = 0\cdot895$; $R_{1\cdot236}^2 = 0\cdot922$; $R_{1\cdot23456}^2 = 0\cdot932$. Later, the same author (Melton 1958c) again used the multiple correlation technique to investigate the control over valley-side slope exercised by the independent variables of basin relief, basin area, basin perimeter and total channel length. Morisawa (1959) made a similar study in an attempt to explain the control over peak runoff intensity in certain Appalachian plateau watersheds exercised by basin area, rainfall intensity, rainfall frequency, relief ratio, circularity ratio and frequency of first order streams. This gave a multiple correlation coefficient of 0·9478 and $R_{1\cdot234567}^2 = 0\cdot898$. The tedious nature of this multiple correlation technique, especially if carried out without the assistance of an electronic computer, can be avoided by adopting a simpler, non-parametric ranking procedure used by Melton (1958b) for the study of interactions between 15 morphometric, climatic and surficial factors measured from 59 drainage basins. Using hand-sorted punched cards for simply arranging these parameters in order of magnitude (Melton 1958d), correlation sets were built up, by means of a non-parametric measure of correlation (Kendall's 'tau'—Siegel 1956, p. 213), revealing some extremely interesting associations of properties.

A parallel, and in some of its phases identical method of multivariate analysis is represented by multiple regression. This employs the concept of trend surfaces as representing relationships between factors, involves less stringent statistical assumptions than does multiple correlation (in particular it does not employ the technique of progressively holding the strongest variables constant at subsequent stages in the computation, as in some multiple correlation methods), and has proved especially susceptible to treatment by electronic computer methods (Krumbein 1959b). Krumbein (1959b) used this method to 'sort out' the relative importance of all combinations of the independent variables of mean grain size $(X_1)$, standard deviation of

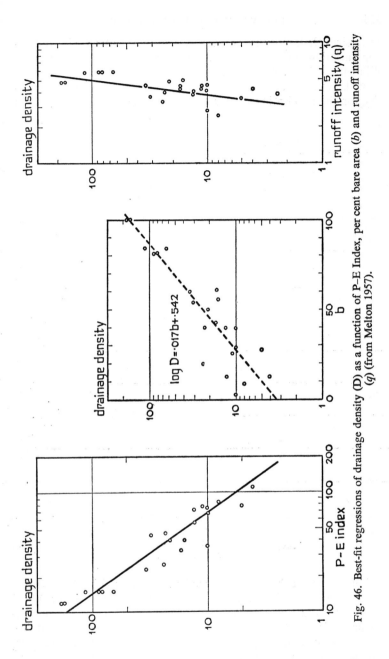

Fig. 46. Best-fit regressions of drainage density (D) as a function of P–E Index, per cent bare area (b) and runoff intensity (q) (from Melton 1957).

grain sizes $(X_2)$, moisture content $(X_3)$ and porosity $(X_4)$ in controlling variations in the dependent variable of beach firmness $(X_0)$ at Wilmette, Illinois. Assuming, once again, that a linear relationship exists between these variables (although this is by no means a necessity for the application of this technique), the best-fit regression is

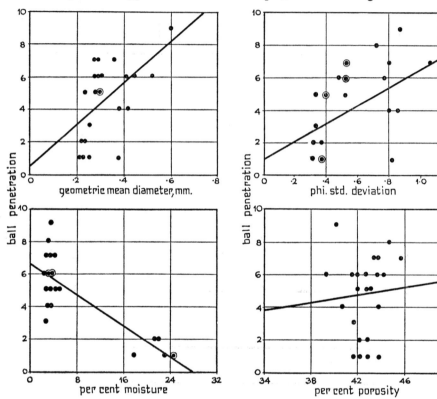

Fig. 47. Best-fit linear regressions of ball penetration as a function of geometric mean diameter, phi standard deviation of grain sizes, per cent moisture and per cent porosity fitted to sand data from Wilmette beach, Lake Michigan (from Krumbein 1959b).

calculated for each of the independent variables (Fig. 47) and the most important independent variable, together with its individual effect on $X_0$ is calculated by the greatest reduction of the sum of squares (Fig. 48). On this assumption that the strength of the relationship between $X_0$ and any of the independent variables (i.e. $X_r$) can be estimated in terms of the amount by which the fitted least squares

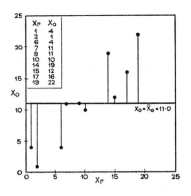

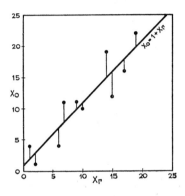

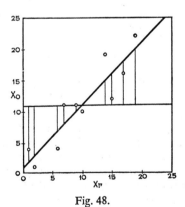

Fig. 48.

*Above:* Graphic representation of total sum of squares of dependent variable $X_0$.

*Middle:* Graphic representation of sum of squares of deviations (residuals) from the best-fit linear regression line fitted to the points shown above.

*Below:* Graphic representation of the sum of squares associated with the best-fit regression line. This sum of squares is a measure of the extent to which the independent variable ($X_r$) reduces the sum of squares of the dependent variable ($X_0$) (from Krumbein 1959b).

function reduces the total sum of squares in $X_0$, the percentages of the total variation of $X_0$ which are explained individually by the independent variables were obtained as follows: $X_3$ explains 69·79 per cent, $X_1$ 33·92 per cent, $X_2$ 20·48 per cent and $X_4$ 0·96 per cent. Thus, individually, moisture content appears as the most important control over beach firmness. It is obvious, however, that important redundancies exist, in that individually the four factors explain more than the total variation observed in beach firmness, and together total 125·15 per cent. 'This indicates that some variables, taken one at a time, show stronger relations than they would show if taken in combination with other independent variables' (Krumbein 1959b, p. 580). This recognition of replication leads the investigator on to the second step in the analysis, on the assumption that the 'reduction in the sum of squares of the dependent variable is counted for all lines, planes or surfaces fitted to the observed data to provide a criterion for estimating the relative importance of the independent variables in controlling the behaviour of the dependent variable' (Krumbein 1959b, p. 576). Thus each pair of independent variables is plotted against $X_0$ and best-fit planes calculated for each relationship. As in the first step, the paired factors can then be ranked in order of their reduction of the sum of squares with respect to these planes. In this way it is found that $X_1$ and $X_3$ explain 74·00 per cent, $X_2$ and $X_3$ 70·71 per cent, $X_3$ and $X_4$ 69·81 per cent, $X_1$ and $X_4$ 39·26 per cent, $X_1$ and $X_2$ 35·72 per cent, and $X_2$ and $X_4$ 25·42 per cent. In all paired combinations mean grain size is confirmed as the second most important control over beach firmness, and Fig. 49 is a graphical expression of the composite simultaneous control of $X_1$ and $X_3$ over $X_0$, which are related by the best-fit plane $X_0 = 4·60 + 5·29X_1 - 0·20X_3$. It is further apparent that the paired reduction by $X_1$ and $X_3$ is not much greater than by $X_3$ alone, and it can be assumed that grain size tends to 'repeat' information already supplied by measures of moisture content. Computer methods, which are important in this second step, become vital in the third step when all combinations of the independent variables in threes are plotted as best-fit surfaces against $X_0$ (in this instance comprising an $E_3$ phase space problem). The final step in the beach firmness problem involves the calculation of the reduction in the sum of squares achieved by all four independent variables operating simultaneously as an $E_4$ phase space 'surface' of the form $X_0 = a + bX_1 + cX_2 + dX_3 + eX_4$. This yields a reduction of only 76·60 per cent, and the residual unexplained variation of 23·40 per cent raises questions regarding the accuracy of the initial measurements, the assumed linear relationships, the number of factors assumed, etc.

A much larger unexplained variation of about 75 per cent resulted from the recent attempt by King (1961) to relate the spacing of American cities to the assumed independent variables of size, average size of associated farms, the local rural farm population density, percentage of population employed in manufacturing, population density, and value of land and buildings per acre. In this instance it seems that the large residual variation may have resulted from the mixing of

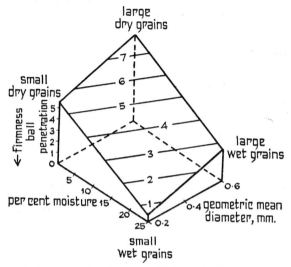

Fig. 49. Linear component trend surface of ball penetration on moisture content and mean grain size of the beach sand data given in Fig. 47 (from Krumbein 1959b).

cities associated with regions of strikingly differing historical development. Thus statistical methods, although providing a standardized, rigorous, conservative and objective framework for the extracting of the maximum amount of information from numerical data, are only an adjunct and not a substitute for the initital qualitative stage of any investigation. This qualitative stage is entirely a matter for the exercise of experience and controlled intuition, in which statistical methods are of no help—although they may subsequently be used to test the efficiency of this qualitative framework. Statistical methods are tools which assist and test imagination. Some of these tools, however, like Galileo's telescope, may prove to be vehicles which enable human imagination and intellectual grasp to operate on higher planes than ever before. For the geomorphologist, multivariate analysis may well be such a tool.

## Postscript

After the preparation of this chapter the extremely comprehensive work entitled *Statistical Analysis in the Geological Sciences* (John Wiley and Sons, New York, 483 pp.) by R. L. Miller and J. S. Kahn has appeared. This valuable manual and reference work will be of great interest to all those who are concerned with the application of statistical techniques to the natural sciences.

## Acknowledgements

My debt to the writings of Professors William C. Krumbein and Arthur N. Strahler has been so patently obvious in almost every page I have written to make any further acknowledgement here superfluous. Indeed, any account of the applications of statistical methods to geology in general, or to geomorphology in particular, is largely a catalogue of the achievements of these two men, and of their associates and students. It is a pleasure, however, for me to thank them here for the example which they have set me as the result of my personal association with them. Most of any merit which this chapter possesses can be attributed to them—the mistakes are my own.

## References

Anderson, E., 1947. 'Field studies of Guatemalan maize.' *Ann. Missouri Botanical Garden*, 34, 433–51.

Bates, R. E., 1939. 'Geomorphic history of the Kickapoo region, Wisconsin.' *Bull. Geol. Soc. Amer.*, 50, 819–80.

Bishop, M. S., 1960. *Subsurface Mapping*. Wiley, New York.

Box, G. E. P., 1954. 'The exploration and exploitation of response surfaces: some general considerations and examples.' *Biometrics*, 10, 16–60.

Box, G. E. P., and Youle, P. V., 1955. 'The exploration and exploitation of response surfaces: an example of the link between the fitted surface and the basic mechanism of the system.' *Biometrics*, 11, 287–323.

Boyer, M. C., 1954. 'Estimating the manning coefficient from an average bed roughness in open channels.' *Trans. Amer. Geophys. Union*, 35, 957–61.

Bracey, H. E., 1953. 'Towns as rural service centres: an index of centrality with special reference to Somerset.' *Trans. Inst. Brit. Geog.*, No. 19, 95–105.

Bridgman, P. W., 1931. *Dimensional Analysis*. Yale, New Haven.

Broscoe, A. J., 1959. 'Quantitative analysis of longitudinal stream profiles of small watersheds.' *Dept of Geol. Columbia Univ., ONR Project NR 389–042, Tech. Rept.* No. 18.

Brown, W. F., 1955. 'Mininum variance in gravity analysis, Part I.' *Geophysics*, 20, 807–28.

Brown, W. F., 1956. 'Minimum variance in gravity analysis, Part II.' *Geophysics*, 21, 107–41.

Bucher, W. H., 1941. 'The nature of geological enquiry and the training required for it.' *Amer. Inst. Min. Metall. Eng., Tech. Pub.*, 1377.

Burma, B. H., 1949. 'Multivariate analysis—a new analytical tool for paleontology and geology.' *Journ. Paleo.*, 23, 95–103.

Calef, W., and Newcomb, R., 1953, 'An average slope map of Illinois.' *Ann. Assn. Amer. Geog.*, 43, 305–16.

Carter, C. S., and Chorley, R. J., 1961. 'Early slope development in an expanding stream system.' *Geol. Mag.*, 98, 117–30.

Chadwick, J. G., 1961. 'Correlation between geographical distributions.' *Geography*, 46, 25–30.

Chamberlin, T. C., 1897. 'The method of multiple working hypotheses.' *Journ. Geol.*, 5, 837–48.

Chayes, F., 1942a. 'Statistical analysis of two-dimensional fabric diagrams', Chapter 22 *in* H. W. Fairbairn, *Structural Petrology of Deformed Rocks*. Addison-Wesley, Reading, Mass.

Chayes, F., 1942b. 'Statistical analysis of three-dimensional fabric diagrams', Chapter 23 *in* H. W. Fairbairn, *Structural Petrology of Deformed Rocks*. Addison-Wesley, Reading, Mass.

Chenoweth, P. A., 1952. 'Statistical methods applied to Trentonian stratigraphy in New York.' *Bull. Geol. Soc. Amer.*, 63, 521–60.

Chisholm, M., 1960. 'Correspondence with R. E. Dickinson regarding commuting in West Germany.' *Ann. Assn. Amer. Geog.*, 50, 187–8, 296, 491–2.

Chorley, R. J., 1957a. 'Climate and morphometry.' *Journ. Geol.*, 65, 628–38.

Chorley, R. J., 1957b. 'Illustrating the laws of morphometry.' *Geol. Mag.*, 94, 140–150.

Chorley, R. J., 1958a. 'Group operator variance in morphometric work with maps.' *Amer. Journ. Sci.*, 256, 208–18.

Chorley, R. J., 1958b. 'Aspects of the morphometry of a "poly-cyclic" drainage basin.' *Geog. Journ.*, 124, 370–4.

Chorley, R. J., 1959. 'The geomorphic significance of some Oxford soils.' *Amer. Journ. Sci.*, 257, 503–15.

Clarke, J. I., and Orrell, K., 1958. 'An assessment of some morphometric methods.' *Dept. of Geog., Univ. of Durham, Occasional papers* No. 2.

Coates, D. R., 1958. 'Quantitative geomorphology of small drainage basins of southern Indiana.' *Dept. of Geol. Columbia Univ., ONR Project NR 389–042, Tech. Rept.* No. 10.

Coates, D. R., 1959. 'Influence of scale in geomorphic map analysis.' *Amer. Assn. Adv. Sci.*, Section E (Chicago), Dec. 1959 (mimeographed).

Cochran, W. G., Mosteller, F., and Tukey, J. W., 1954. 'Principles of sampling.' *Journ. Amer. Stat. Assn.*, 49, 13–35.

Court, A., 1952. 'Some new statistical techniques in geophysics.' *Advances in Geophysics*, 1, 75–85.

Croxton, F. E., and Cowden, D. J., 1939. *Applied General Statistics.* (1st. edn.) Prentice-Hall, New York.

Croxton, F. E., and Cowden, D. J., 1955. *Applied General Statistics.* (2nd edn.) Pitman, London.

Curray, J. R., and Griffiths, J. C., 1955. 'Sphericity and roundness of quartz grains in sediments.' *Bull. Geol. Soc. Amer.*, 66, 1075–96.

Davies, G. L., 1958. 'Irish erosion surfaces—A statistical analysis.' *Adv. Sci.*, 56, 385–8.

Dawson, K. R., 1958. 'The application of multivariate variance analysis to mineralogical variation, Preissac-Lacorne batholith, Abitibi County, Quebec.' *The Canadian Mineralogist*, 6, 222–33.

Dickinson, R. E., 1959. 'The geography of commuting in West Germany.' *Ann. Assn. Amer. Geog.*, 49, 443–56.

Dixon, W. J., and Massey, F. J., 1957. 'Introduction to statistical analysis.' (2nd edn.) McGraw-Hill, New York.

Duncan, O. D., Cuzzort, R. P., and Duncan, B., 1961. *Statistical Geography: Problems in Analysing Areal Data.* The Free Press of Glencoe, Ill.

Duncan, W. J., 1953. 'Physical similarity and dimensional analysis.' Arnold, London.

Dury, G. H., 1959. 'Analysis of regional flood frequency on the Nene and the Great Ouse.' *Geog. Journ.*, 125, 223–9.

Dury, G. H., 1960. 'Misfit streams: Problems in interpretation, discharge and distribution.' *Geog. Rev.*, 50, 219–42.

Einstein, H. A., 1950. 'The bed-load function for sediment transportation in open channel flows.' *U.S. Dept. Agr., Tech. Bull.* 1026.

Fenneman, N. M., 1931. *Physiography of the Western United States.* McGraw-Hill, New York.

Fenneman, N. M., 1938. *Physiography of the Eastern United States.* McGraw-Hill, New York.

Fisher, R. A., 1926. 'The arrangement of field experiments.' *Journ. of the Ministry of Agriculture*, 33, 511.

Fisher, R. A., 1953. 'The expansion of statistics.' *Journ. Roy. Stat. Soc.*, 116, 1–6.

Fisher, R. A., 1960. *The Design of Experiments.* (7th edn.) Oliver and Boyd, Edinburgh.

Forgotson, J. M., 1960. 'Review and classification of quantitative mapping techniques.' *Bull. Amer. Assn. Petrol. Geols.*, 44, 83–100.

Garrison, W. L., 1959–60. 'Spatial structure of the economy.' *Ann. Assn. Amer. Geog.*, 49, 232–9, 471–82; 50, 357–73.

Garrison, W. L., and Marble, D. F., 1958. 'Analysis of highway networks: A linear programming formulation.' *Proc. Highway Res. Board.*, 37, 1–17.

Gilbert, G. K., 1877. *Report on the Geology of the Henry Mountains.* U.S. Geol. Survey, Washington D.C.

Gilbert, G. K., 1914. 'The transportation of debris by running water.' *U.S. Geol. Surv. Prof. Paper* 86.

Gilchrist, B., and Cressman, G. P., 1954. 'An experiment in objective analysis.' *Tellus*, 6, 309–18.

Godwin, H., 1941. 'Pollen analysis and Quaternary geology.' *Proc. Geol. Assn.*, 52, 328–61.

Grant, F. S., 1954. 'A theory for the regional correction of potential field data.' *Geophysics*, 19, 23–45.

Grant, F. S., 1957. 'A problem in the analysis of geophysical data.' *Geophysics*, 22, 309–44.

Griffiths, J. C., 1953. 'Estimation of error in grain size analysis.' *Journ. Sed. Petrol.*, 23, 75–84.

Griffiths, J. C., 1959. 'Size and shape of rock fragments in Tuscarora scree, Fishing Creek, Lamar, Central Pennsylvania.' *Journ. Sed. Petrol.*, 29, 391–401.

Griffiths, J. C., 1960. 'Aspects of measurement in the geosciences.' *Mineral Industries*, 29, No. 4.

Griffiths, J. C., and Rosenfeld, M. A., 1954. 'Operator variation in experimental research.' *Journ. Geol.*, 62, 74–91.

Gumbel, E. J., 1954. 'Applications of the circular normal distribution.' *Journ. Amer. Stat. Assn.*, 49, 267–97.

Gumbel, E. J., Greenwood, J. A., and Durand, D., 1953. 'The circular normal distribution.' *Journ. Amer. Stat. Assn.*, 48, 131–52.

Hack, J. T., 1957. 'Studies of longitudinal stream profiles in Virginia and Maryland.' *U.S. Geol. Surv. Prof. Paper* 294-B.

Hansen, M. H., Hurwitz, W. N., and Madow, W. G., 1953. *Sample Survey Methods and Theory*, Vol. 1. Wiley, New York.

Hanson-Lowe, J., 1935. 'The clinographic curve.' *Geol. Mag.*, 72, 180–4.

Hartshorne, R., 1959. *Perspective on the Nature of Geography*. Rand McNally, Chicago.

Hollingworth, S. E., 1938. 'The recognition and correlation of high-level erosion surfaces in Britain: a statistical study.' *Quart. Journ. Geol. Soc.*, 94, 55–84.

Horton, R. E., 1945. 'Erosional development of streams and their drainage basins: Hydrophysical approach to quantitative morphology.' *Bull. Geol. Soc. Amer.*, 56, 275–370.

Johnson, D. W., 1919. *Shore Processes and Shoreline Development*. Wiley, New York.

Jones, O. T., 1924. 'The upper Towy drainage system.' *Quart. Journ. Geol. Soc.*, 80, 568–609.

Jones, O. T., 1952. 'The drainage systems of Wales and the adjacent regions.' *Quart. Journ. Geol. Soc.*, 107, 201–25.

Judson, S., and Andrews, G. W., 1955. 'Pattern and form of some valleys in the Driftless Area, Wisconsin.' *Journ. Geol.*, 63, 328–36.

King, L. J., 1961. 'A multivariate analysis of the spacing of urban settlements in the United States.' *Ann. Assn. Amer. Geog.*, 51, 222–33.

Kinsman, B., 1957. 'Proper and improper use of statistics in geophysics.' *Tellus*, 9, 408–18.

Krumbein, W. C., 1934. 'The probable error of sampling sediments for mechanical analysis.' *Amer. Journ. Sci.*, 27, 204–14.

Krumbein, W. C., 1937. 'Sediments and exponential curves.' *Journ. Geol.*, 45, 577–601.

Krumbein, W. C., 1939. 'Preferred orientation of pebbles in sedimentary deposits.' *Journ. Geol.*, 47, 673–706.

Krumbein, W. C., 1953a. 'Statistical designs for sampling beach sand.' *Trans. Amer. Geophys. Union*, 34, 857–68.

Krumbein, W. C., 1953b. 'Latin square experiments in sedimentary petrology.' *Journ. Sed. Petrol.*, 23, 280–3.

Krumbein, W. C., 1953c. 'Design of experiments for statistical analysis of geological data.' *Journ. Geol.*, 61, 510–32.

Krumbein, W. C., 1955a. 'Experimental design in the earth sciences.' *Trans. Amer. Geophys. Union*, 36, 1–11.

Krumbein, W. C., 1955b. 'Statistical analysis of facies maps.' *Journ. Geol.*, 63, 452–70.

Krumbein, W. C., 1956. 'Regional and local components in facies maps.' *Bull. Amer. Assn. Petrol. Geols.*, 40, 2163–94.

Krumbein, W. C., 1958. 'Measurement and error in regional stratigraphic analysis.' *Journ. Sed. Petrol.*, 28, 175–85.

Krumbein, W. C., 1959a. 'Trend surface analysis of contour-type maps with irregular control-point spacing.' *Journ. Geophys. Res.*, 64, 823–34.

Krumbein, W. C., 1959b. 'The "sorting out" of geological variables illustrated by regression analysis of factors controlling beach firmness.' *Journ. Sed. Petrol.*, 29, 575–87.

Krumbein, W. C., 1960a. 'The "geological population" as a framework for analysing numerical data in geology.' *Liv. and Man. Geol. Journ.*, 2, 341–68.

Krumbein, W. C., 1960b. 'Some problems in applying statistics to geology.' *Applied Statistics.*, 9, 82–91.

Krumbein, W. C., 1960c. *Lectures on sedimentary-stratigraphic map analysis.* Queen Mary College, London (mimeographed).

Krumbein, W. C., 1960d. 'Stratigraphic maps from data observed at outcrop.' *Proc. Yorks. Geol. Soc.*, 32, 353–66.

Krumbein, W. C., and Miller, R. L., 1953. 'Design of experiments for statistical analysis of geological data.' *Journ. Geol.*, 61, 510–32.

Krumbein, W. C., and Pettijohn, F. J., 1938, *Manual of Sedimentary Petrography.* Appleton-Century-Crofts Inc., New York.

Krumbein, W. C., and Slack, H. A., 1956. 'Statistical analysis of low-level radioactivity of Pennsylvanian black fissile shale in Illinois.' *Bull. Geol. Soc. Amer.*, 67, 739–62.

Krumbein, W. C., and Sloss, L. L., 1958. 'High-speed digital computers in stratigraphic and facies analysis.' *Bull. Amer. Assn. Petrol. Geols.*, 42, 2650–69.

Krumbein, W. C., and Tukey, J. W., 1956. 'Multivariate analysis of mineralogic, lithologic, and chemical composition of rock bodies.' *Journ. Sed. Petrol.*, 26, 322–37.

Langbein, W. B., 1940. 'Determination of Manning's *n* from vertical-velocity curves.' *Trans. Amer. Geophys. Union, 21st Ann. Meeting, Section on Hydrology*, 618–20.

Langbein, W. B., and Schumm, S. A., 1958. 'Yield of sediment in relation to mean annual precipitation.' *Trans. Amer. Geophys. Union*, 39, 1076–84.

Leighly, J., 1955. 'What has happened to physical geography?' *Ann Assn. Amer. Geog.*, 45, 309–18.

Leopold, L. B., Bagnold, R. A., Wolman, M. G., and Brush, L. M., 1960. 'Flow resistance in sinuous or irregular channels.' *U.S. Geol. Surv. Prof. Paper* 282-D.

Leopold, L. B., and Maddock, T., 1953. 'The hydraulic geometry of stream channels and some physiographic implications.' *U.S. Geol. Surv. Prof. Paper* 252.

Leopold, L. B., and Miller, J. P., 1956. 'Ephemeral streams—Hydraulic factors and their relation to the drainage net.' *U.S. Geol. Surv. Prof. Paper* 282-A.

Leopold, L. B., and Wolman, M. G., 1957. 'River channel patterns: Braided, meandering and straight.' *U.S. Geol. Surv. Prof. Paper* 282-B.

Lewis, W. V., 1943. 'Some aspects of percolation in South East England.' *Proc. Geol. Assn.*, 54, 171–84.

Linton, D. L., 1951. 'The delimitation of morphological regions.' Chapter 11 in *London Essays in Geography*, ed. by L. D. Stamp and S. W. Wooldridge. Longmans, London.

Lippitt, L., 1959. 'Statistical analysis of regional facies change in Ordovician Cobourg Limestone in northwestern New York and southern Ontario.' *Bull. Amer. Assn. Petrol. Geols.*, 43, 807–16.

Little, J. M., 1940. *Erosional Topography and Erosion*, A. Carlisle, San Francisco.

Longuet-Higgins, M. S., 1952. 'On the statistical distribution of the heights of sea waves.' *Journ. Marine Res.*, 11, 245–66.

McCarty, H. H., 1958. 'Science, measurement, and area analysis.' *Econ. Geog.*, 34, facing p. 283.

McGill, J. T., 1959. 'Coastal classification maps: A review.' *Proc. 2nd Coastal Geog. Conf., Louisana State Univ.*, 1–21.

Mahalanobis, P. C., 1950. 'Why statistics?' *Sankhyā: The Indian Journal of Statistics*, 10, 195–228.

Manning, J. C., 1953. 'Application of statistical estimation and hypothesis testing to geologic data.' *Journ. Geols.*, 61, 544–56.

Melton, M. A., 1957. 'An analysis of the relations among elements of climate, surface properties, and geomorphology.' *Dept. of Geol. Columbia Univ., ONR Project NB 389-042, Tech. Rept*, No. 11.

Melton, M. A., 1958a. 'List of sample parameters of quantitative properties of landforms; their use in determining the size of geomorphic experiments.' *Dept. of Geol. Columbia Univ., ONR Project NR 389-042, Tech. Rept.* No. 16.

Melton, M. A., 1958b. 'Correlation structure of morphometric properties of drainage systems and their controlling agents.' *Journ. Geol.*, 66, 442–60.

Melton, M. A., 1958c. 'Geometric properties of mature drainage systems and their representations in an $E_4$ phase space.' *Journ. Geol.*, 66, 35–54.

Melton, M. A., 1958d. 'Use of punched cards to speed statistical analysis of geomorphic data.' *Bull. Geol. Soc. Amer.*, 69, 355–7.

Melton, M. A., 1959. 'A derivation of Strahler's channel-ordering system.' *Journ. Geol.*, 67, 345–6.

Melton, M. A., 1960. 'Intravalley variation in slope angles related to micro-climate and erosional environment.' *Bull. Geol. Soc. Amer.*, 71, 133–44.

Miller, J. P., 1959. 'Geomorphology in North America.' *Polish Geog. Rev.*, 31, 567–87.

Miller, R. L., 1956. 'Trend surfaces: their application to analysis and description of environments of sedimentation. 1. The relation of sediment-size parameters to current-wave systems and physiography.' *Journ. Geol.*, 64, 425–46.

Miller, V. C., 1953. 'A quantitative geomorphic study of drainage basin characteristics in the Clinch Mountain area, Virginia and Tennessee.' *Dept. of Geol. Columbia Univ., ONR Project NR 389–042, Tech. Rept.* No. 3.

Morisawa, M. E., 1957. 'Accuracy of determination of stream lengths from topographic maps.' *Trans. Amer. Geophys. Union*, 38, 86–8.

Morisawa, M. E., 1959. 'Relation of quantitative geomorphology to stream flow in representative watersheds of the Appalachian plateau province.' *Dept. of Geol. Columbia Univ., ONR Project 389–042, Tech. Rept.* No. 20.

Moroney, M. J., 1960. *Facts from Figures.* (3rd edn.) Penguin Books, London.

Murphy, N. F., 1949. 'Dimensional analysis.' *Bull. Virginia Poly. Inst. Eng. Exp. Sta.*, Series no. 73, Vol. 42, No. 6.

Nagel, E., 1939. 'Principles of the theory of probability.' in *International Encyclopedia of Unified Science*, Univ. of Chicago Press, Vol. 1, No. 6.

Oldham, C. H. G., and Sutherland, D. B., 1955. 'Orthogonal polynomials; their use in estimating regional effect.' *Geophysics*, 20, 295–306.

Olsen, J. S., and Potter, P. E., 1954. 'Variance components of cross-bedding direction in some basal Pennsylvanian sandstones of the eastern interior basin: Statistical methods.' *Journ. Geol.*, 62, 26–49.

Peltier, L. C., 1959. 'Area sampling for terrain analysis.' *Amer. Assn. Adv. Sci.*, Section E (Chicago), Dec. 1959 (mimeographed).

Pincus, H. J., 1953. 'The analysis of aggregates of orientation data in the earth sciences.' *Journ. Geol.*, 61, 482–509.

Pincus, H. J., 1956. 'Some vector and arithmetic operations in two-dimensional orientation variates, with applications to geologic data.' *Journ. Geol.*, 64, 533–57.

Potter, P. E., and Siever, R., 1955. 'A comparative study of Upper Chester and Lower Pennsylvanian stratigraphic variability.' *Journ. Geol.*, 63, 429–51.

Quenouille, M. H., 1950. *Introductory Statistics.* Pergamon, London.

Raisz, E., and Henry, J., 1937. 'An average slope map of southern New England.' *Geog. Rev.*, 27, 467–72.

Ray, R. G., and Fischer, W. A., 1960. 'Quantitative photography—A geologic research tool.' *Photogrammetric Eng.*, 26, 143–50.

Reynolds, O., 1883. 'An experimental investigation of the circumstances which determine whether the motion of water shall be direct or sinuous, and of the law of resistance in parallel channels.' *Phil. Trans. Roy. Soc. London*, 174, 935–82.

Reynolds, R. B., 1956. 'Statistical methods in geographical research.' *Geog. Rev.*, 46, 129–31.

Robinson, A. H., 1956. 'The necessity of weighting values in correlation analysis of areal data.' *Ann. Assn. Amer. Geog.*, 46, 233–6.

Robinson, A. H., and Bryson, R. A., 1957. 'A method for describing quantitatively the correspondence of geographical distributions.' *Ann. Assn. Amer. Geog.*, 47, 379–91.

Robinson, A. H., Lindberg, J. B., and Brinkman, L. W., 1961. 'A correlation and regression analysis applied to rural farm population densities in the Great Plains.' *Ann. Assn. Amer. Geog.*, 51, 211–21.

Rosenfeld, M. A., and Griffiths, J. C., 1953. 'An experimental test of visual comparison technique in estimating two dimensional sphericity and roundness of quartz grains.' *Amer. Journ. Sci.*, 251, 553–85.

Rubey, W. W., 1938. 'The force required to move particles on a stream bed.' *U.S. Geol. Surv. Prof. Paper* 189.

Russell, R. J., 1949. 'Geographical geomorphology.' *Ann. Assn. Amer. Geog.*, 39, 1–11.

Scheffé, H., 1953. 'A method of judging all contrasts in the analyses of variance.' *Biometrika*, 40, 87–104.

Schumm, S. A., 1956. 'Evolution of drainage system and slopes in badlands at Perth Amboy, New Jersey.' *Bull. Geol. Soc. Amer.*, 67, 597–646.

Schumm, S. A., 1960a. 'The shape of alluvial channels in relation to sediment type.' *U.S. Geol. Surv. Prof. Paper* 352-B.

Schumm, S. A., 1960b. 'The effect of sediment type on the slope and stratification of some modern fluvial deposits.' *Amer. Journ. Sci.*, 258, 177–84.

Shulits, S., 1941. 'Rational equation of river-bed profile.' *Trans. Amer. Geophys. Union*, 22, 622–31.

Siegel, S., 1956. *Nonparametric Statistics for the Behavioral Sciences.* McGraw-Hill, New York.

Simpson, S. M., 1954. 'Least square polynomial fitting to gravitational data and density plotting by digital computers.' *Geophysics*, 19, 255–269.

Smith, G.-H., 1935. 'The relative relief of Ohio.' *Geog. Rev.*, 25, 272–84.

Smith, K. G., 1950. 'Standards for grading texture of erosional topography.' *Amer. Journ. Sci.*, 248, 655–68.

Smith, K. G., 1958. 'Erosional processes and landforms in Badlands National Monument, South Dakota.' *Bull. Geol. Soc. Amer.*, 69, 975–1008.

Smith, W. L., and Flanagan, F. J., 1956. 'Use of statistical methods to detect radioactivity change due to weathering of a granite' *Amer. Journ.. Sci.*, 254, 316–24.

Stevens, S. S., 1946. 'On the theory of the scales of measurement.' *Science*, 103, 677–80.

Strahler, A. N., 1950. 'Equilibrium theory of erosional slopes approached by frequency distribution analysis.' *Amer. Journ. Sci.*, 248, 673–96, 800–14.

Strahler, A. N., 1952a. 'Hypsometric (area-altitude) analysis of erosional topography.' *Bull. Geol. Soc. Amer.*, 63, 1117–42.

Strahler, A. N., 1952b. 'Dynamic basis of geomorphology.' *Bull. Geol. Soc. Amer.*, 63, 923–38.

Strahler, A. N., 1954a. 'Quantitative geomorphology of erosional landscapes.' *Comptes Rendus, Sect. 13, Int, Geol. Cong.* (Algiers), 1952, 341–54.

Strahler, A. N., 1954b. 'Statistical analysis in geomorphic research.' *Journ. Geol.*, 62, 1–25.

Strahler, A. N., 1956. 'Quantitative slope analysis.' *Bull. Geol. Soc. Amer.*, 67, 571–96.

Strahler, A. N., 1957. 'Objective field sampling of physical terrain properties.' *Ann. Assn. Amer. Geog.*, 47, 179–80 (Abstract).

Strahler, A. N., 1958. 'Dimensional analysis applied to fluvially eroded landforms.' *Bull. Geol. Soc. Amer.*, 69, 279–300.

Svensson, H., 1956. 'Method for exact characterizing of denudation surfaces, especially peneplains, as to the position in space.' *Lund Studies in Geog.*, Series A, No. 8.

Swartz, C. A., 1954. 'Some geometrical properties of residual maps.' *Geophysics*, 19, 46–70.

Tanner, W. F., 1958. 'The zig-zag nature of type I and type IV curves.' *Journ. Sed. Petrol.*, 28, 372–5.

Tanner, W. F., 1959. 'Sample components obtained by the method of differences.' *Journ. Sed. Petrol.*, 29, 408–11.

Thompson, D'Arcy W., 1942. *On Growth and Form.* Cambridge U.P., England.

Thompson, W. R., 1957. 'The coefficient of localization: An appraisal.' *Southern Economic Journ.*, 23, 320–5.

Thornton, E. H., 1960. 'Irish erosion surfaces.' *Geol. Mag.*, 97, 345–6.

Tippett, L. H. C., 1952. *Technological Applications of Statistics.* Williams and Norgate, London.

Van Burkalow, A., 1945. 'Angle of repose and angle of sliding friction. An experimental study.' *Bull. Geol. Soc. Amer.*, 56, 669–708.

Von Bertalanffy, L., 1950. 'The theory of open systems in physics and biology.' *Science*, 111, 23–9.

Von Richthofen, F. F., 1886. *Führer für Forschungsreisende.* R. Oppenheim, Berlin.

Walker, H., and Lev, J., 1953. *Statistical Inference.* Holt, New York.

Whitten, E. H. T., 1959. 'Composition trends in a granite: modal variation and ghost stratigraphy in part of the Donegal Granite, Eire.' *Journ. Geophys. Res.*, 64, 835–48.

Whitten, E. H. T., 1961. 'Quantitative areal modal analysis of granite complexes.' *Bull. Geol. Soc. Amer.*, 72, 1331–60.

Williams, W. T., and Lambert, J. M., 1959. 'Multivariate methods in plant ecology I: association-analysis in plant communities.' *Journ. Ecol.*, 47, 83–101.

Williams, W. T., and Lambert, J. M., 1960. 'Multivariate methods in plant ecology II: the use of an electronic digital computer for association-analysis.' *Journ. Ecol.*, 48, 689–710.

Wolman, M. G., 1954. 'A method for sampling coarse river-bed material.' *Trans. Amer. Geophys. Union*, 35, 951–6.

Wolman, M. G., 1955. 'The natural channel of Brandywine Creek, Pennsylvania.' *U.S. Geol. Surv. Prof. Paper* 271.

Wolman, M. G., and Leopold, L. B., 1957. 'River flood plains: some observations on their formation.' *U.S. Geol. Surv. Prof. Paper* 282-C.

Wolman, M. G., and Miller, J. P., 1960. 'Magnitude and frequency of forces in geomorphic processes.' *Journ. Geol.*, 68, 54–74.

Wood, W. F., and Snell, J. B., 1957. 'The dispersion of geomorphic data around measures of central tendency.' *Ann. Assn. Amer. Geog.*, 47, 184–5.

Wood, W. F., and Snell, J. B., 1957. 'The dispersion of geomorphic data around measures of central tendency and its application.' *H.Q. Quartermaster Research and Development Command, Natick, Mass., Environmental Analysis Branch, Research Study Report EA—8.*

Woodford, A. O., 1951. 'Stream gradients and Monterey Sea Valley.' *Bull. Geol. Soc. Amer.*, 62, 799–852.

Wooldridge, S. W., 1928. 'The 200-foot platform in the London Basin.' *Proc. Geol. Assn.*, 39, 1–26.

Wooldridge, S. W., 1958. 'The trend of geomorphology.' *Trans. Inst. Brit. Geog.*, No. 25, 29–35.

Wooldridge, S. W., and Linton, D. L., 1955. *Structure, Surface and Drainage in South-East England.* Philip, London.

Zernitz, E. R., 1932. 'Drainage patterns and their significance.' *Journ. Geol.*, 40, 498–521.

Zobler, L., 1957. 'Statistical testing of regional boundaries.' *Ann. Assn. Amer. Geog.*, 47, 83–95.

Zobler, L., 1958. 'Decision making in regional construction.' *Ann. Assn. Amer. Geog.*, 48, 140–8.

# Index